BMW 1600 1966–73 Autobook

By Kenneth Ball
Graduate, Institution of Mechanical Engineers
Associate Member, Guild of Motoring Writers
and the Autopress Team of Technical Writers.

BMW 1600 1966–71
BMW 1600–2 1971–73
BMW 1600TI 1966–71

Autopress Ltd. Golden Lane Brighton BN1 2QJ England

The AUTOBOOK series of Workshop Manuals is the largest in the world and covers the majority of British and Continental motor cars, as well as all major Japanese and Australian models. For a full list see the back of this manual.

CONTENTS

Acknowledgement

Introduction

Chapter 1	The Engine	9
Chapter 2	The Fuel System	31
Chapter 3	The Ignition System	41
Chapter 4	The Cooling System	47
Chapter 5	The Clutch	53
Chapter 6	The Gearbox	63
Chapter 7	Propeller Shaft, Rear Axle and Rear Suspension	73
Chapter 8	Front Suspension and Hubs	85
Chapter 9	The Steering Gear	93
Chapter 10	The Braking System	99
Chapter 11	The Electrical System	117
Chapter 12	The Bodywork	129
Appendix		141

ISBN 0 85147 356 3

First Edition 1970
Reprinted 1971
Second Edition, fully revised 1971
Third Edition, fully revised 1972

Printed and bound in Brighton England for Autopress Ltd by G Beard & Son Ltd

ACKNOWLEDGEMENT

My thanks are due to BMW Concessionaires for their unstinted co-operation and also for supplying data and illustrations.

I am also grateful to a considerable number of owners who have discussed their cars at length and many of whose suggestions have been included in this manual.

Kenneth Ball G I Mech E
Associate Member Guild of Motoring Writers
Ditchling Sussex England.

INTRODUCTION

This do-it-yourself Workshop Manual has been specially written for the owner who wishes to maintain his car in first class condition and to carry out his own servicing and repairs. Considerable savings on garage charges can be made, and one can drive in safety and confidence knowing the work has been done properly.

Comprehensive step-by-step instructions and illustrations are given on all dismantling, overhauling and assembling operations. Certain assemblies require the use of expensive special tools, the purchase of which would be unjustified. In these cases information is included but the reader is recommended to hand the unit to the agent for attention.

Throughout the Manual hints and tips are included which will be found invaluable, and there is an easy to follow fault diagnosis at the end of each chapter.

Whilst every care has been taken to ensure correctness of information it is obviously not possible to guarantee complete freedom from errors or to accept liability arising from such errors or omissions.

Instructions may refer to the righthand or lefthand sides of the vehicle or the components. These are the same as the righthand or lefthand of an observer standing behind the car and looking forward.

CHAPTER 1

THE ENGINE

1 :1 Description
1 :2 Removing the engine
1 :3 Removing and replacing cylinder head
1 :4 Removing and refitting camshaft
1 :5 Cylinder head dismantling and reassembly
1 :6 Servicing the cylinder head
1 :7 Timing chain and timing gear
1 :8 Pistons, rings and connecting rods
1 :9 Removing and refitting flywheel
1 :10 Removing and refitting crankshaft
1 :11 Cylinder block and crankcase
1 :12 Oil pump removal and refitting
1 :13 Oil pump dismantling and reassembly
1 :14 Fullflow filter
1 :15 Factory exchange engine installation
1 :16 Exhaust emission control unit
1 :17 Fault diagnosis

1 :1 Description

The overhead camshaft engine as shown in **FIG 1 :1** is of traditional BMW design and is located at the front of the car in unit with the gearbox. It is tilted to the right in the engine compartment at an angle of 30 deg. to allow for a better position enabling a lower body line to be styled, giving good visibility to the driver. The combustion chamber is of hemispherical swirl action design, with specially shaped piston crowns to give intensive swirl action and thorough ignition of the charge at all engine speed, giving greater engine flexibility.

A five main bearing crankshaft drives the overhead camshaft by a tensioned double tracked chain moving around the crankshaft and camshaft sprocket gears. The inlet and exhaust valves are set in line along the cylinder head and are of the inverted 'V' arrangement adding to the efficiency of the specially designed combustion chambers.

The offset gudgeon pins are retained in the piston using wire circlips. The pistons have two compression rings and one oil control ring, all three located above the gudgeon pin. The connecting rods are fitted with renewable bearing shells lined with a special alloy. The crankshaft runs in similar bearings but end thrust is taken by the centre main bearing which has flanges on either side.

Lubrication is affected using a rotor driven pump located beneath the crankshaft and driven from the front end of the crankshaft by means of a single track chain. A micronic fullflow oil filter is used and the oil pressure controlled by a pressure relief valve located in the pump body.

Full details of the engine specifications are given in Technical Data at the end of this manual, together with an extensive coverage of further technical information.

1 :2 Removing the engine

The usual operations of decarbonizing and top overhaul can be done without removing the power unit.

If the operator is not a skilled automobile engineer it is suggested he will find much useful information in 'Hints on Maintenance and Overhaul' at the end of this manual and that he should read this before starting work. It must be stressed that any supports must be firmly based and

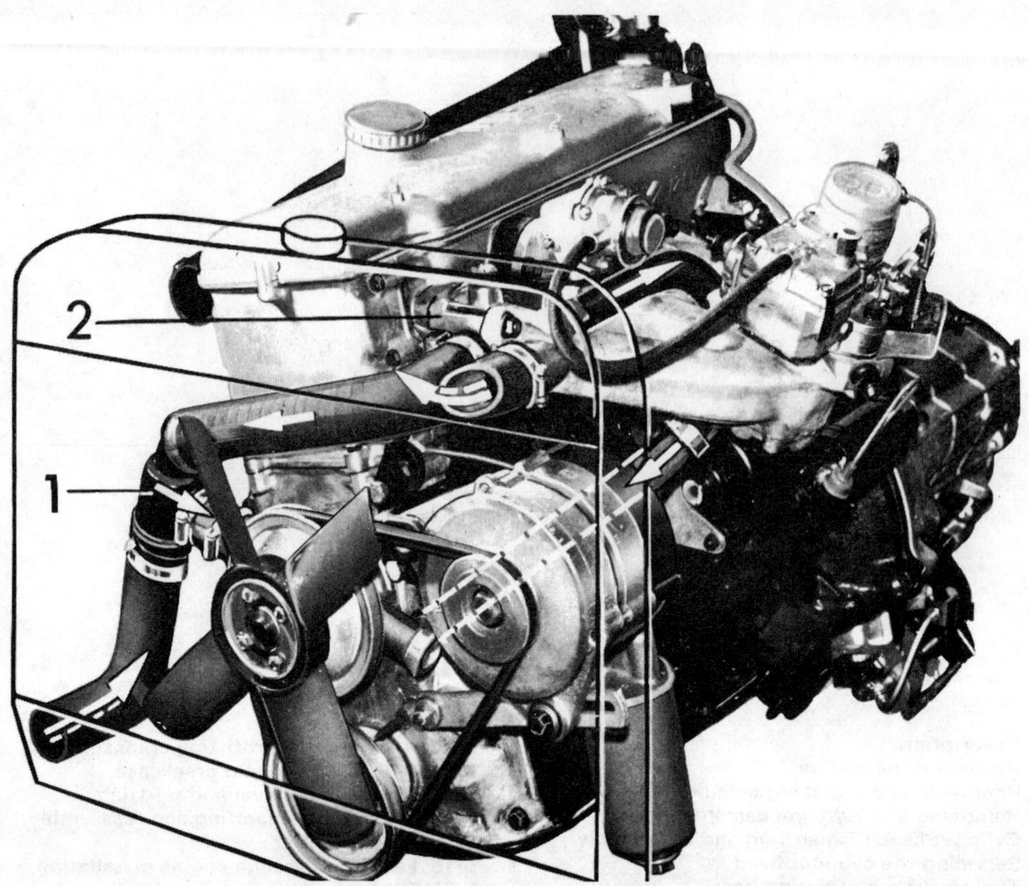

FIG 1 : 1 BMW 1600 engine

not likely to collapse during the operation or serious injury could result. To remove the engine proceed as follows:

1 Open the bonnet and cover both the wing surfaces with wing covers. Remove the pre-heater 1 (see **FIG 1 : 2**), and air filter housing 2. Detach the earth cable from the battery. Mark the relative bonnet and hinge positions using a pencil and then remove the bonnet after releasing the hinge bolts.

2 Remove the cable from the starter support arm, the cables from the ignition switch, the starter motor, the distributor, the thermometer element, oil pressure switch and generator or alternator. In each case make a note of the respective cable colours and their locations to facilitate reassembly.

3 Remove the radiator cap and open both the water draining cock at the base of the radiator and the drain cock located on the side of the cylinder block. Release the coolant at the distribution union and also at the bottom of the radiator. Unscrew the radiator mounting bolts from the front panel and carefully lift away the radiator. Take great care that the radiator matrix is not damaged by the fan blades. Slacken the hot water hose clip at the cylinder head and also at the inlet manifold.

4 Carefully release the fuel hose at the carburetter and plug the end to ensure that fuel does not syphon from the exposed end. Disconnect the choke control cable at the carburetter and also the throttle control rod on the carburetter and pull away the rod from its support on the bulkhead.

5 Refer to **FIG 1 : 3** and disconnect the pullrod on the intermediate shaft and slacken the bearing support from the longitudinal stay. Disconnect the return spring and lift away the intermediate shaft together with the pushrod.

6 Slacken the lefthand power unit mounting silentbloc bush.

7 From the inside of the car push up the gearchange lever gaiter together with the foam packing and using a pair of circlip pliers remove the circlip.

8 Using a garage hydraulic jack raise the vehicle and support on firmly based stands. Using a garage crane or lifting tackle support the weight of the engine. From the underside of the car release the three nuts securing the exhaust downpipe from the exhaust manifold flange. Remove the two retaining nuts for the exhaust downpipe support located on the underside of the gearbox casing.

9 Refer to **FIG 1 :4** and remove the crossmember 9 and bolts 10. Locate and disconnect the reversing lamps switch terminals and also slacken the retaining screw holding the speedometer drive cable to the gearbox casing and gently pull out the speedometer cable. Remove the four propeller shaft flange to gearbox drive flange retaining bolts. Refer to **FIG 1 :5** and slacken the centre bearing support 13. This will enable the propeller shalt to be gently eased back from the gearbox and also release it from the rear propeller shaft. Lift away the front shaft.

10 Refer to **FIG 1 :6** and slacken the internal hexagonal bolt 15 and push out the bearing pin. Firmly press the gearchange lever upwards so releasing it from the control rod bracket. Finally slacken the righthand power unit support and gently lower the gearbox and using the garage crane or lifting tackle lift the power unit through the bonnet aperture.

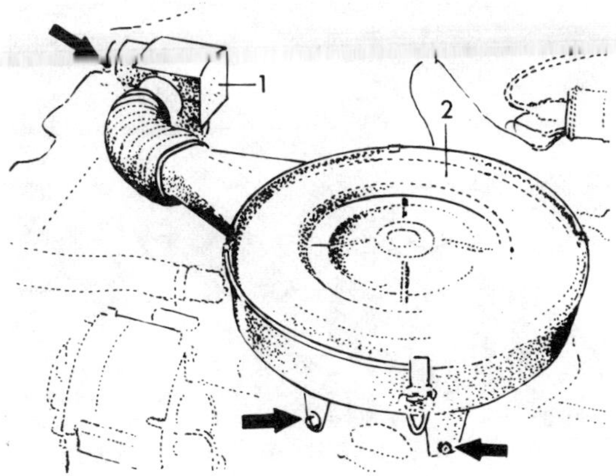

FIG 1 :2 Air filter and pre-heater

Refitting the unit to the car:

Refitting is the reverse procedure to dismantling but the following points should be noted:

1 Upon the reassembling the threaded pins of the exhaust manifold system always coat with Molykote paste to ensure ease of dismantling at a later time.
2 Refer to **FIG 1 :7** and set the stop A to give a clearance of 0.118 inch.
3 Refer to **FIG 1 :6** and ensure that the bearing pin 14 is so positioned that the Allen screw correctly seats in the centring recess as arrowed.
4 Refer to **FIG 1 :5** and ensure that the propeller shafts centre bearing is pre-stressed by 0.08 inch (2mm).
5 Ensure that the front propeller shaft drive flange bolts are tightened to a torque wrench setting of 21.8 lb ft.
6 Referring to **FIG 1 :8** ensure that the bearing support is correctly located so that it is at 90 deg. to the power unit.
7 Ensure that the starter lever is firmly pressed against its stop and that the instrument panel control is set to the bottom notch.
8 It is important that the alternator connections are correct upon reassembly. The red cable should be connected to the B terminal.
9 When refilling the cooling system the heater control lever should be set to the position 'hot'. Fill with water and replace the radiator cap and rotate until it engages in the second retaining notch. The water should then be allowed to heat up to its normal operating temperature of approximately 80°C. Once the thermostat has opened, place a large rag over the radiator cap and relieve the pressure by turning it back so that the cap engages in the first retaining notch. Finally check the water level and tighten down the radiator cap to its fully closed position.

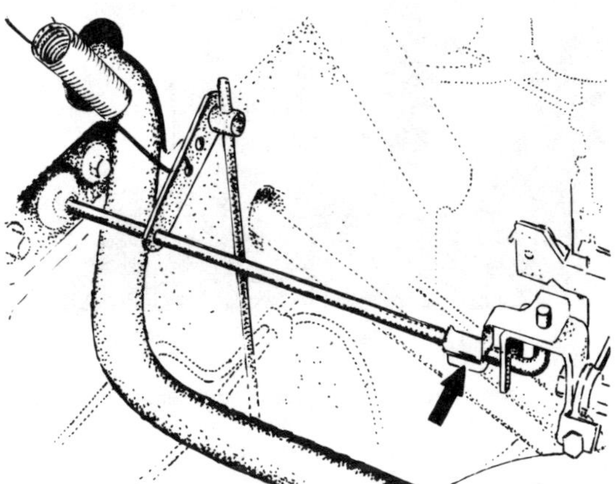
FIG 1 :3 Carburetter intermediate control shaft

1 :3 Removing and replacing cylinder head

To remove the cylinder head proceed as follows:

1 Open the bonnet and using protective aprons cover the wing surfaces. Detach the earth cable from the battery. Open the radiator drain tap.
2 Carefully ease the breather tube away from the cylinder head cover. Remove the radiator hose from the thermostat housing. Remove the vacuum hose

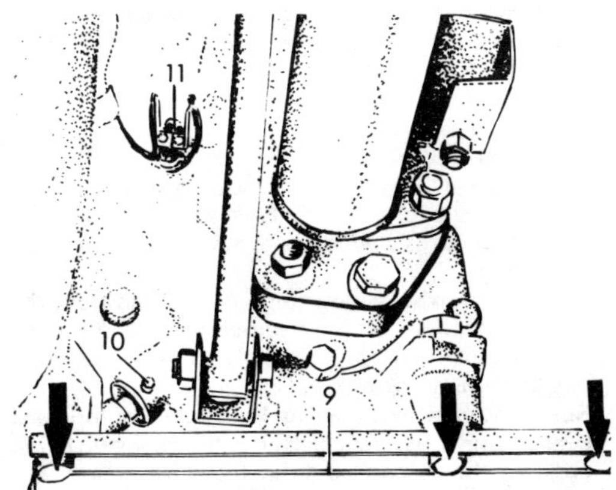

FIG 1 :4 Gearbox mounting crossmember

FIG 1:5 **Propeller shaft centre bearing support**

FIG 1:6 **Gearchange lever pivot pin**

from the check valve. Release and remove the fuel supply hose from the fuel pump.

3 Carefully unscrew the thermostat contact from its location in the thermostat housing. Disconnect the throttle linkage and also the bowden cable from the automatic choke control lever using a pair of engineers pliers to hold the lever securely. Remove the bowden cable sleeve from the bowden cable pivot mounting and gently pull away.

4 Remove the water hose from the induction manifold. Release the dip stick holder fastening nut. Release the heater hose from the cylinder head.

5 Carefully remove the low-tension cable connector from the side of the distributor and also the connection to the oil pressure warning switch. Release and lift away the distributor cap and also the HT cable from the ignition coil. Note the position of the spark plug leads and remove these leads from the spark plug.

6 Release the exhaust downpipe connection from the exhaust manifold flange. Remove the cylinder head cover retaining nuts and carefully lift away the cover together with its gasket.

7 Rotate the engine so that No. 1 cylinder is at top dead centre which is indicated by the pointer being opposite the second notch in the drive pulley. The notch in the camshaft flange must also coincide with the notch marked at the top of the cylinder head.

8 Release the eight bolts retaining the top camshaft sprocket cover and lift away. Loosen the camshaft drive chain tensioner closure plug and unscrew by hand with extreme caution as this is under the influence of heavy pressure. With the plug removed take out the spring and the piston (see **FIG 1:10**).

9 To remove the camshaft drive sprocket bend back the lockplate corners away from the retaining bolts and remove the fastening bolts. Carefully lift away the sprocket and using a piece of wire tie up the chain onto the side of the generator to ensure that it does not drop and become disengaged from the camshaft.

10 Remove the cylinder head retaining bolts in the order shown in **FIG 1:9** and carefully lift away the cylinder head. Also lift away the cylinder head gasket taking care not to damage it so that it can be inspected if necessary.

Reassembly:

Reassembly is the reverse procedure to dismantling. The following points should however be noted:

1 Before reassembling the cylinder head to the cylinder block, all the mating surfaces must be perfectly clean. Ensure that the cylinder head bolt threads are free from dirt.

2 Only BMW cylinder head gaskets are to be used and must be checked to ensure that all cooling waterways holes match up with those on the cylinder block.

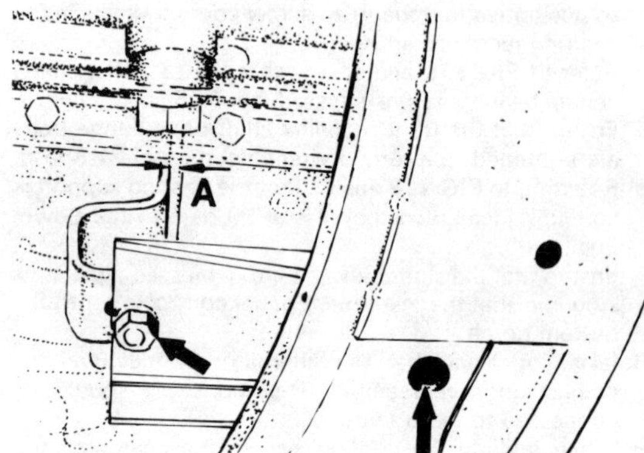

FIG 1:7 **Engine support mounting clearance**

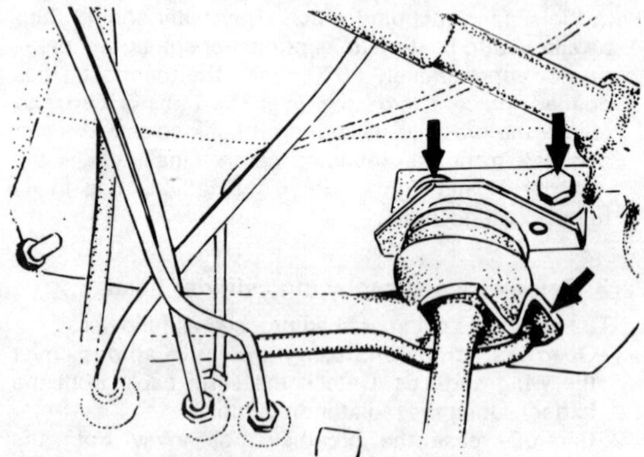
FIG 1:8 **Bearing support mounting**

3 The cylinder head retaining bolts must be tightened in the order shown in **FIG 1:9** using a torque wrench setting of 43.4 lb ft. Allow the engine to operate at normal running temperature and then allow to cool to approximately 35°C. Then recheck the cylinder head retaining bolt torque wrench setting to ensure the correct loading of 43.4 lb ft. Finally check and correct the valve clearance as described in **Section 1:4**.

4 When refitting the camshaft drive sprocket to the camshaft the work will be made easier if the chain tensioner is relieved by inserting a screwdriver between the tensioning arm and the timing chain gearbox cover. It should be noted that if the timing chain tensioner is of the sprocket type only pistons of 2.519 inch (64mm) in length should be installed otherwise the timing chain could be very noisy in operation or it could slip (see **FIG 1:10**). Alternatively, a piston 2.441 inch (62 mm) long should be used with a tensioning strip type. Upon reassembly the chain tensioner should be bled preferably before the camshaft sprocket is replaced. To do this lay the piston with its recess against the tensioning arm in its housing, carefully slide in the spring with the taper wound end resting inside the closure plug and using an oil can completely fill the housing with oil. Lightly screw home the closure plug. Using a screwdriver move the tensioning arm to and fro until oil starts to issue from the closure plug. Then hold the tensioning lever breast forward and tighten the closure plug.

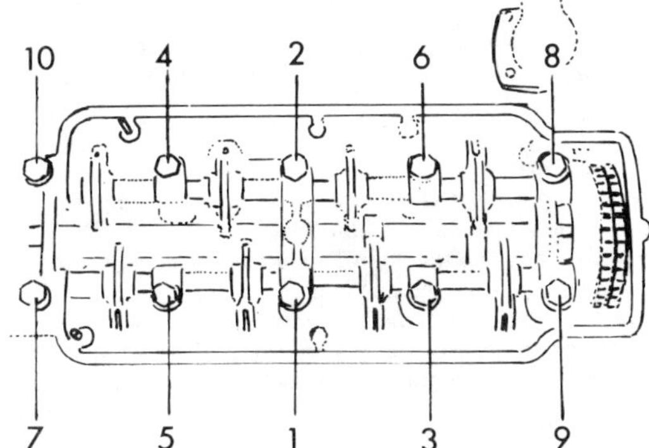

FIG 1:9 Cylinder head bolt tightening sequence

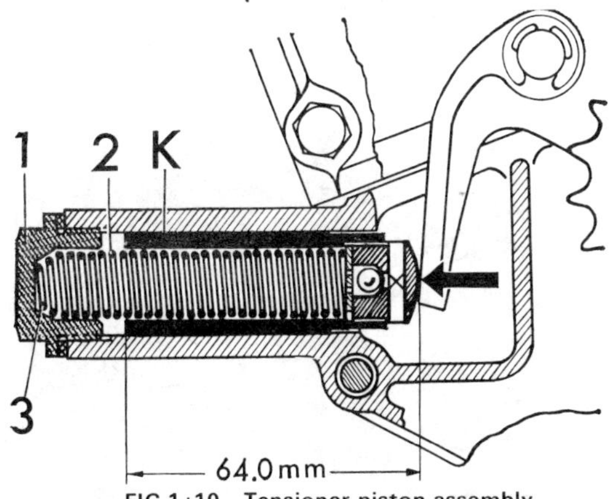

FIG 1:10 Tensioner piston assembly

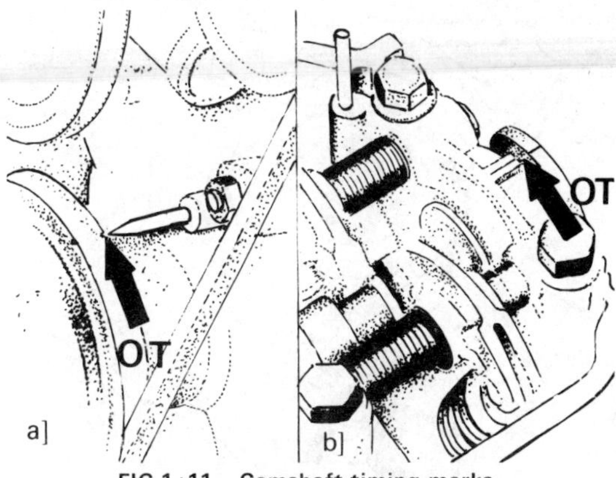

FIG 1:11 Camshaft timing marks

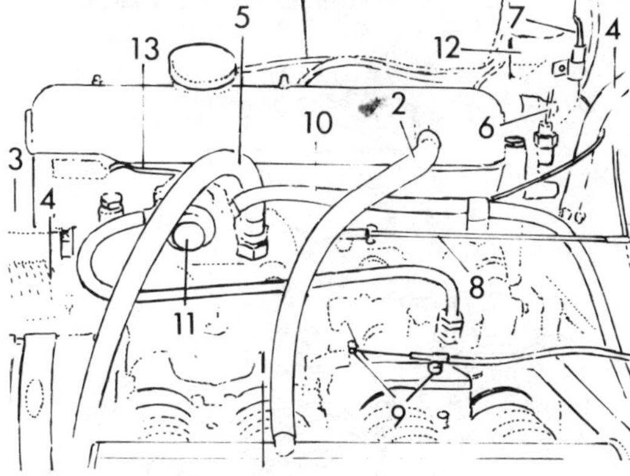

FIG 1:12 Preparatory dismantling to removing camshaft

Key to Fig 1:12 1 Air filter 2 to 5 Hose connections 6 and 7 Electrical connections 8 Throttle linkage 9 Choke cable 10 Fuel pipe 11 Fuel pump 12 Distributor 13 Thermal connection

If a timing chain tensioner of the tensioning rail type is fitted, bleed the piston by moving the rail backwards and forwards until oil emerges from the closure plug. In both cases tighten the closure plug to a torque wrench setting between 22 to 29 lb ft. Once the tensioner has been reassembled correctly, the camshaft should be rotated until the notch marked in the camshaft flange is opposite to the notch marked on the top of the cylinder head (see **FIG 1:11**). Then mount the sprocket with the chain fitted onto the camshaft flange and reassemble the four retaining bolts together with their lockplates.

5 The gearbox top cover and mating surfaces should be thoroughly clean and dry and then coated with a fine layer of Atmosit and fitted into place. Locate the two bolts holding the upper and lower gearbox casing together and just tighten. Follow by replacing the remaining six bolts checking on the final tightness of the first two bolts that were inserted. This will ensure that no oil leaks occur when the engine is back in service.

6 Upon reassembling the threaded pins of the exhaust manifold system always coat with Molykote paste to ensure ease of dismantling at a later time.

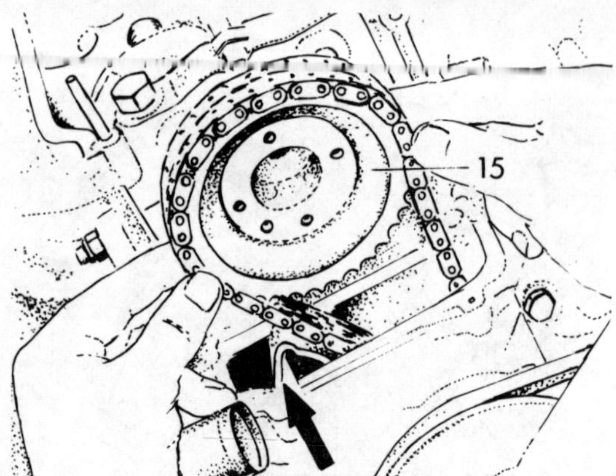

FIG 1:13 Camshaft sprocket removal

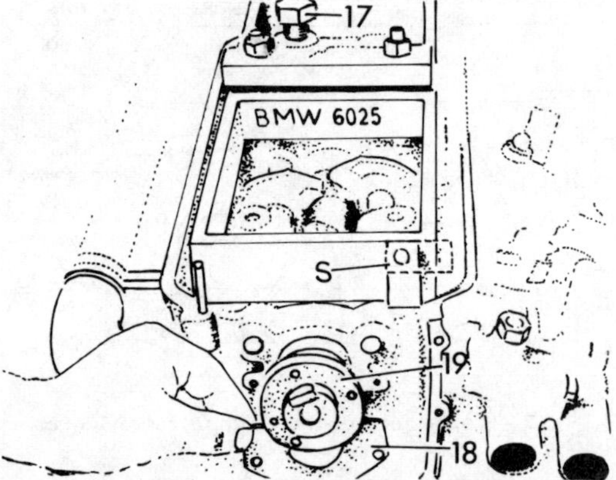

FIG 1:14 Compression frame in position on head

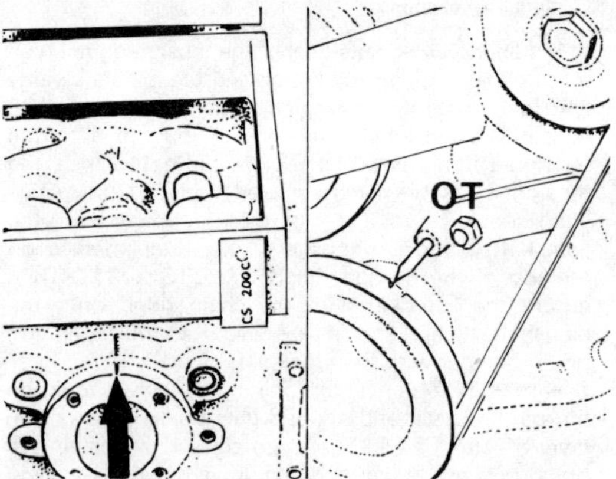

FIG 1:15 Camshaft timing marks

7 When reassembling the bowden cable to the choke lever always ensure that the choke lever is up against its limit stop and that the signal contact on the dashboard is pressed down into its lowest position. This will ensure correct control.

1:4 Removing and refitting camshaft

To remove the camshaft proceed as follows:

1 Open the bonnet and cover the wing surfaces with wing covers. Detach the earth cable from the battery. Refer to **FIG 1:12** and remove the air filter, cylinder head cover hose connections to the distributor and oil pressure switch. Disconnect the accelerator linkage, the choke control cable and the fuel supply line to the fuel pump. Remove the fuel pump, the distributor and the thermometer connection.

2 Disconnect the exhaust downpipe at the exhaust manifold flange. Remove the cylinder head cover and the upper timing chain cover, releasing the bolts in the order shown in **FIG 1:24.**

3 Release the lockplates of the camshaft sprocket retaining bolts and remove the four bolts. Inspect the chain tensioner and if it is of the sprocket type insert a screwdriver between the tensioner sprocket and the timing case cover and then carefully lift away the camshaft chain sprocket as shown in **FIG 1:13.**

4 Unscrew the cylinder head retaining bolts as shown in **FIG 1:9** and detach the splash oil pipe running the length of the cylinder head.

5 It is recommended that BMW tool No. 6025 is used for the dismantling of the cylinder head otherwise unnecessary damage could be caused to the various components. Place the cylinder head onto the rocker clamp and locate the compression frame in position as shown in **FIG 1:14**. Secure it, the two supports S must be swung out to the side as shown in the diagram. Screw up the bolt 17 until the camshaft can be withdrawn after first removing the guide plate.

Reassembly:

Reassembly is the reverse procedure to dismantling but the following points should be noted:

1 Upon reassembling the camshaft to the engine make sure that No. 1 cylinder is at TDC and that the notch on the camshaft flange is correctly aligned with the mark on the top of the cylinder head (see **FIG 1:15**).

2 Ensure that the mating surfaces on the upper and lower timing case covers and the cylinder head are thoroughly

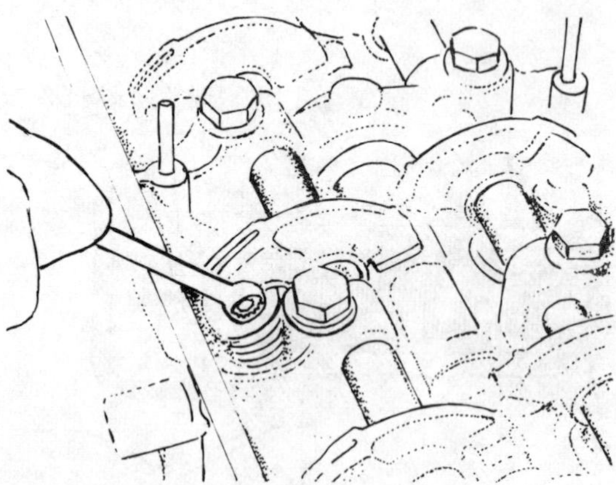

FIG 1:16 Valve clearance adjustment

clean and then coat with a thin layer of Atmosit, then screw up the two bolts clamping the upper and lower case covers together and replace the six retaining bolts to the front of the cylinder head. Finally check the tightness of the first two bolts inserted. This will ensure that there are no oil leaks in service.

3 When reassembling the exhaust downpipe to the manifold coat the threads with Molykote G paste to ensure ease of dismantling at a later time.

Valve clearance adjustment:

The overhead valve clearance must be adjusted whilst the engine is cold and stationary. To complete the adjustment proceed as follows:

1 The order of checking the clearance in the same sequence as the firing order of 1, 3, 4, 2, working with paired cylinders at the TDC position.

TDC cylinder number	*Valve overlap cylinder number*
1	4
3	2
4	1
2	3

2 Using metric feeler gauge if available check the clearance between rocker and valve stem.

Inlet .15 to .20 mm (.0059 to .00787) inch
Outlet .15 to .20 mm (.0059 to .00787) inch

3 To adjust the clearance use a ring spanner and loosen the lockscrew as shown in **FIG 1:16.** Turn the eccentric slightly using a piece of strong wire, as shown in **FIG 1:17,** and recheck clearance with feeler gauge. Continue adjustment until clearance is correct.

4 To lock the eccentric, hold in place at its correct position and tighten the ball screw gently.

5 Adjust each rocker in turn and when completed replace head cover and run engine until normal operating temperature when if the clearances have been correctly set no valve gear noise should be heard.

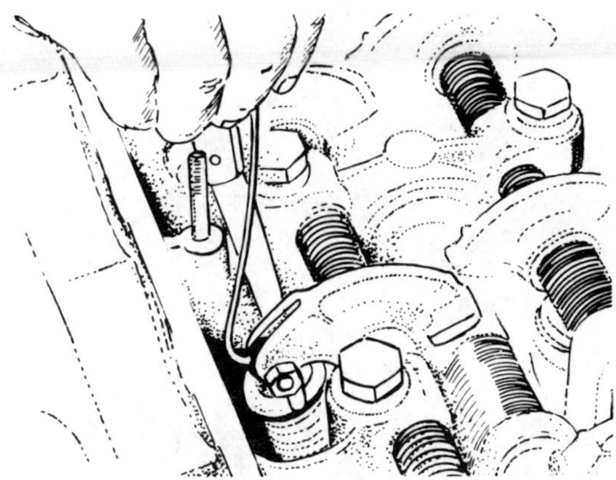

FIG 1:17 Eccentric adjustment

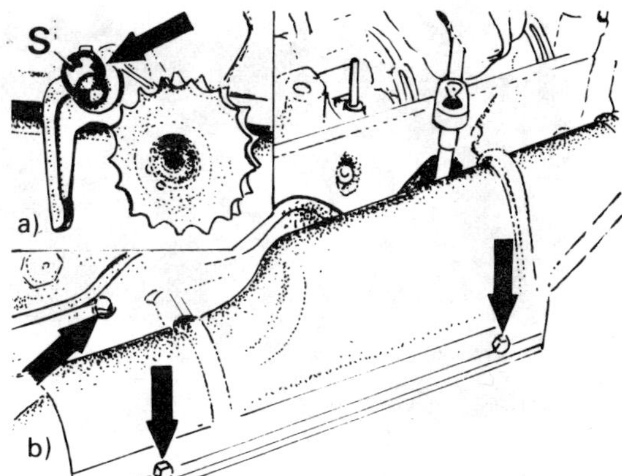

FIG 1:18 Tension sprocket retaining clip

1:5 Cylinder head dismantling and reassembly

To dismantle the cylinder head it should first be removed from the engine as detailed in **Section 1:3** and then proceed as follows:

1 Remove the retaining spring clip S from the tensioning lever of the sprocket type timing chain tensioner if fitted, and pull off the tensioning lever together with the wheel (see **FIG 1:18**).

2 Carefully place the cylinder head on a soft wood base on the work bench and remove the guide jacket bolts and lift away the guide jacket. Release the exhaust manifold nuts and lift away the manifold (see **FIG 1:19**).

3 Remove the two nuts holding the fuel pump to the cylinder head and lift away the fuel pump. Release the fastening nuts from the thermostat housing and the induction manifold and lift away the thermostat housing together with the induction manifold.

4 Remove the distributor clamp bolt and lift out the distributor. Release the four retaining bolts holding the distributor flange casting to the front of the cylinder head and lift away.

5 Remove the spark plugs and release the fastening bolts from the guide plate. Attach the rocker arm holder BMW tool 601 as shown in **FIG 1:20** and tighten the nuts evenly until the camshaft is free. Carefully lift away the camshaft and remove the guide plate. Remove the rocker arm holding tool BMW.601 and push the rocker arms and thrust rings on the rocker shaft far enough to one side to permit removal of the retaining

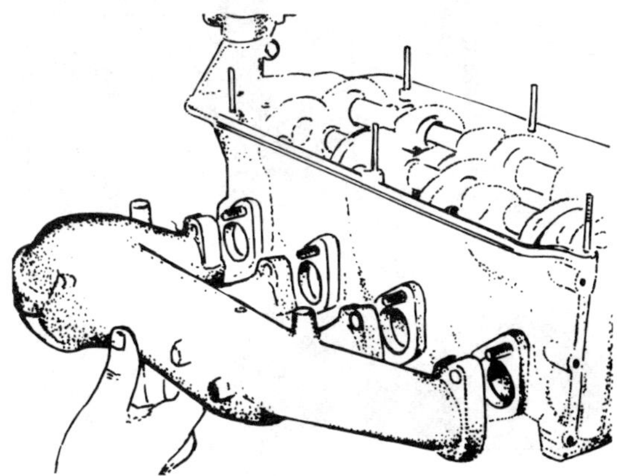

FIG 1:19 Exhaust manifold removal

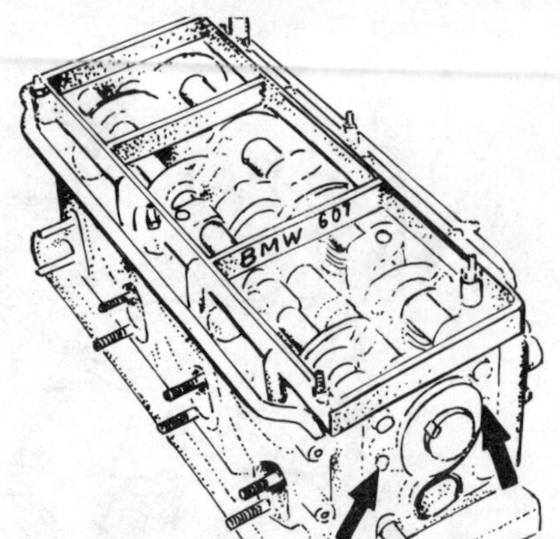

FIG 1 : 20 **Rocker arm holder in position**

FIG 1 : 21 **Camshaft guide plate**

FIG 1 : 22 **Rocker shaft removal**

circlips. Using a suitably sized drift drive the rocker shafts out towards the front of the cylinder head as shown in **FIG 1 : 22.**

6 Using BMW valve lifter 603 remove the valves and valve springs.

Reassembly:

Reassembly is the reverse procedure to dismantling but the following points should be noted:

1 The rocker shafts should be correctly aligned enabling the cylinder head bolts to be correctly refitted.

2 Upon reassembling the camshaft, the guide plate F (see **FIG 1 : 21**), also serves to retain the rocker shafts 'K'. The groove must be aligned to be in contact with the cylinder head and the inner edges of guide plate F must be clean and free from bruising. Once the guide plate has been assembled the camshaft must still be able to revolve freely. Position the camshaft so ensuring the notch in the camshaft flange is opposite to the notch made in the cylinder as shown in **FIG 1 : 11.**

3 The mating faces of the distributor flange F (see **FIG 1 : 21**) and the cylinder head front face must be coated with a non-hardening sealing compound. The distributor must be replaced so that the vacuum chamber is to the right of the engine when viewed facing forward as shown in the diagram. Finally reset the ignition timing as detailed in **Chapter 3.**

4 Before refitting the fuel pump ensure that the companion flange is not damaged and that the insulation flange thickness with gaskets and plunger length are correct specification. Refer to **Chapter 2** for full information.

1 : 6 Servicing the cylinder head

1 Remove the cylinder head and camshaft as detailed in the previous Section. If decarbonizing is intended, plug all the waterways in the top face of the cylinder block with pieces of rag. Scrape the carbon from the combustion spaces in the head before removing the valves to avoid damage to the seats.

2 **FIG 1 : 23** shows the valve assembly as assembled into the cylinder head. To remove the valves use BMW valve lifter 602. Remove the valve after marking it to ensure correct reassembly. Clean the ports free from carbon and examine the valves seats and stems.

3 The valve stems must not show any signs of 'picking up' or wear, neither should they be bent. If satisfactory, but the valve seats show pitting too deep for removal by grinding paste, have the seats reground at a garage. If the seat is too far gone or has been burnt, fit new valves. Cylinder head seatings may also be badly worn or pitted and these may be recut once the glass-hard glaze has been removed. If the seats are then too wide they can be reduced by using a special facing cutter. Seatings which are beyond recutting can be restored by having special inserts fitted.

4 To grind-in valves put a light spring under the head of the valve and use a medium grey carborundum paste unless the seats are in very good condition, when fine-grade paste may be used at once. Use a suction-cup tool and grind with a semi-rotary movement, letting the valve rise off the seat occasionally by pressure of the spring under the head. Use grinding paste sparingly. When both seats have a smooth grey matt finish clean away every trace of the grinding paste from both the port and valve.

5 If, on inspection, the valve guides are found to be worn they may be renewed. To remove the valve

guides, heat the cylinder head in an oven to approximately 180°C. Using a suitably sized drift press out the valve guides into the combustion chamber. The new valve guides may be fitted into the combustion chamber from the rocker shaft side of the cylinder head. Finally ream out the valve guides using a .315 inch diameter reamer.

6 Inspect the valve springs for weakness or signs of hairline cracks and that they conform to the specification as detailed in General Data. From chassis No. 933766 a single spring is used, replacing the double (inner and outer) spring. For the single spring it is essential to use the type 'E' lower washer.

7 Finish decarbonizing by cleaning carbon from the piston crowns. Clean off thoroughly and make sure that the faces of the head and the block are free from any oil or dirt.

Reassembly:

Reassembly is the reverse procedure to dismantling. Ensure that the valve stems are well lubricated before insertion in their guides. The oil seal rings A (see **FIG 1:23**), must always be renewed. A damaged oil seal ring will result in an increase in oil consumption. The oil seal ring should be located in the spring washer as shown in the diagram.

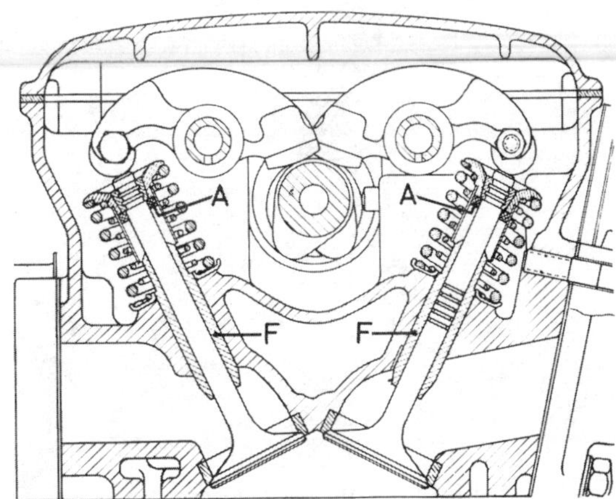

FIG 1:23 Overhead valve layout

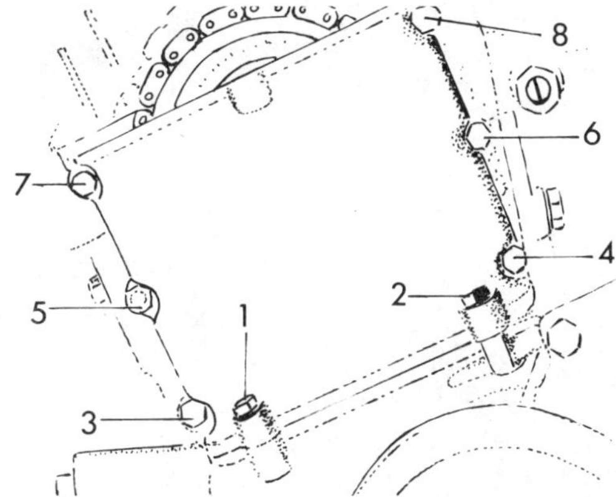

FIG 1:24 Timing gear front cover retaining bolts

1:7 Timing chain and timing gear

To remove the timing chain proceed as follows:

1 Remove the engine as detailed in **Section 1:2.**

2 Remove the engine oil sump drain plug and drain the oil.

3 Remove the supporting yoke with the silentbloc on the righthand side and if available fasten the engine to receiving plate BMW.6001 fitted into the assembly support No. BMW.6000.

4 Carefully remove the oil sump retaining bolts and lift away the sump.

5 Remove the six cylinder head cover retaining bolts and lift away the cover. Carefully rotate the crankshaft so that No. 1 cylinder is set to the TDC position. This is indicated by the tip of the pointer needle pointing to the notch in the pulley (see **FIG 1:11**). In this position the notch marked in the crankshaft flange must be opposite to the notch in the cylinder head.

6 Release the eight bolts from the top timing gear cover in the order shown in **FIG 1:24** and lift away the cover. Loosen the camshaft drive chain tensioner closure plug and unscrew by hand with extreme caution as this is under the influence of heavy spring pressure. With the plug removed, take out the spring and the piston.

7 Carefully unscrew the pulley fastening nut 1 (see **FIG 1:25**), open the tabwashers 2 and 3 for the fan fastening bolts, unscrew the bolts and carefully lift away the fan.

8 Loosen the generator clamping bolts, ease back the adjustment and lift off the fan belt. Using a universal two leg puller with suitably threaded legs extract the pulley as shown in **FIG 1:26.**

9 Unscrew the generator or alternator mounting bracket and lift away. Release the hose clamp on the right-

FIG 1:25 Fan pulley assembly

hand end of the rubber return hose, release the water pump retaining bolts and carefully lift away the water pump.

10 Remove the timing chain tensioner as previously described, open the tabwashers on the sprocket fastening bolts and remove together with the sprocket and timing chain.

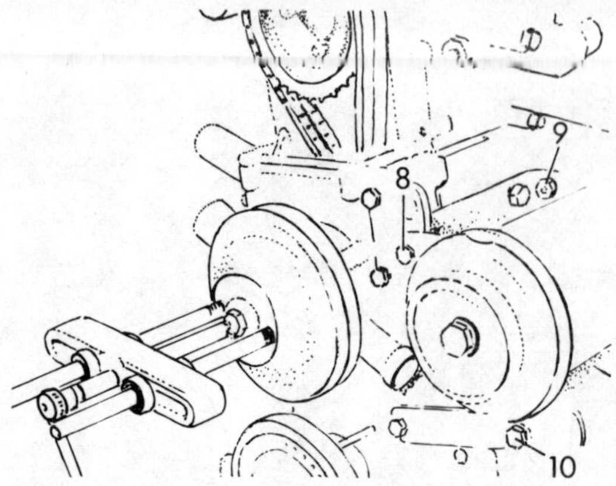

FIG 1:26 Water pump pulley removal

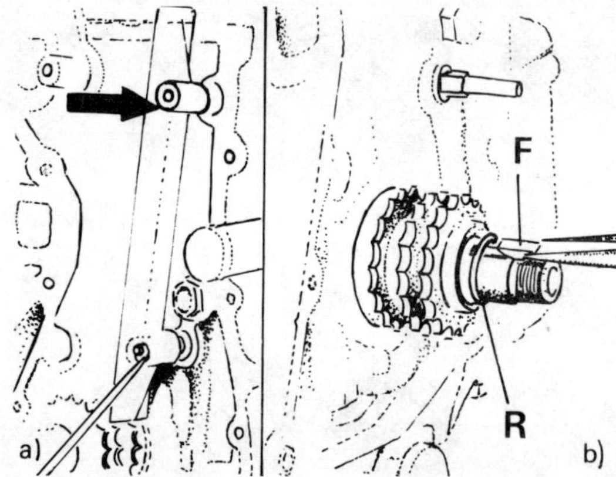

FIG 1:27 Timing gear tensioner and crankshaft oil seal

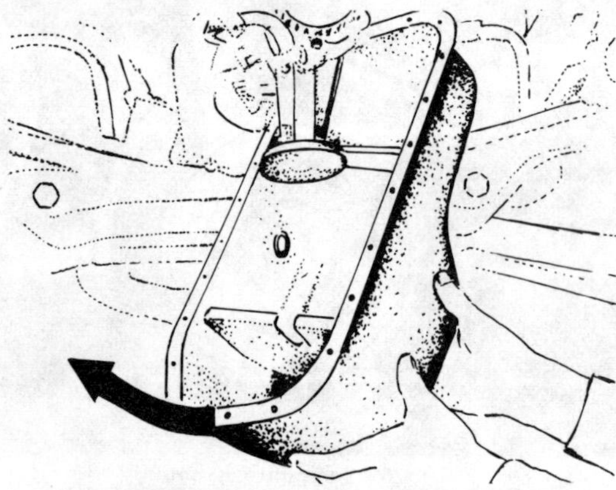

FIG 1:28 Oil sump removal

11 Carefully loosen the nut securing the crankshaft pulley, having first locked the crankshaft against movement by wedging a piece of wood between a crankshaft crank web and the crankcase.

12 Remove the six fastening bolts from the lower timing gear cover and lift away the timing gear cover, taking care not to damage the packing ring oil seal. Lift away the chain. The seal may be removed by carefully pressing it inwards. To refit a new seal, heat the timing gearbox cover to approximately 100°C in an oven and insert the seal from behind.

13 Using a screwdriver and a pair of circlip pliers release the tensioning wheel retainer and lift away the tensioning wheel. This is only applicable if the sprocket type tensioner is fitted.

14 Remove the three retaining bolts securing the sprocket to the oil pump. Ease forward the sprocket and lift away together with the driving chain.

15 Release the two oil pump housing retaining bolts and carefully ease downwards the oil pump housing so releasing it from the locating dowel sleeves. Remove the sliding rail retainers and lift away the sliding rails.

16 Lift away the key from the front of the crankshaft and remove the O-ring. Using a universal puller remove the sprocket wheel from the end of the crankshaft.

Reassembly:

Reassembly is the reverse procedure to dismantling but the following points should be noted:

1 The little O-ring fitted at the front of the crankshaft must always be renewed.

2 When refitting the retainers the machined surface (arrowed) must always face towards the retainer as shown in **FIG 1:27.**

3 Adjust the chain tensioner by fitting the appropriate packing plate as shown in **FIG 1:46.** Care must be taken to ensure that the position of the oil bore in the packing plate is correctly located otherwise failure in lubrication will occur. The correct chain tension should be so adjusted as to permit slight depression of the chain under light thumb pressure.

4 When refitting the crankshaft pulley retaining nut tighten to a torque wrench setting of 101.3 lb ft.

5 When reassembling the camshaft sprocket chain and tensioner the tensioner must be bled before the sprocket is assembled. The piston should be placed with its recess against the tensioning arm. Fit the spring with the taper wound end resting against the closure plug. Screw in the closure plug lightly. Using an oil can fill the oil space with oil. Ensure that the camshaft flange notch is correctly aligned with the notch marked in the cylinder head. Mount the sprocket and chain onto the camshaft flange and refit the four retaining bolts using new tabwashers.

6 When reassembling the water pump it is imperative that new copper gaskets are fitted.

7 When refitting the fan pulley retaining nut tighten to a torque wrench setting of 28.9 lb ft. It is essential that the fan blades are not held for additional leverage to enable the nut to be tightened but increase the fan belt tension and hold the water pump pulley.

8 When assembling the upper timing gearbox cover to the lower timing gearbox cover coat the mating surfaces with a suitable sealing compound. Fit the two cover retaining bolts but do not tighten fully and follow with the remaining six bolts as shown in **FIG 1:24.** Finally tighten the first two bolts.

9 Whenever the cylinder head cover gasket has been disturbed it must be renewed, otherwise this could cause an oil leak.

1 :8 Pistons, rings and connecting rods

The piston assemblies may be removed from the engine whilst it is in location in the vehicle. The operation is very straightforward and presents no difficulties. To remove the piston assemblies proceed as follows:

1 Remove the cylinder head as detailed in **Section 1 : 3**.

2 Drain the oil from the engine sump into a container of suitable capacity. Release the oil sump retaining bolts and carefully ease the sump forward until contact is made with the oil suction baffleplate. Gently turn the sump to the left as shown in **FIG 1 : 28** and remove.

3 Ensure that the connecting rods and end caps are suitably marked for correct reassembly. Rotate the engine until No. 1 piston is at BDC, release the connecting rod bolts, separate the end cap from the connecting rod and carefully push the piston and connecting rod upwards. Repeat for the remaining three piston assemblies.

4 Using a small screwdriver or suitably pointed tool release one of the gudgeon pin retaining wire clips as shown in **FIG 1 : 29** and push out the gudgeon pin. This operation may be done whilst the piston is cold. Mark all components for correct reassembly.

Piston rings:

To remove the rings slide a piece of steel like a disused .020 inch feeler gauge under one end and pass it round under the ring, at the same time gently pressing the raised part over onto the piston land above. Always remove and refit rings over the top of the piston. Clean carbon deposit from the ring groove with a piece of broken ring but do not remove metal, otherwise oil consumption will increase.

Before fitting new rings always remove the cylinder bore glass with special garage equipment and check the ring gap in the bore. Place a piston about 1 inch down the bore and press the new ring down onto it. Measure the gap between the ring ends with a feeler gauge as shown in **FIG 1 : 30** and file the ends if necessary until the gap is .0118 to .0177 inch for No. 1 and 2 rings. No. 3 ring should be set to have a gap of .0098 to .0157 inch. Check the piston ring side clearance using a feeler gauge as shown in **FIG 1 : 31**. The clearance should be .0024 to .0034 inch for No. 1 ring, .0014 to .0024 inch for No. 2 ring and .0098 to .0157 for No. 3 ring. Finally check the piston fitting clearance using an internal and external micrometer. The piston should be measured as shown in **FIG 1 : 32** with dimension 'A' .433 inch. The correct piston clearance is .0016 inch.

Reassembly of pistons:

This is the reverse procedure to dismantling but the following points should be noted:

1 Only pistons of the same weight classification should be fitted to an engine otherwise out of balance could occur. The piston crowns are marked with a + or — sign as shown in **FIG 1 : 34.**

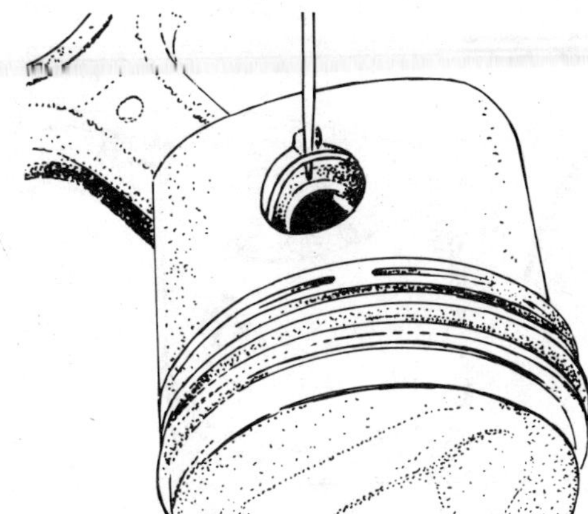

FIG 1 : 29 Gudgeon pin retaining circlip removal

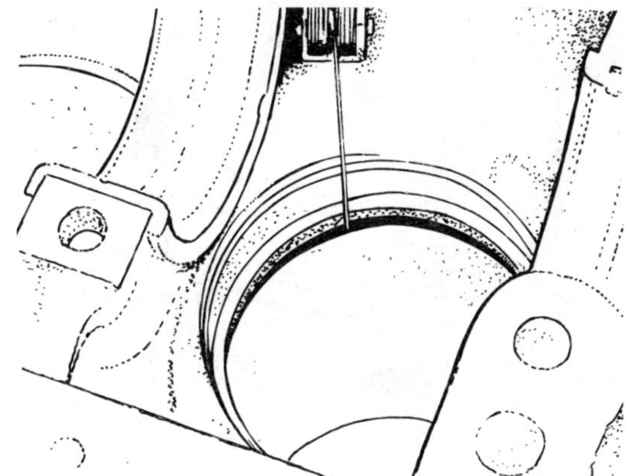

FIG 1 : 30 Piston ring gap measurement

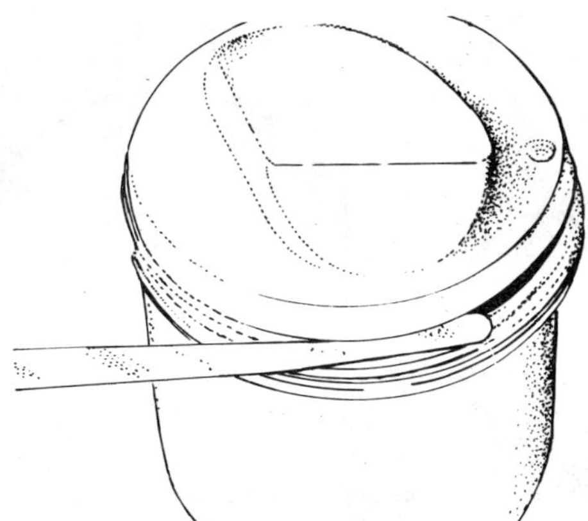

FIG 1 : 31 Piston ring side clearance

2 The piston rings are of the following type, rectangular ring, stopped ring and equal chamfer oil scraper ring. Each ring has a top and bottom and must not be fitted the wrong way round.

3 The gudgeon pins are specially colour coded and must not be intermixed.

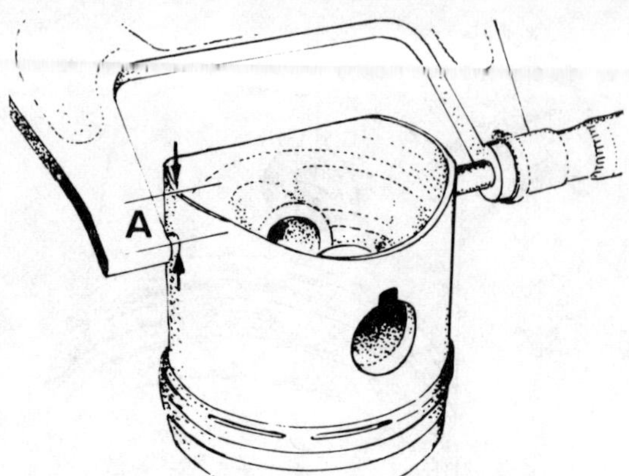

FIG 1:32 Piston diameter measurement

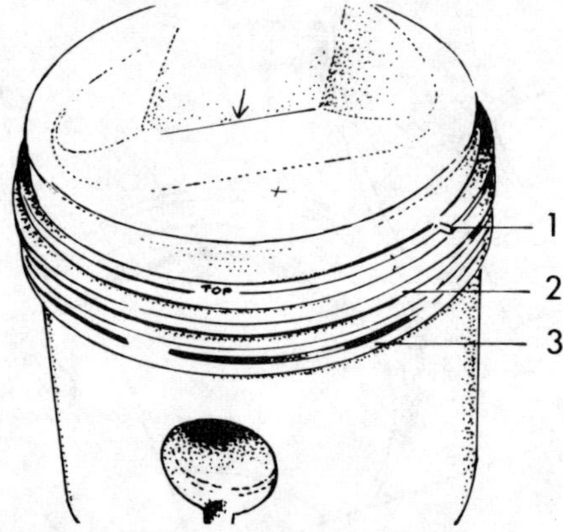

FIG 1:33 Piston ring location

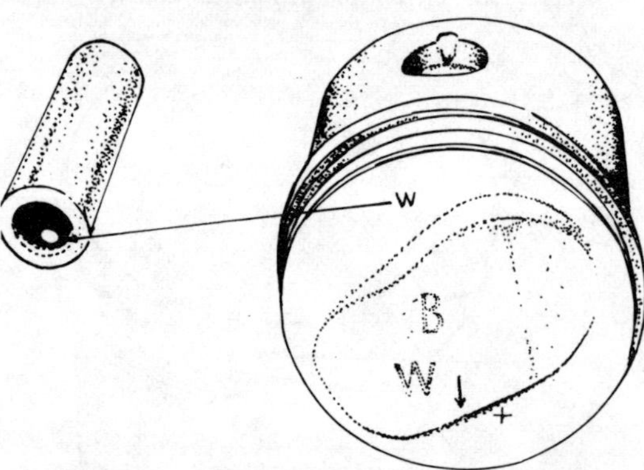

FIG 1:34 Piston and gudgeon pin identification

W stamped on piston crown—white mark on inside of pin.

S stamped on piston crown—black mark on inside of pin.

See Technical Data for further information.

4 Before refitting the pistons to the engine set the ring gap at 180 deg. to each other thus ensuring the best ring seal (see **FIG 1:35**).

Connecting rods:

Big-end bearing liners are renewable. Ensure that the running clearances compare with the information in Technical Data.

Inspection:

Examine the internal face of the rod bearing inserts and if light scratches are noticed carefully remove them by using a hand scraper. Should however deep notches or signs of wear be evident the bearings must be renewed.

The clearance between the connecting rod bearing and journal must be checked by using 'Plastigage' type PG1 calibrated wire as follows:

1 Thoroughly wipe all components with a non-fluffy rag.
2 The piston connecting rod assemblies should be prepared ready for assembly to the crankshaft. Place a piece of calibrated wire on the journal. Fit the connecting rod bearing end caps and tighten to a torque wrench setting of between 37.5 to 41.2 lb ft. Do **not** rotate the connecting rod.
3 Remove the end caps and determine the amount of clearance by comparing width of the flattened 'Plastigage' with the graduations on the envelope as shown in **FIG 1:41**. Compare their result with the specification in Technical Data.
4 Should the clearance be greater than the figures stated, the connecting rod bearings must be replaced by undersize bearings and the crankshaft specially reground at BMW. On no account file either the rod or the cap to take up wear.

Reassembly:

Reassembly is the reverse procedure to dismantling but the following points should be noted:

1 Ensure that the numbers stamped on the connecting rod and end cap match. Also check that connecting rods of the same weight classification are being fitted. This classification is coded using coloured spots (see **FIG 1:36**).
2 The oil drilling supplying the gudgeon pin lubrication should be assembled to face forwards in the direction of travel.

FIG 1:35 Piston ring gap location

3 Check that the piston ring slots are 180 deg. to each other and thoroughly lubricate piston and bearing upon fitting (see **FIG 1 : 35**).

4 The connecting rod and bolts are special 12K expansion bolts and must not be reused. Always fit new bolts on reassembly and tighten to a torque wrench setting of between 37 to 41.2 lb ft.

1 : 9 Removing and refitting flywheel

The flywheel may be removed with the engine in situ but with gearbox and clutch removed. To complete this operation proceed as follows:

1 Before the flywheel is removed from the engine it is advisable to check for any distortion due to heat from excessive clutch use. Attach a dial gauge to the cylinder block and position so that the probe is in contact with the friction face as shown in **FIG 1 : 37**. At a radius of 200 mm (7.874 inch) the maximum runout allowed is .10 mm (.004 inch). The flywheel face is specially hardened and the maximum allowable skimming thickness is .012 + .0039 inch. Care must be taken to ensure that the inside wall thickness of the friction face is not less than .531 inch.

2 Lever off the locking plate for the six flywheel to crankshaft retaining bolts as shown in **FIG 1 : 38** and release the retaining bolts, having first locked the flywheel using BMW tool No. 6013 or using other suitable means. Carefully lift away the flywheel.

3 Reassembly is the reverse procedure to dismantling. A new locking plate must be fitted taking care it is pushed squarely onto the bolt heads.

1 : 10 Removing and refitting crankshaft

Drain the engine oil sump and remove the engine as detailed in **Section 1 : 2**. Thoroughly clean the outside of the engine and then proceed as follows:

1 Remove the lower half of timing gear cover and the oil pump and accessories as detailed in **Section 1 : 7**.

2 Check the crankshaft end float with a dial gauge located on flywheel as shown in **FIG 1 : 39** by levering the crankshaft endwise using a screwdriver. This should be between .0024 to .0064 inch. If the clearance is excessive a new centre main bearing incorporating thrust washers must be fitted (see **FIG 1 : 40**).

3 Remove the flywheel as described in **Section 1 : 9** and release the crankshaft end cover.

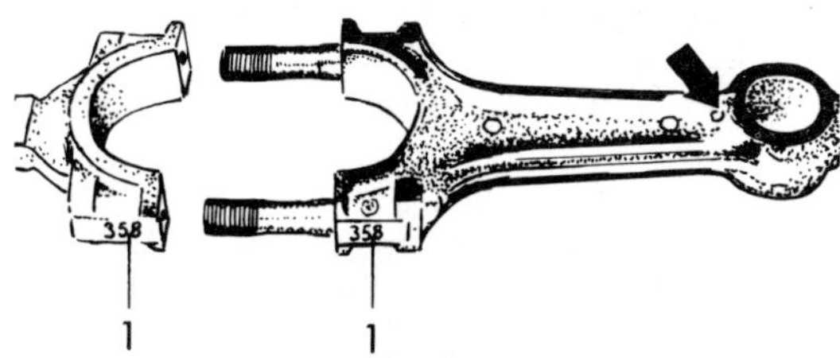

FIG 1 : 36 Connecting rod identification

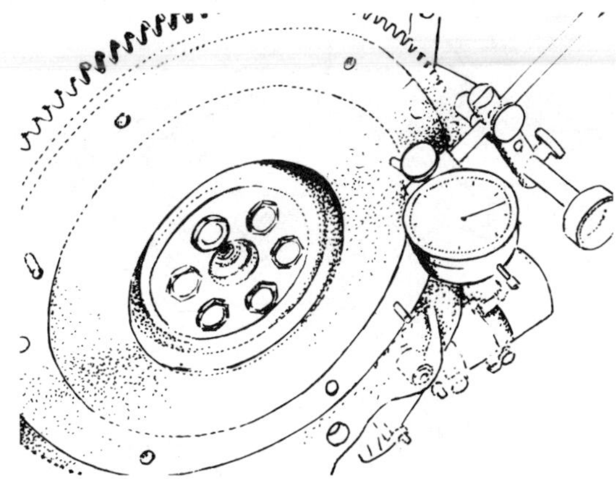

FIG 1 : 37 Checking flywheel runout

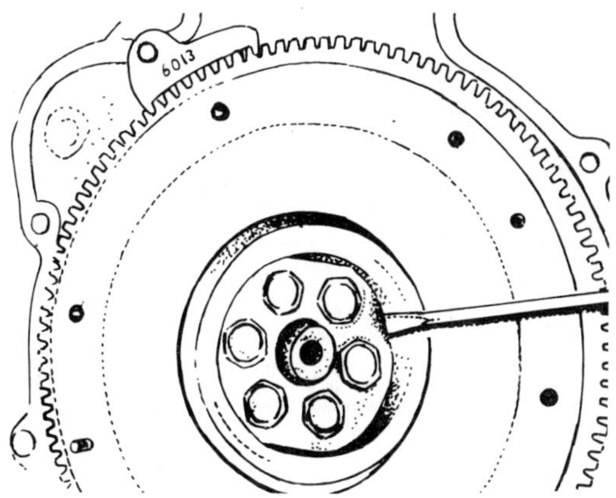

FIG 1 : 38 Flywheel retaining bolt lockplate

FIG 1 : 39 Checking crankshaft end float

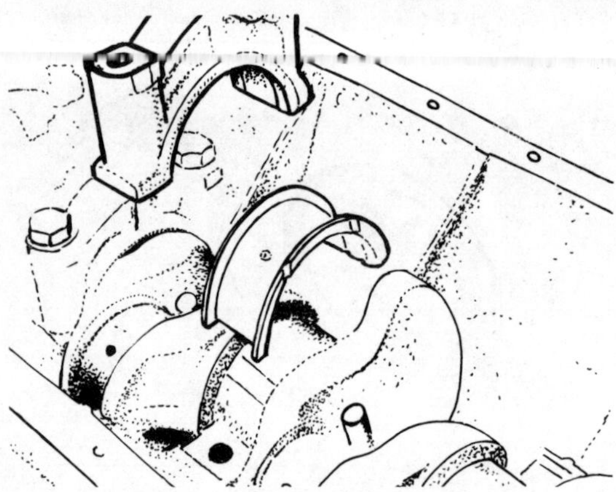

FIG 1:40 Crankshaft master bearing

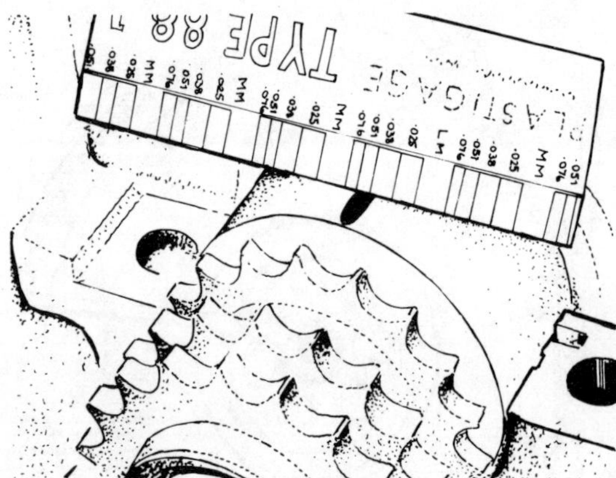

FIG 1:41 Bearing clearance measurement

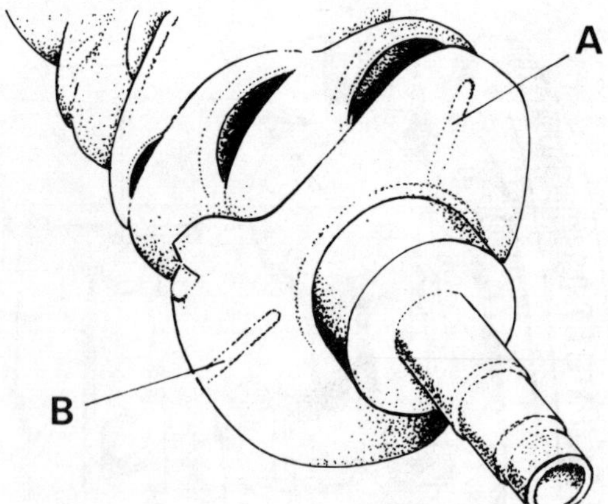

FIG 1:42 Crankshaft journal size identification

4 Using a dial gauge suitably positioned check the crankshaft sealing ring which if worn or distorted must be renewed.
5 Inspect the gearbox first motion shaft grooved ball-bearings for signs of wear or overheating and fit new if necessary.
6 Ensure the connecting rods and end caps are suitably marked for correct reassembly and remove the end cap bolts.
7 Ensure the main bearing end caps are suitably marked for correct reassembly and remove the retaining bolts. It should be noted the centre main bearing is the master bearing and it is this which determines the crankshaft end float. This bearing is colour coded according to crankshaft journal diameter and end float.
8 Carefully lift out the crankshaft.

Cleaning crankshaft and oil passages:

To thoroughly clean the crankshaft and oil drillings wash in paraffin ensuring penetration of paraffin into the oil drillings and use a compressed air line to pass air through the drillings. Wipe dry with a non-fluffy rag.

Main bearings:

Minor scratches on the main bearing inserts can be smoothed out by carefully using a hand scraper. Should there be signs of seizure excess wear or grooves, fit new bearing inserts.

If the inspection reveals that the bearing inserts are satisfactory to check their clearance to the crankshaft journals proceed as follows:

1 Place a piece of 'Plastigage' calibrated wire on the journal and install the main bearing caps and shell bearings. Tighten the main bearing cap bolts to a torque wrench setting of between 42 and 45.6 lb ft. **Do not** rotate the crankshaft.
2 Remove the caps and compare the width of the flattened 'Plastigage' with the graduation scale on the envelope (see **FIG 1:41**). The number within the graduation on the envelope indicates the correct bearing clearances. The correct clearance of main bearing to journal is between .0019 and .0027 inch. Should the clearance not be within the wear limit replace bearings. If this still gives an oversize reading the crankshaft will have to be specially reground at BMW. Two sizes of undersize bearings are available. Full dimension details are given in Technical Data. Never file the bearing caps in an attempt to take up wear.

A colour coding is used for reground crankshaft (see **FIG 1:42**).

Main bearing journal (B):

1 Colour stripe — 1st undersize
2 Colour stripes — 2nd undersize

Big-end bearing journal (A):

1 Colour stripe — 1st undersize—red or blue
2 Colour stripes — 2nd undersize—red or blue

For an original diameter crankshaft a red or blue colour spot is marked on the counterweight as shown in **FIG 1:43**.

General inspection:

The crankshaft must be thoroughly inspected for signs of cracking at the crankpin and journals as well as the webs. If there are any signs of failure the crankshaft must be renewed.

Should there be any deep notches or the journals found to be oval in excess of .002 inch then the journals should be reground.

Before refitting the crankshaft to the engine always ensure that the oil passages are thoroughly clean and there are no signs of metal dust from the grinding process.

Crankpin and journal alignment:

1 Support the ends of the crankshaft on V-blocks on a surface plate and using a dial indicator gauge check the centre main bearing for runout. The maximum permissible runout is .0008 inch at the centre main bearing.
2 Check for alignment of crankpins.
3 Check for crankpin and journal ovality.
4 Check for crankpin and journal taper.
5 Flywheel mounting flange. Fit the flywheel, turn the crankshaft and set the dial indicator to edge of flange. Maximum runout should not exceed $.012 \pm .0039$ inch.

Should any distortion be found it must be corrected by means of careful use of an arbor press.

Refitting crankshaft:

Reassembly of the crankshaft is the reverse procedure to dismantling. The following points should be noted:

1 If an undersize crankshaft is being used it is essential that the corresponding bearing shells are used.
2 Ensure that the main bearing end caps are correctly located and it is best policy to fit new bolts. Tighten to a torque wrench setting of between 42 and 45.6 lb ft. The oil filter bracket is secured with No. 2 main bearing end cap.
3 Check that the connecting rods are installed in the same positions as noted on removal from engine. Always use new end caps bolts and tighten to a torque wrench setting of between 37.6 and 41.2 lb ft.
4 When reassembling the gearbox drive shaft ballbearing in the end of the crankshaft, always pack the ballbearing race with a high melting point grease. Fit the coverplate with its projection facing outwards. It is recommended that the felt washer be soaked in hot fat and finally drive on the end cap as far as it will go (see **FIG 1:44**).
5 Before reassembling the crankshaft rear cover smear with Atmosit at the contact face with the oil sump.

1:11 Cylinder block and crankcase

Cleaning:

Immerse the complete crankcase in a wash tank containing a water and soda solution and thoroughly wash using a pressure jet. Ensure that all oilways are thoroughly cleaned. Using a compressed air jet blow away traces of moisture and finally wipe internally and externally with a non-fluffy rag.

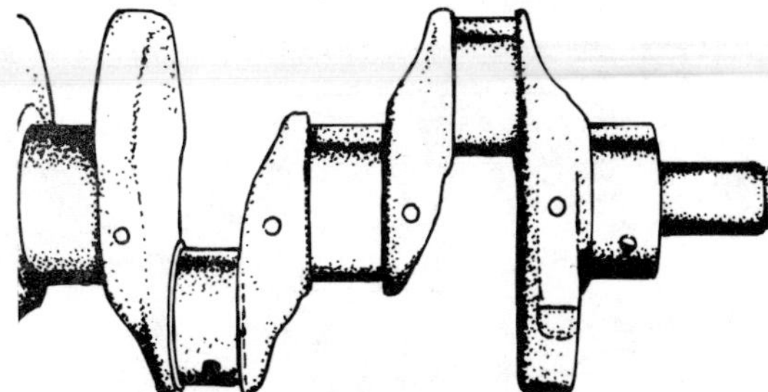

FIG 1:43 Crankshaft journal size identification

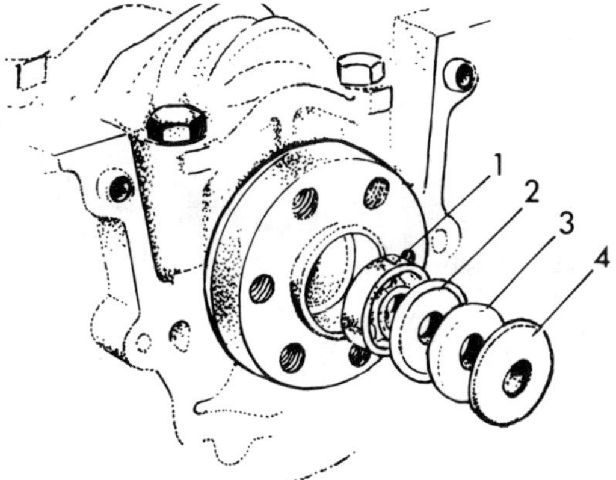

FIG 1:44 Gearbox drive shaft ballbearing assembly

Key to Fig 1:44 1 Bearing 2 Coverplate 3 Felt washer 4 Cap

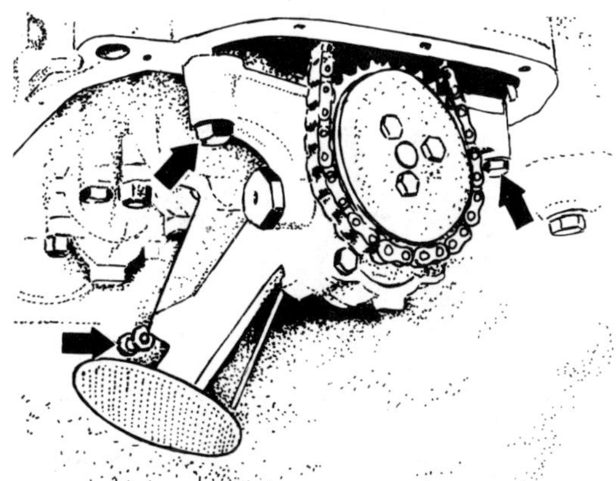

FIG 1:45 Oil pump mounting location

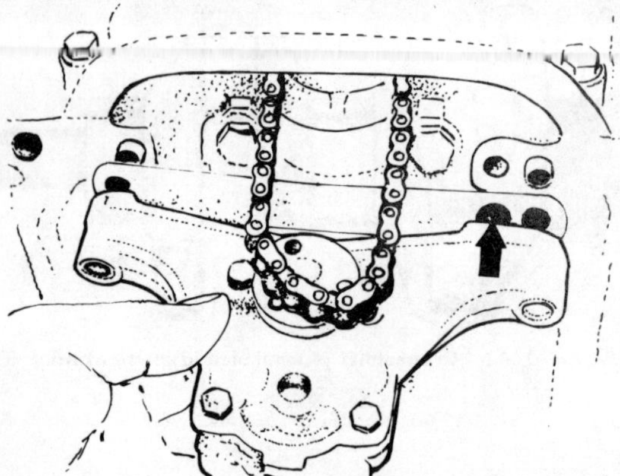

FIG 1:46 Oil pump removal—note packing shim location

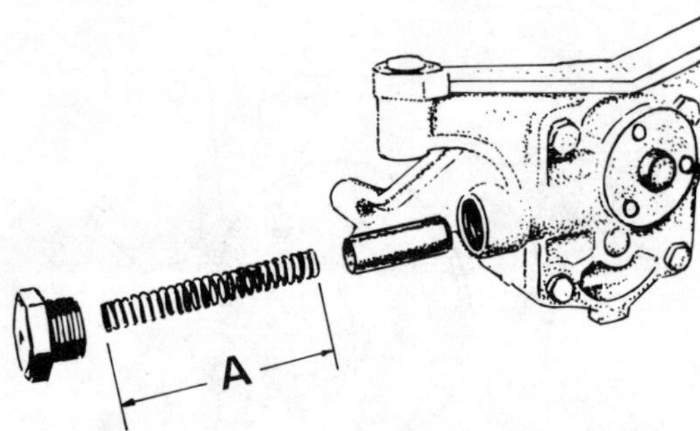

FIG 1:47 Oil pressure relief valve

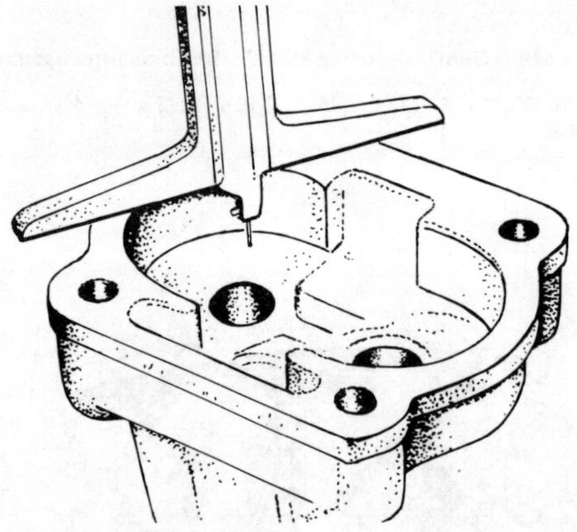

FIG 1:48 Oil pump body wear

Cylinder bores:

Examine the cylinder bores and if light scoring marks are detected it is suggested that the block is taken to a garage and refaced using fine emerycloth, wrapped around a hone.

Check the cylinder bore dimensions at the top and bottom of the bore to check for taper as well as ovality. Full dimensional details are given in Technical Data.

Cylinder head mating face:

The cylinder block may show distortions on the head mating face and may be checked by using a straight edge and feeler gauge placed diagonally across the face and also longitudinally. If distortion is detected a surface grinder should be used, care being taken to remove as little metal as possible.

1:12 Oil pump removal and refitting

The oil pump may be removed with the engine in situ. Raise the front of the vehicle, place on firmly based stands and proceed as follows:

1 Release the oil sump retaining bolts and carefully pull the sump forward until contact is made between the oil filter and the baffle plate. Gently turn the oil sump towards the left and ease down forwards and lift away from the underside of the car (see **FIG 1:28**).

2 Remove the three bolts holding the chain sprocket to the pump and remove the sprocket. Remove the two oil pump retaining bolts, the retaining plate mounting nuts and carefully remove the oil pump assembly downwards making note of any chain tension shims that may be in position between the pump and the underside of the crankcase (see **FIG 1:45** and **1:46**).

Reassembly:

Reassembly is the reverse procedure to removal but the following points should be noted:

1 Adjust the chain tension with the specially shaped shims placed between the oil pump and the crankcase. The correct adjustment is obtained when the chain can be depressed under light thumb pressure. Always ensure that the oil hole in the shim mates up with the oil hole in the crankcase otherwise failure of lubrication system will result.

2 To ensure that no oil leaks occur between the oil sump flange and the underside of the crankcase always check the alignment of the bolt holes and realign if necessary.

1:13 Oil pump dismantling and reassembly

Before dismantling the oil pump thoroughly clean the outside using an oil solvent and blow dry carefully, using compressed air jet. To dismantle the pump proceed as follows:

1 Unscrew the pressure relief valve spring retaining plug as shown in **FIG 1:47.** Carefully lift away the spring and plunger. Check the length of the spring which should be 2.68 inches. It is very important that the length of the spring is not altered and should the original one fitted to the oil pump be greater than the specified length, then a new spring must be fitted.

2 Release the four body retaining bolts and separate the two halves of the pump body. Thoroughly clean the mating flange of the body and using a depth gauge as shown in **FIG 1:48** check the amount of wear at the position shown. The maximum amount of wear permissible is .002 inch.

3 Using a set of feeler gauges check the backlash between the two gears as shown in **FIG 1:49**. The clearance when new should be between .001 and .002 inch. The maximum permissible backlash is .003 inch.
4 Using a vernier or other suitable measuring instrument, check the hub-to-pinion contact face dimension 'A' (see **FIG 1:50**). This dimension should be 1.358± .004 inch.
5 Thoroughly check all gear teeth for signs of excessive wear or pitting, and also the main pump body for hairline cracks or signs of distortion. New parts should be fitted as required.

Reassembly:

Reassembly is the reverse procedure to dismantling. It is considered advisable that whilst attention is being given to the oil pump, the oil filter located on the underside of the crankcase should be removed and thoroughly cleaned. Check the filter medium for damage or clogging and either clean or fit a new filter as necessary.

On later cars the gear type oil pump is replaced by a rotor type pump and in the event of a new type pump being fitted as a replacement the following instructions should be followed.

Refer to **FIG 1:51**. Remove the gear type pump, the pivot pin 1 and washer 2 and the screw plug 3. Insert the new sealing washer 4 and secure the pipe 5 with the new pivot pin 6 and lock washer 7.

Fit the new rotor type pump with sprocket and 24 link chain and adjust the chain tension as described in **Section 1:12**, being most careful to mate up the hole in the shim with the oil hole in the crankcase.

Dismantling and reassembly:

Lift out the sealing ring, plunger and spring. Check that the free length of the spring is 68 mm (2.677 inch) and renew it if it differs from this measurement. **Pull**, not push, off the driven flange. Separate the components of the pump and after washing them they should be examined for excessive wear or damage and renewed if necessary.

Reassembly is quite straightforward, but great care must be given to checking the dimensions indicated.

Check the fitting of the inner rotor on its shaft (see **FIG 1:52**). Check the measurements between the flange and the inner rotor shown in **FIG 1:53**.

Check the running clearances between: The outer rotor and pump housing (see **FIG 1:54**). The inner and outer rotors (see **FIG 1:55**). The pump housing and rotor sealing face (see **FIG 1:56**). If the maximum clearances are exceeded the components must be renewed.

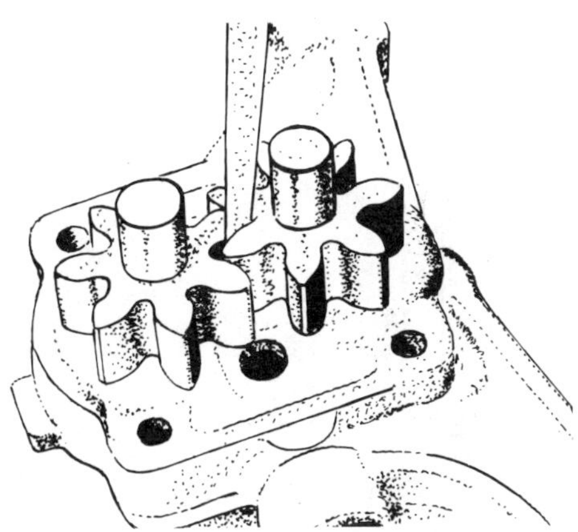

FIG 1:49 Oil pump gear backlash

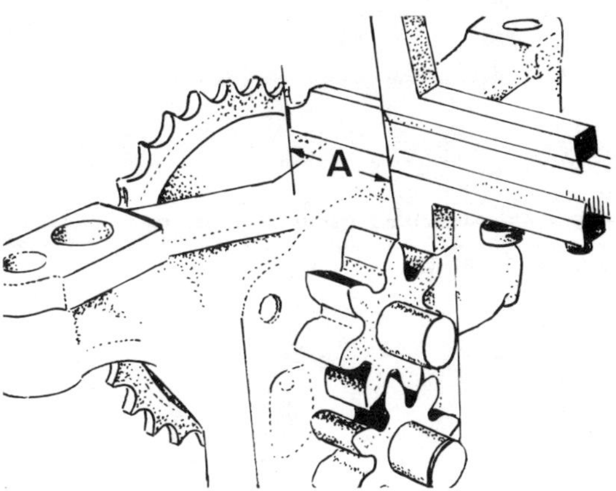

FIG 1:50 Oil pump gear location

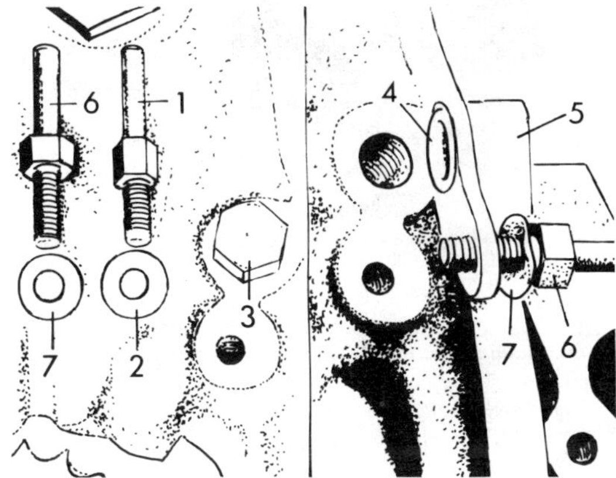

FIG 1:51 View showing details of old and new pump fitting procedure.

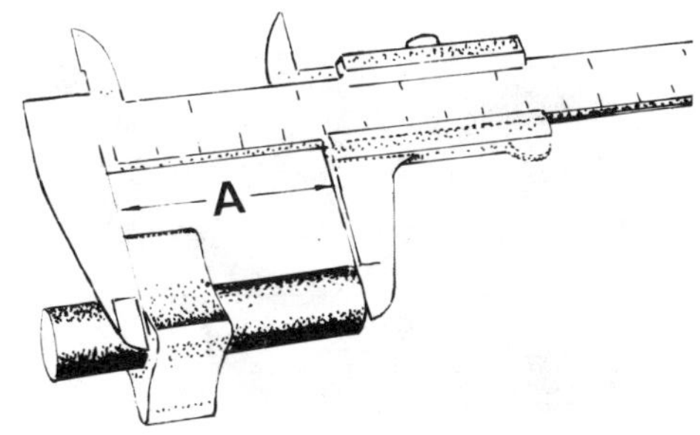

FIG 1:52 Fitting inner rotor on shaft. A=51 mm (2.007 inch)

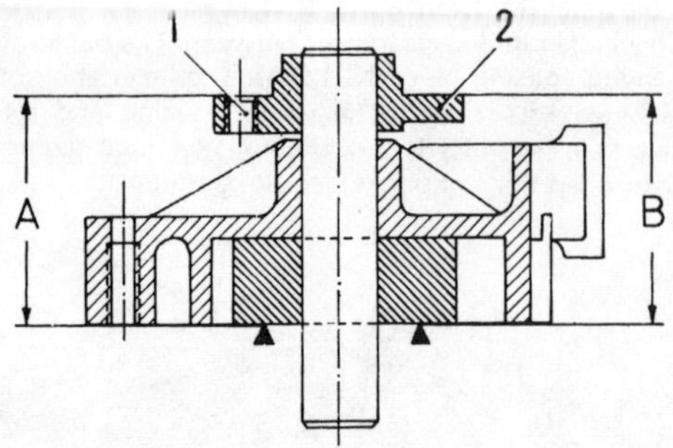

FIG 1:53 Measuring flange to inner rotor distance. Flange 1 A=42.7±.01 mm (1.681±.0004 inch). Flange 2 B=42.5±.01 mm (1.673±.0004 inch)

FIG 1:54 Clearance between outer rotor and pump housing .05 to .20 mm (.0020 to .0079 inch)

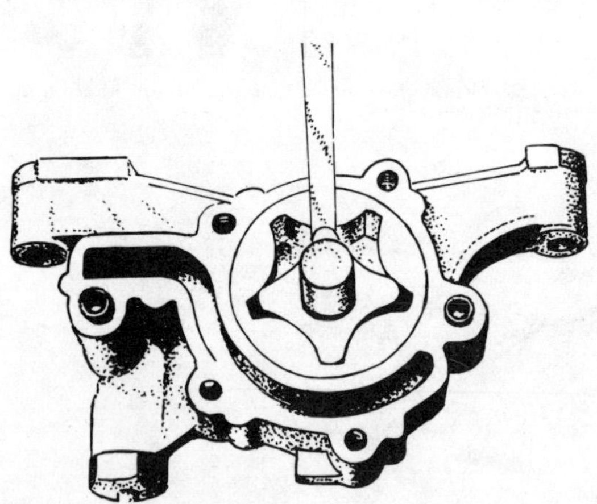

FIG 1:55 Clearance between inner and outer rotors .09 to .27±.03 mm (.0035 to .0106±.0012 inch)

1:14 Fullflow filter

A fullflow oil filter of the renewable element type is located on the side of the engine underneath the generator.

It is recommended that the filter element be renewed every 4000 miles, and to remove the old element proceed as follows:

1 Disconnect the battery before starting work on the filter. Unscrew the centre bolt, the head of which is located at the base of the filter bowl. Carefully remove the bowl holding upright as it will be full of oil.

2 Discard the old oil into a suitable container and remove the element and clean the inside of the bowl with fuel. Do not attempt to clean the element as nothing useful can be gained by doing so.

3 Remove the old oil seals and fit new as supplied with the new filter element. Place the element in the bowl and fill the bowl with clean engine oil. Tighten the filter bowl retaining bolt.

FIG 1:56 Clearance between pump housing and rotor sealing face .034 to .084 mm (.0013 to .0033 inch)

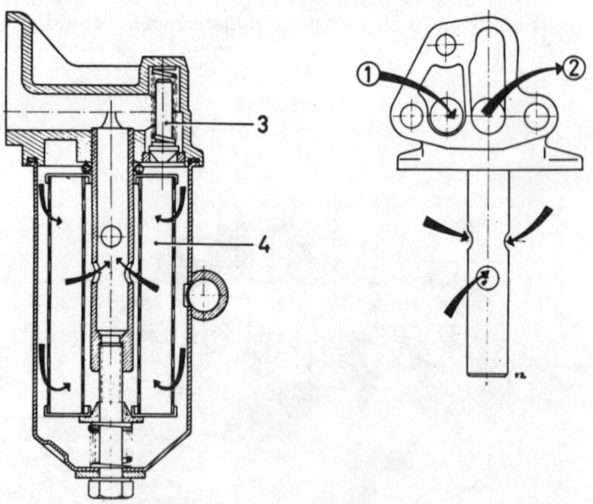

FIG 1:57 Full flow filter

Key to Fig 1:57 1 Oil supply from pump 2 Oil supply to lubrication points 3 Bypass valve 4 Filter element

4 Reconnect the battery and start the engine. Immediately check for signs of oil leaks between the filter bowl and its main body as it is essential that there are no leaks from the filter as this could lead to complete failure of the engine lubrication system.

1:15 Factory exchange engine installation

Should it be necessary to fit a factory reconditioned engine it is recommended that the replacement engine be prepared before the unit is assembled to the vehicle.

1 Remove the original power unit as fully described in **Section 1:2.**
2 Remove the two fastening bolts for the support bracket S (see **FIG 1:58**). Detach the fastening bolts detailed 1 and 2 for the coverplate A from the gearbox and lift away the plate.
3 Remove the starter motor fastening bolts and lift away the starter motor.
4 Remove the fastening bolts holding the engine and gearbox crankcase. Also release the lefthand silentbloc from the crankcase (see **FIG 1:60**).

Reassembly of units to replacement engine:

1 Replace the two silentbloc mountings with limit stops to the crankcase.
2 Fit the gearbox to the engine and tighten the fastening bolts to a torque wrench setting of 18.1 lb ft.
3 Fit the starter and tighten the retaining bolts to a torque wrench setting of 34 lb ft.
4 Refit the gearbox coverplate ensuring that it is located the correct way round.
5 Refit the two fastening bolts for the support bracket.
6 Refit the engine as described in **Section 1:2.**

1:16 Exhaust emission control unit

Description:

To ensure that the exhaust emission control unit is operating satisfactorily the carburetter requires to be correctly adjusted using an exhaust gas analyzer. Also to ensure effective operation the ignition timing has to be accurately set using a stroboscope. Normally this equipment is not available to car owners and it is therefore suggested that this work be entrusted to the local garage. For reference purposes full details of the two adjustments are given.

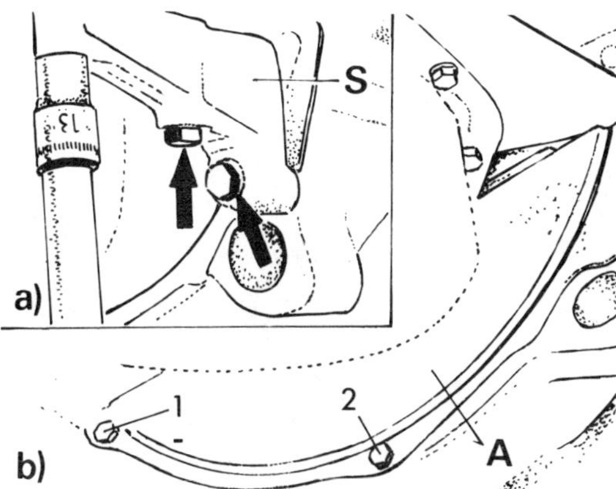

FIG 1:58 Support bracket location

Carburetter adjustment:

1 Refer to **FIG 1:59** and detach the air hose **1** from the non-return valve and connect the exhaust gas analyzer to the exhaust tail pipe.
2 Run the engine at a fast idle speed to allow it to come up to normal operating temperature and then using an electric tachometer set the engine idle speed to 1000 rev/min.
3 Use the slow-running mixture adjustment screw, refer to **Chapter 2,** set the CO content to 7 ± 1 per cent.
4 Recheck the engine idling speed to 1000 rev/min if necessary and repeat the operation until the required value is obtained. Finally reset to normal idling speed.

Ignition timing:

1 Using electronic engine tuning equipment check that the distributor dwell angle is correct.
2 Detach the vacuum advance pipe from the distributor.
3 Set the engine speed to a fast idle and allow to come up to normal operating temperature. Reset the engine idle speed with the assistance of an electric tachometer to 2000 rev/min.

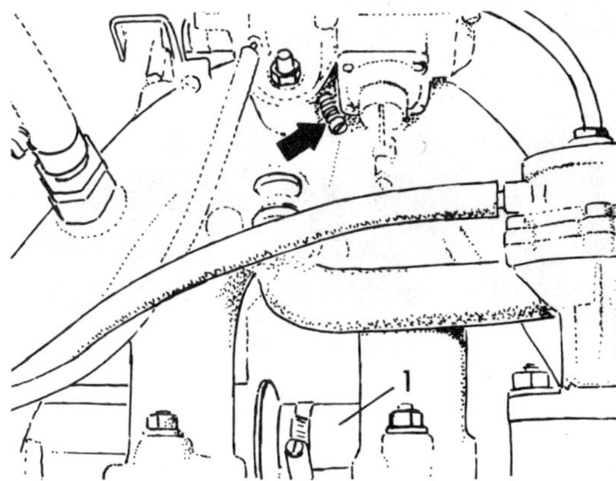

FIG 1:59 Non-return valve and idling adjustment screw

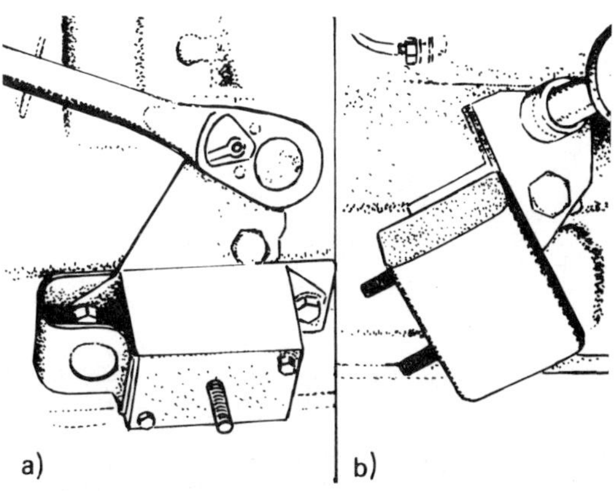

FIG 1:60 Engine mountings

FIG 1 : 61 Flywheel engine timing steel ball and datum mark

FIG 1 : 62 Front timing marks

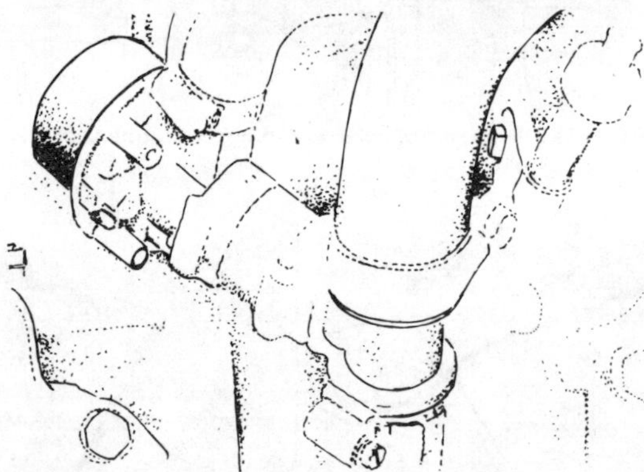

FIG 1 : 63 Control valve

4 Connect the stroboscope into the ignition system and point towards the aperture in the gearbox bellhousing so that the steel ball located in the flywheel can be seen.

5 Adjust the ignition timing as necessary so that the centre of the steel ball is visible at the datum location as shown in **FIG 1 : 61**.

Should the engine flywheel not be fitted with a steel ball or there is no inspection opening in the gearbox bellhousing the static ignition timing must be set using the marks on the V-belt pulley. Refer to **FIG 1 : 62** where it will be seen that the upper notch in the pulley is the TDC timing notch, the next notch is the static ignition timing notch and the lower notch is for ignition timing using a strobe light at 2000 rev/min.

After either of the above two methods of checking and adjusting the ignition timing reset the engine idle speed.

Exhaust gas control valve:

This component is very reliable in operation and only needs renewing should difficulty be experienced in the setting of the carburetter to give correct exhaust gas compensation or persistent backfiring in the exhaust system whilst the throttle control is closed. The location is shown in **FIG 1 : 63.**

Air pump:

To check the operation of the air pump, carefully remove the blow-off pipe from the air pump and lightly press the hand on the pressure relief valve. With the assistance of a second operator allow the engine speed to increase slowly. Normally the pressure release valve will open between 1700 to 2000 rev/min. If the release valve should open earlier the pressure regulator unit should be renewed by first releasing the hose and extracting the pressure regulator unit with the assistance of two screwdrivers. A new pressure regulator unit should be pushed into position (see **FIG 1 : 64**). Should the pressure release valve only open at an engine speed in excess of 2000 rev/min then the air pump must be renewed. This operation is very straightforward only requiring the removal of the hoses and retaining bolts together with the mounting bushes. These should be checked for wear and renewed as necessary. Tighten the retaining bolts to a torque wrench setting of 59 lb ft (see **FIG 1 : 65**).

The lower mounting bolt locates in an elongated hole on the mounting bracket and the V-belt tension should be adjusted by easing the air pump away from the engine oil sump using hand pressure only. When correctly adjusted it should be possible to depress the belt between .2 and .4 inch.

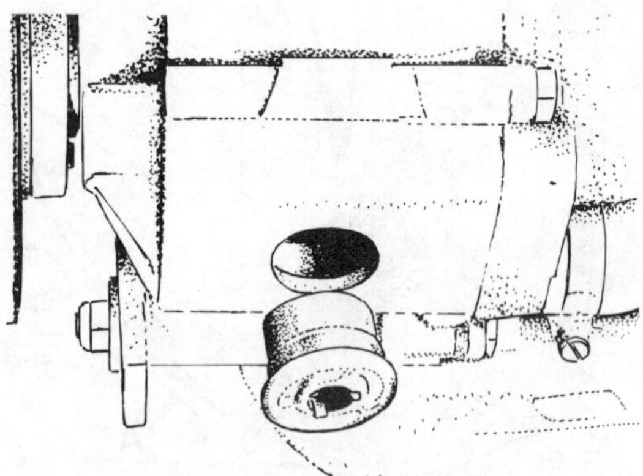

FIG 1 : 64 Pressure regulator unit

Non-return valve:

The non-return valve is located in the manifold as shown in **FIG 1:66**. To remove the valve first detach the heat deflection shield, release the hose and pipe clip in the underside of the manifold and unscrew the non-return valve from the pipe manifold.

Injection pipes:

The injection pipes are located in the exhaust system inside the exhaust manifold. If new pipes are being inserted they should be screwed into the manifold to the length marked on the injection pipe as shown in **FIG 1:67**.

$A = 37 \text{ mm } {}^{+0}_{-1} \text{ mm } (1{\cdot}456 \; {}^{+0}_{-.04} \text{ inch})$.

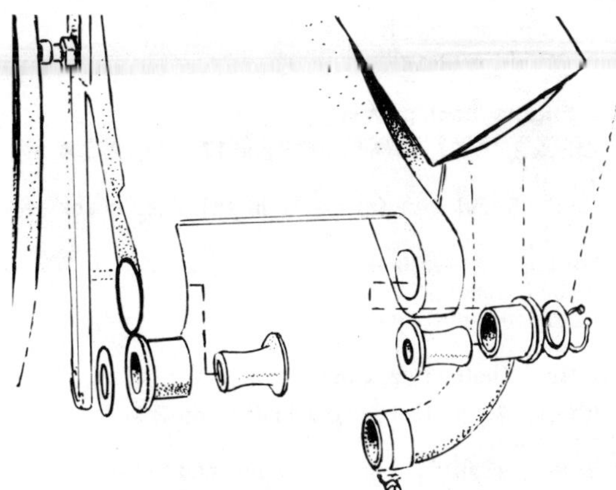

FIG 1:65 Air pump mountings

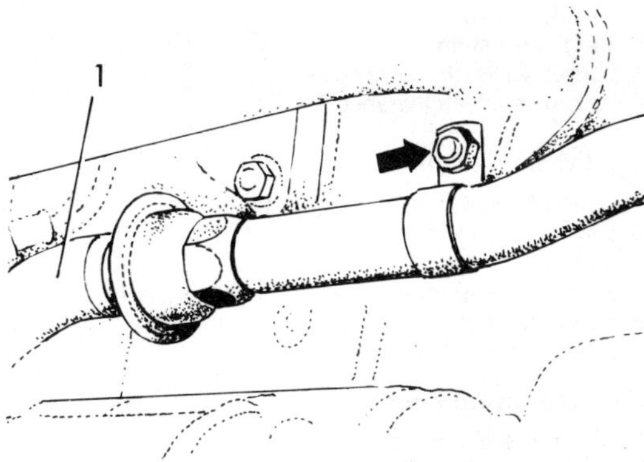

FIG 1:66 Non-return valve location

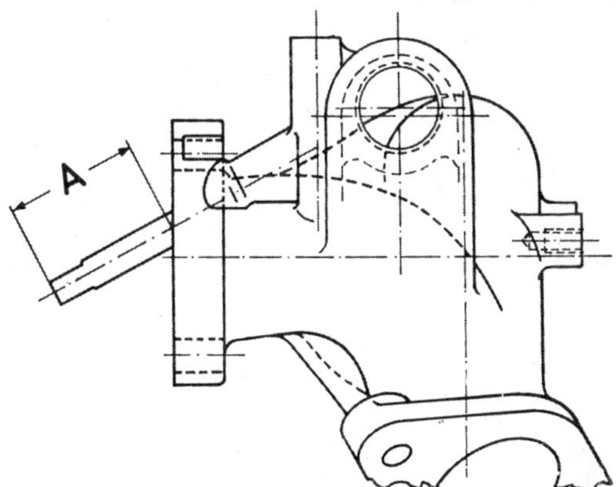

FIG 1:67 Exhaust manifold injection pipe

1:17 Fault diagnosis

(a) Engine will not start

1 Defective coil
2 Faulty distributor capacitor (condenser)
3 Dirty, pitted or incorrectly set contact breaker points
4 Ignition wires loose or insulation faulty
5 Water on sparking plug leads
6 Corrosion of battery terminals or battery discharged
7 Faulty or jammed starter
8 Sparking plug leads wrongly connected
9 Vapour lock in fuel pipes
10 Defective fuel pump
11 Overchoking
12 Underchoking
13 Blocked petrol filter or carburetter jets
14 Leaking valves
15 Sticking valves
16 Valve timing incorrect
17 Ignition timing incorrect

(b) Engine stalls

1 Check 1, 2, 3, 4, 10, 11, 12, 13, 14 and 15 in (a)
2 Sparking plugs defective or gaps incorrect
3 Retarded ignition
4 Mixture too weak
5 Water in fuel system
6 Petrol tank vent block
7 Incorrect valve clearance

(c) Engine idles badly

1 Check 2 and 7 in (b)
2 Air leak at manifold joints
3 Slow-running jet blocked or out of adjustment
4 Air leak in carburetter
5 Over-rich mixture
6 Worn piston rings
7 Worn valve stems or guides
8 Weak exhaust valve springs
9 Exhaust emission control valve failure

(d) Engine misfires

1 Check 1, 2, 3, 5, 8, 10, 13, 14, 15, 16, 17 in (a); 2, 3, 4 and 7 in (b)
2 Weak or broken valve springs
3 Exhaust emission control valve failure

(e) Engine overheats

See Chapter 4

(f) Compression low

1 Check 14 and 15 in (a); 6 and 7 in (c) and 2 in (d)

2 Worn piston ring grooves
3 Scored or worn cylinder bores

(g) Engine lacks power

1 Check 3, 10, 11, 13, 14, 15, 16 and 17 in (a); 2, 3, 4 and 7 in (b)
2 Check 6 and 7 in (c) and 2 in (d). Also check (e) and (f)
3 Leaking joint washers
4 Fouled sparking plugs
5 Automatic advance not operating

(h) Burnt valves or seats

1 Check 14 and 15 in (a); 7 in (b) and 2 in (d). Also check (e)
2 Excessive carbon around valve seat and head

(j) Sticking valves

1 Check 2 in (d)
2 Bent valve stem
3 Scored valve stem or guide
4 Incorrect valve clearance

(k) Excessive cylinder wear

1 Check 11 in (a) and see Chapter 4
2 Lack of oil
3 Dirty oil
4 Piston rings gummed up or broken
5 Badly fitting piston rings
6 Connecting rods bent

(l) Excessive oil consumption

1 Check 6 and 7 in (c) and check (k)
2 Ring gaps too wide
3 Oil return holes in piston choked with carbon
4 Scored cylinders
5 Oil level too high
6 External oil leaks
7 Ineffective valve stem oil seals

(m) Crankshaft and connecting rod bearing failure

1 Check 2 in (k)
2 Restricted oilways
3 Worn journals or crankpins
4 Loose bearing caps
5 Extremely low oil pressure
6 Bent connecting rod

(n) Internal water leakage

1 See Chapter 4

(o) Poor circulation

1 See Chapter 4

(p) Corrosion

1 See Chapter 4

(q) High fuel consumption

1 See Chapter 2

(r) Engine vibration

1 Loose generator bolts
2 Fan blades out of balance
3 Incorrect clearance for front engine mounting rubbers
4 Exhaust pipe mountings too tight
5 Incorrect adjustment of power unit stabilizer

CHAPTER 2

THE FUEL SYSTEM

2:1 Description
2:2 Fuel pump operating principle
2:3 Routine maintenance
2:4 Pump removal, dismantling and examination
2:5 Reassembly, installation and adjustment
2:6 Carburetter removal and refitting Solex 38.PDSI
2:7 Carburetter operation and adjustment, Solex 38.PDSI
2:8 Dual carburetter removal and refitting Solex 40.PHH
2:9 Carburetter operation and adjustment, Solex 40.PHH
2:10 Air cleaner
2:11 Petrol tank
2:12 Fault diagnosis

2:1 Description

All the models described in this manual use a mechanical diaphragm fuel feed pump driven from the overhead camshaft. Two types of carburetter are fitted, the Solex 36 or 38.PDSI and the Solex 40.PHH. Each version being dealt with, supplying all necessary information for servicing and adjustment.

2:2 Fuel pump operating principle

Refer to **FIGS 2:1** and **2:2**. An eccentric on the rotating camshaft actuates the operating lever 13 via a pushrod which depresses the diaphragm 14 and so creates a depression in the pumping chamber located in the upper body 7. Under atmospheric pressure, petrol passes through the pipeline connection from the fuel tank to the inlet valve into the pumping chamber. The return spring located under the diaphragm then raises the diaphragm, expelling the petrol through the outlet valve and pipeline to the float chamber of the carburetter.

When the float chamber is full of petrol, the pressure in the pipeline and the pump chamber holds the diaphragm depressed against the tension of the return spring.

2:3 Routine maintenance

A poor delivery of fuel to the carburetter may be due to a fault in the fuel pump or related lines. Periodically the pump body screws 6 (see **FIG 2:1**) and upper cover screw 1 should be checked for tightness. The fuel pump lines should be disconnected and checked for freedom of restrictions, chafing and loose connections. The fuel pump filter located underneath the top dome should be removed and cleaned periodically.

2:4 Pump removal, dismantling and examination

The petrol pump is located on the lefthand side of the engine between the induction manifold and thermostat housing. Remove the fuel pump by first disconnecting the fuel inlet and outlet pipes and releasing the two retaining nuts from the studs in the cylinder head. Carefully lift away the pump from the cylinder head.

Dismantling:

1 Refer to **FIG 2:1**. Remove the top dome mounting screw and washer 3. Lift off the dome 2, washer 4 and filter 5. Remove the pump body's interlocking screws 6 and separate the upper half from the lower half of the body.

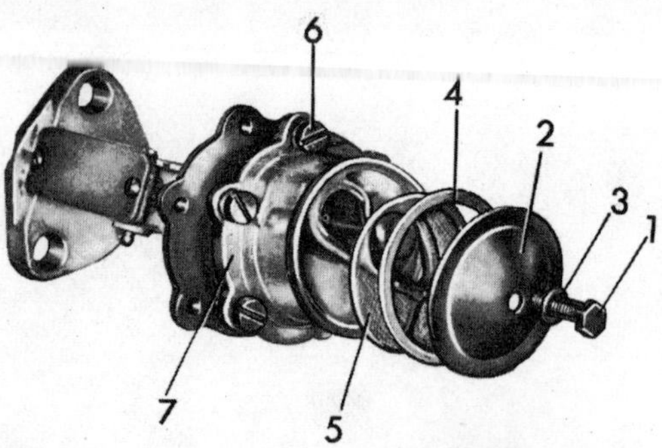

FIG 2:1 Fuel pump upper body

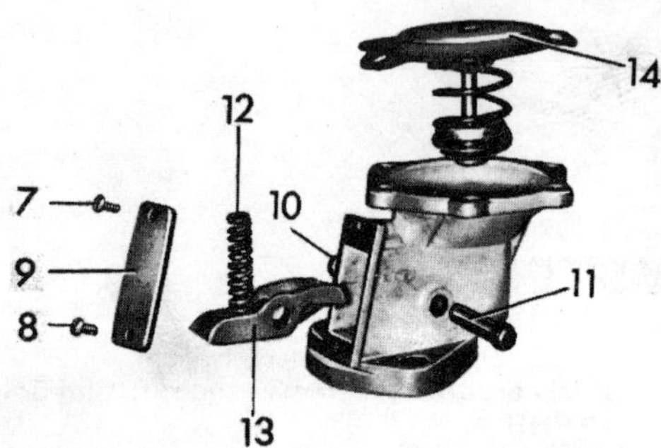

FIG 2:2 Fuel pump lower body

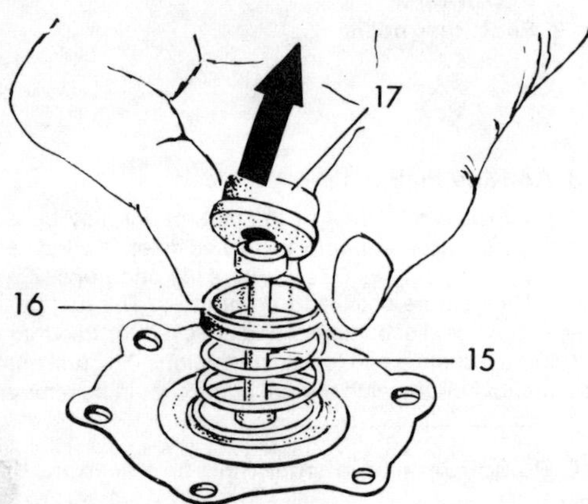

FIG 2:3 Diaphragm assembly

2 Remove the screws 7 and 8 (see **FIG 2:2**) fastening the sealing plate 9 to the lower body. Lift the retaining plate 10 from the pivot 11 and drive out the pivot using a parallel punch and hammer. Lift out spring 12 and pump drive lever 13. Carefully lift out the diaphragm 14.
3 Depress the diaphragm spring 15 (see **FIG 2:3**) and compression collar 16. Carefully ease the collar sideways so disengaging it from the central spindle.
4 Thoroughly wash all components in petrol and blow them dry using a compressed air jet or foot pump. Inspect the valves for evidence of damage and valve springs for weakness or cracks. Check to see that the diaphragm reaction spring 15 and operating lever spring 12 are not distorted or unserviceable. Generally inspect all parts for cracks, distortion or the diaphragm for stiffness and also the pump drive lever for distortion, and pivot pin for wear.

2:5 Reassembly, installation and adjustment

Ensure all parts are clean and dry. Assembling is the reverse procedure to dismantling. Lubricate the pump drive lever 13 and pivot pin 11 before placing them in the lower body.

Reassembly is the reverse procedure to dismantling but the following points should be noted:

1 It is recommended that upon reassembling the diaphragm to the body it is brought to its correct position by BMW gauge 5125. The length of the diaphragm return spring 15 must not under any circumstances be altered.
2 The small inlet and outlet butterfly valves located in the upper body of the pump are not interchangeable and it is recommended that they are renewed in pairs.

Installation and adjustment:

Refer to **FIG 2:4** where it will be seen that the pump is operated by a pushrod which is operated from the camshaft. A special insulating flange is located between the pump body and the cylinder head and the thickness S must be checked against original specification. Should either the plunger length or insulating flange thickness not be to specification then the operating pressure of the pump will be affected.

Pump plunger and flange specification:

Up to Chassis No. 917583.
Insulating flange thickness S with gaskets .19685 inch thick.
Plunger length L.3.59456 inch.
Pump pressure 2.13 to 2.84 lb/sq in.
From Chassis No. 917584.
Insulating flange thickness S with gaskets .78742 inch.
Plunger length L.4.19299 inch.
Pump pressure 3.0 to 3.6 lb/sq in.

2:6 Carburetter removal and refitting Solex 36 or 38.PDSI

To remove the carburetter proceed as follows:

1 Slacken the air inlet hose 1 (see **FIG 2:5**) open the air filter cover clips and ease the rubber connection hose 3 from the cylinder head cover 4 and lift away together with the rubber assembly hose 5.
2 Release and remove the petrol supply hose 6 and vacuum hose 7.
3 Using a screwdriver carefully lift away the intermediate throttle control linkage. Disconnect the automatic choke cable 17 (see **FIG 2:6**), from the lever 18 holding firmly in place with engineers pliers.
4 Carefully disconnect the bowden cable sleeve 19 from the pivot lever 20 and carefully pull away.
5 Remove the two carburetter retaining nuts and lift away the carburetter.

Reassembly:

Reassembly is the reverse procedure to dismantling but the following points should be noted:

1 Once the carburetter has been refitted and all controls connected, the engine should be allowed to run to normal operating temperature and then the idling speed adjusted using the spring-loaded adjustment screw until normal idling speed is obtained.

2 Ensure that the lever 18 (see **FIG 2:6**), lies against its limit stop 21. Also the signal contact located on the dashboard must be pushed down to its lowest position.

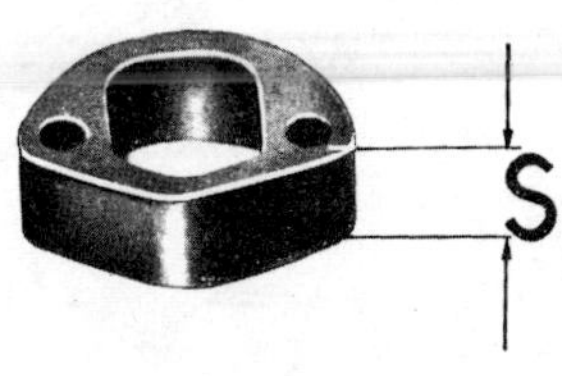

FIG 2:4 Pushrod and spacer

2:7 Carburetter operation and adjustment, Solex 36 or 38.PDSI

Description and operation:

The Solex 36 or 38.PDSI carburetter is of the down-draft design and may be considered to comprise three main parts. The throttle chamber together with the throttle butterfly, the throttle lever and pump intermediate lever and volume control adjustment screw.

The main body of the carburetter consists of a mixing chamber, float chamber, both parts incorporating all the required drillings and jets for the mixing of petrol with air as well as the float chamber with the float which keeps the petrol lever constant. An accelerator pump is mounted on the top of the float chamber and is operated by a control rod and intermediate operating lever. The float chamber cover is secured onto the float chamber by means of retaining bolts. It contains the connection tube for the fuel pipe and located in the underside the needle valve. An air vent tube for the float chamber is positioned in the float chamber cover. In the main venturi tube the strangler assembly is located. On the lower face of the float chamber cover a special control device is fitted with an enrichment valve for enrichment of the charge under full load conditions. Gaskets are placed between the throttle chamber, and the main body and float chamber cover.

The main jet, air correction jet and choke tube are specially matched so as to give the engine maximum performance with a minimum of fuel consumption. It is not recommended that individual carburetter settings are changed but should any adjustment become necessary due to unusual operating conditions or a different type of petrol is being used it is recommended that the agents be contacted for further information.

If a flat spot is noticed when the accelerator pedal is depressed the cause of the trouble is usually in the fuel pump system in the form of a dirty filter or partially blocked feed pipe.

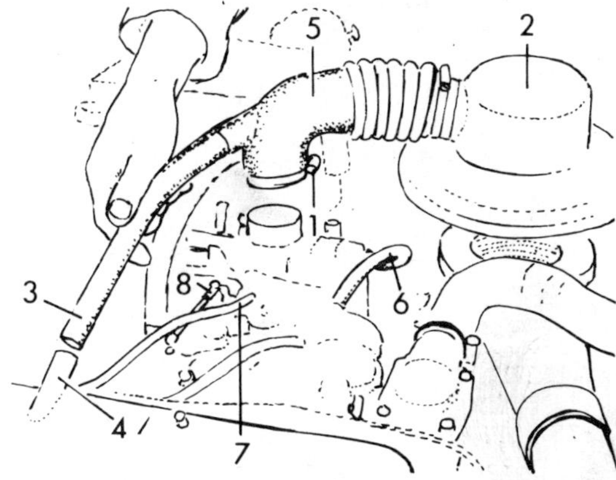

FIG 2:5 Carburetter removal

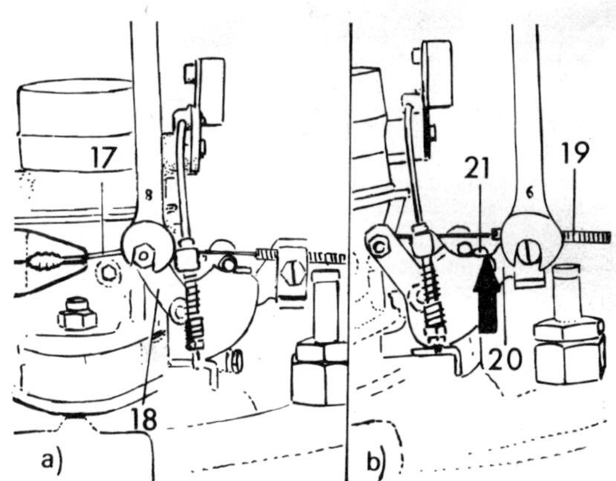

FIG 2:6 Bowden cable release

Dismantling:

Refer to **FIG 2:7** and unscrew the fastening screw on the carburetter top cover 11 and lift away together with gasket 12. Remove the float location plate 13 and carefully lift away the float together with its pivoting shaft.

1 Unscrew the seal plug 15 and remove together with its packing ring. Using a screwdriver of suitable blade width carefully remove the main jet.

2 Unscrew the float needle valve assembly 16 and lift out together with its packing ring 17.

3 Using a screwdriver of suitable blade width, carefully remove the air correction jet 19 and the mixture regulating screw G (see **FIG 2:8**) together with its spring.

4 Using a suitably sized spanner remove the idling jet 20. Unscrew the enrichment valve A and lift away together

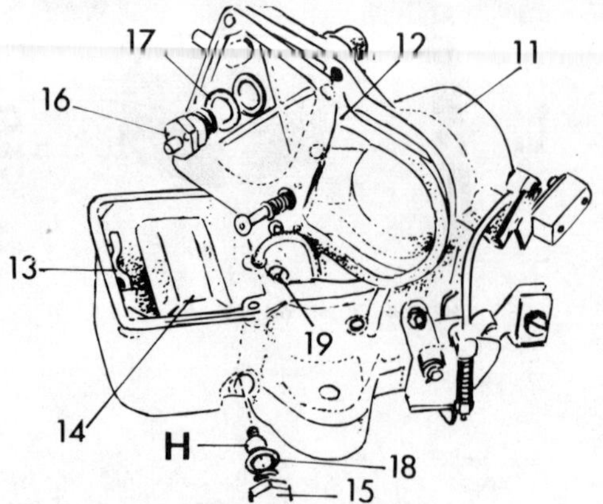

FIG 2:7 Carburetter top cover removed

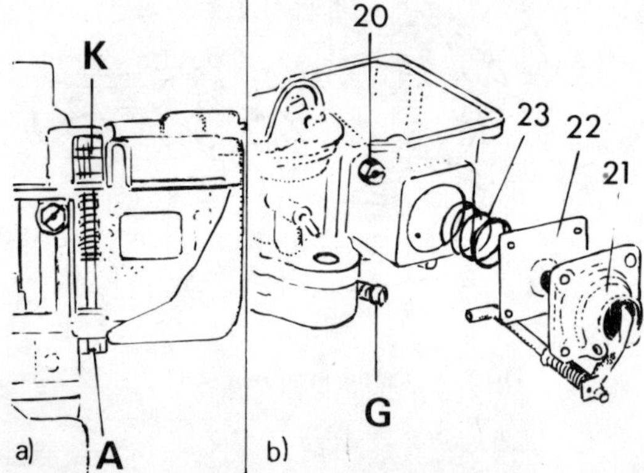

FIG 2:8 Enrichment valve

with its packing ring. The enrichment valve is controlled by a vacuum piston K (see **FIG 2:8**). Disconnect the clamp ring from the pump connection linkage and using a screwdriver unscrew the pump cover retaining screws. Lift away the pump cover 21 together with its connection linkage. Gently lift out the diaphragm 22 together with its spring 23.

5 Thoroughly clean all parts of the carburetter using petrol and dry carefully using a gentle compressed air jet.

Reassembly:

Reassembly is the reverse procedure to dismantling. Wherever gaskets are used they must always be renewed.

Resetting carburetter:

Once the carburetter has been reassembled to the engine, allow the engine to warm up to normal operating temperature and then adjust the idling screw 24 (see **FIG 2:9**) until the engine is at normal idling speed. The idling mixture should be adjusted by rotating the screw 25 together with idling screw 24 so that when the idling mixture is correct the engine is running smoothly at maximum idling speed.

Fuel level check:

To enable the carburetter to act at maximum efficiency the fuel level in the float chamber must be set and to complete this operation proceed as follows:

1 Allow the engine to run until normal operating temperature is reached. Switch off the engine.
2 Remove the fuel hose and immediately plug the end to ensure that no fuel is allowed to drip onto the hot engine. Remove the carburetter cover retaining screws and very carefully lift off the cover together with its gasket.
3 The fuel level shown as dimension N in **FIG 2:10** should be .669 to .748 inch at normal atmospheric pressure. It is recommended that a vernier depth gauge be used for this operation. Allowance should be made for the thickness of the special packing ring 17 (see **FIG 2:7**) located below the float needle valve.
4 Reassemble the carburetter top cover and reconnect the fuel hose.

2:8 Dual carburetter removal and refitting Solex 40.PHH

To remove the carburetter installation proceed as follows:

1 Carefully pull off the breather hose connection to the rocker cover and remove the air filter located on the wheel arch panel.

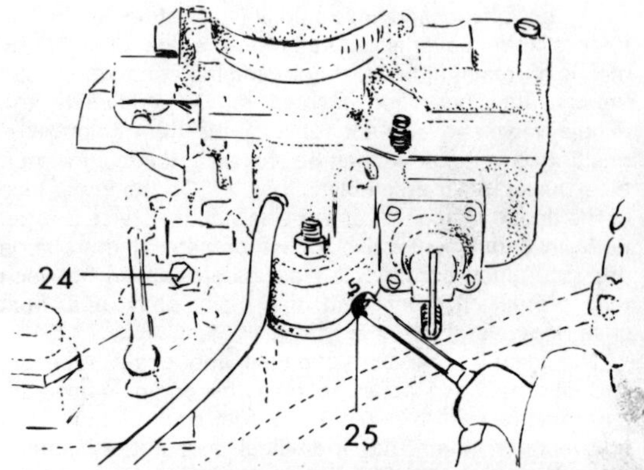

FIG 2:9 Carburetter adjustment screws

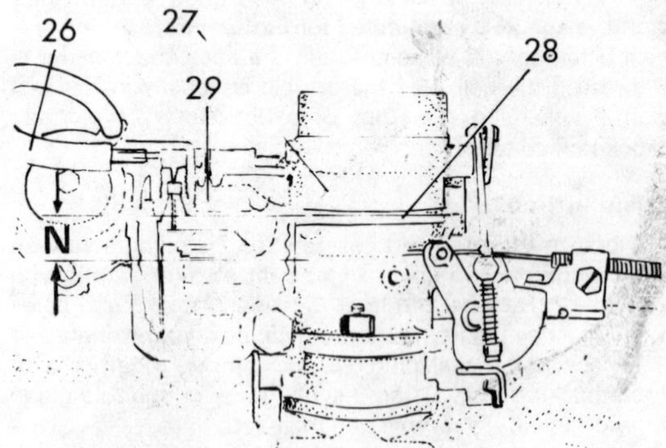

FIG 2:10 Float chamber level

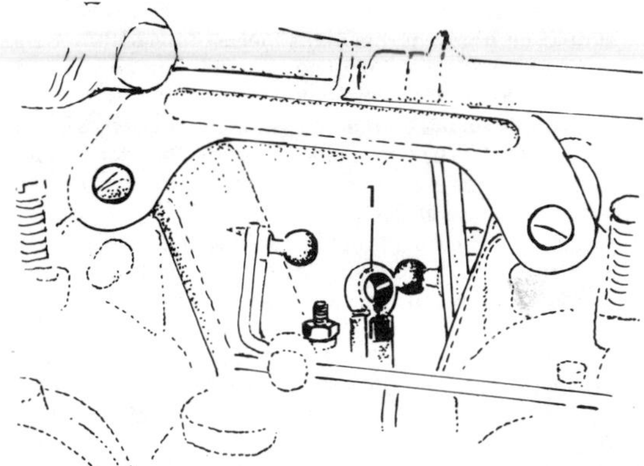

FIG 2:11 Dual carburetter rotary control shaft pullrod connection

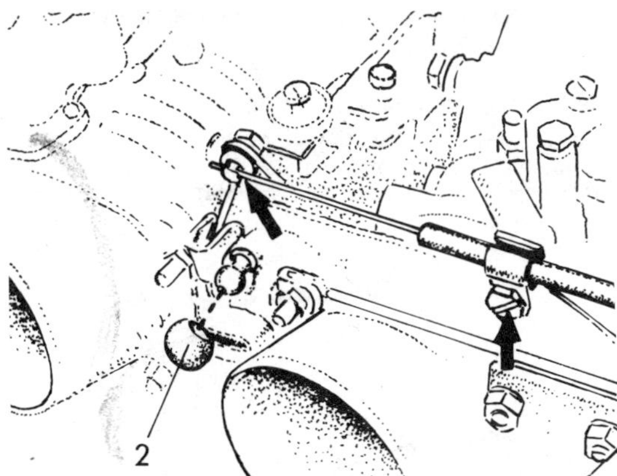

FIG 2:12 Dual carburetter installation starter control cable correct location

2 Gently ease off the fuel supply hoses. Disconnect the pullrod 1 (see **FIG 2:11**) from the rotary shaft and slacken the bearing bracket.

3 Referring to **FIG 2:12** carefully push off the pushrod 2 and disconnect the starter cable from the bearing support as indicated by the arrows.

4 Make a special note as to the correct position of the tensioning spring as shown in **FIG 2:13** so that it may be correctly positioned upon refitting. Release the carburetter to manifolding fastening nuts and carefully lift away the carburetter assembly.

Reassembly:

Reassembly is the reverse procedure to dismantling but the following points should be noted:

1 When reassembling the tension spring located between the two carburetter bodies special care must be taken to ensure that it is correctly positioned.

2 To enable the starter cable to be correctly positioned push the contact on the instrument panel into the bottom notch so fully opening the choke. Refix the choke in this position. Before fitting the front carburetter to the manifold engage the choke lever pin to both carburetters.

2:9 Carburetter operation and adjustment, Solex 40.PHH

Initial setting:

If the carburetters have been removed from the engine or their adjustment is suspect then the initial setting should be checked and reset as follows:

1 With the engine stationary remove the air filter housing from the inner wheel arch panel, and carefully pull off the breather hose from the top of the cylinder head cover and lower it so that the end is facing the distributor.

2 Carefully tighten the idling mixture regulation screws (1 to 4) (see **FIG 2:14**), until they are fully but gently screwed to their seating. Turn back each mixture regulation screw exactly one half a turn.

3 Carefully loosen the synchronization screw (5) and unscrew until it is no longer bearing upon the throttle control lever (7). Unscrew the idling stop screw as far as it will go and screw inwards the synchronization screw 5 until it just comes into contact with the throttle control lever (7). Carefully screw in the idling stop screw (6) until the throttle butterfly lever is just touching. Finally screw in the idling stop screw (6) an extra two turns inwards.

FIG 2:13 Dual carburetter installation control tensioning spring location

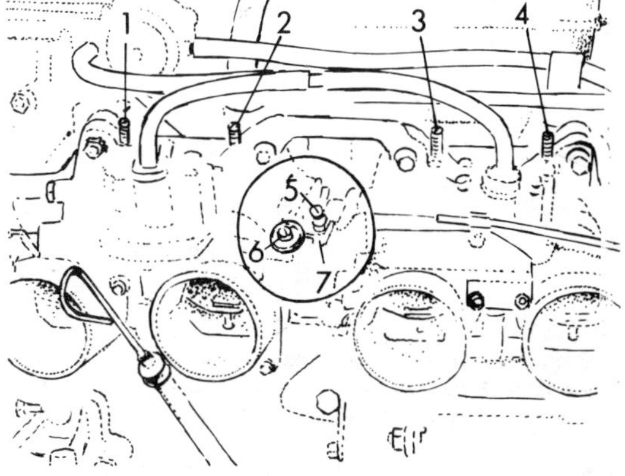

FIG 2:14 Carburetter setting identification

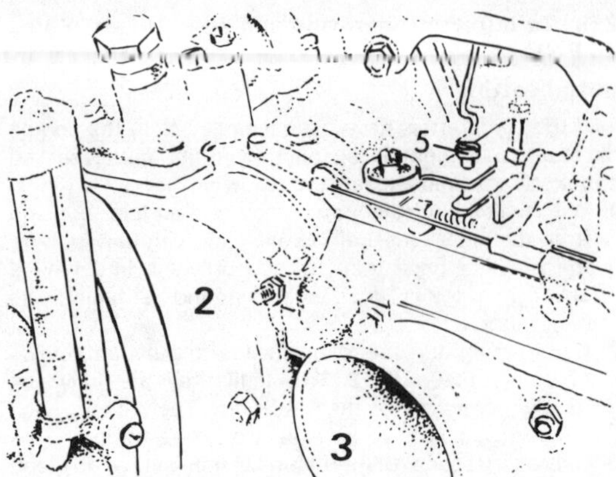

FIG 2:15 Carburetter synchronization

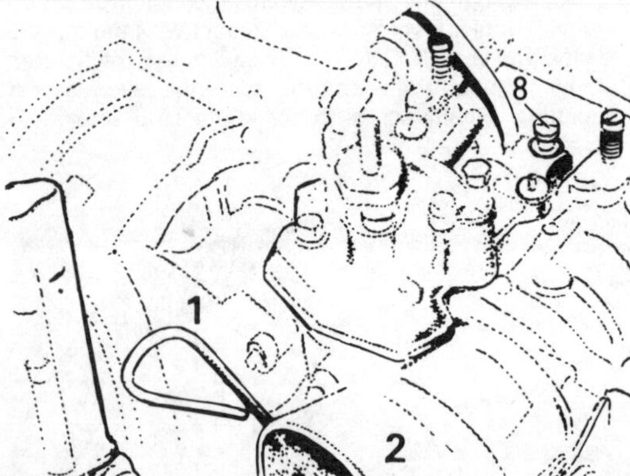

FIG 2:16 Carburetter synchronization

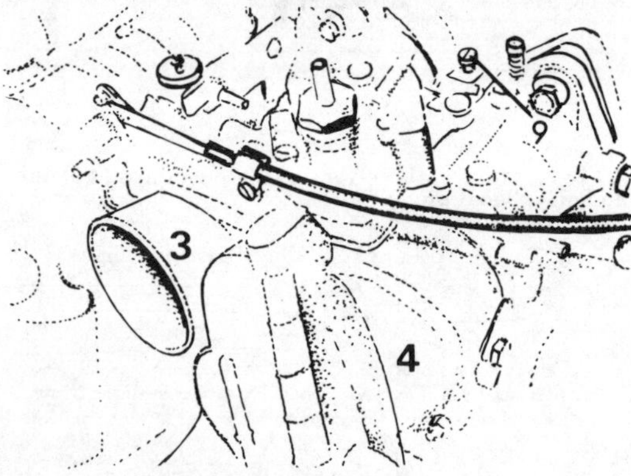

FIG 2:17 Carburetter synchronization

Dual carburetter installation synchronization:

Before the carburetters may be synchronized it is essential that the ignition timing and the valve clearances are checked for correct adjustment and then proceed as follows:

1 Start the engine and allow to run until it reaches its normal operating temperature. Once this has been attained, set the idling speed to 1200 rev/min. It should be noted at this point that all four carburetters must be adjusted to allow equal volume of air passage with the aid of a synchrotester.

2 Adjust the second carburetter (2) of the second cylinder (see **FIG 2:15**), to coincide with the carburetter number 3 of the third cylinder by means of the synchronization screw 5.

3 Adjust the first carburetter of the first cylinder to coincide with the second carburetter of the second cylinder by means of the adjusting screw 8 (see **FIG 2:16**).

4 Adjust the fourth carburetter of the fourth cylinder to coincide with carburetter number three of the third cylinder by means of the adjusting screw (9) (see **FIG 2:17**).

5 With the engine still running and at a fast idle speed adjust the idling mixture by turning the regulation screw inwards or outwards. This setting is correct when the engine reaches the maximum idling speed.

6 Reset the engine idling speed to 800 rev/min and readjust the idling mixture.

Fuel level check and adjustment:

For this test an accurate carburetter fuel level test rig is required as found in many service stations. The information in this section is given for reference purposes so that

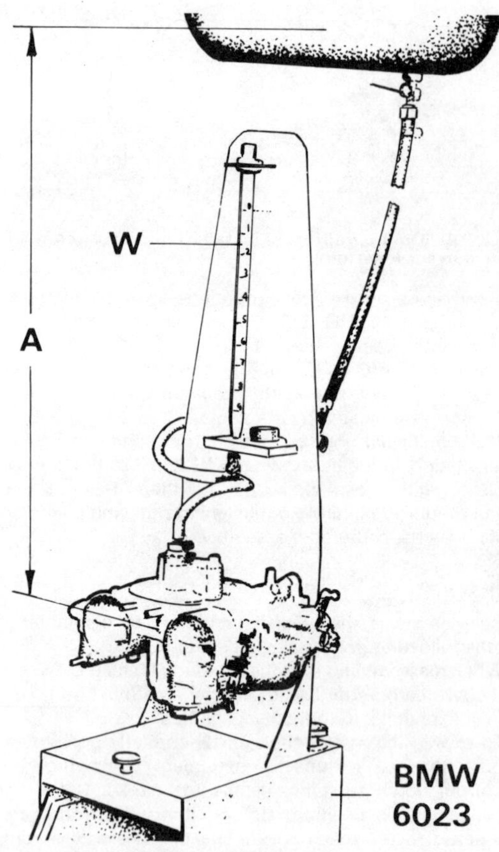

FIG 2:18 Carburetter test rig

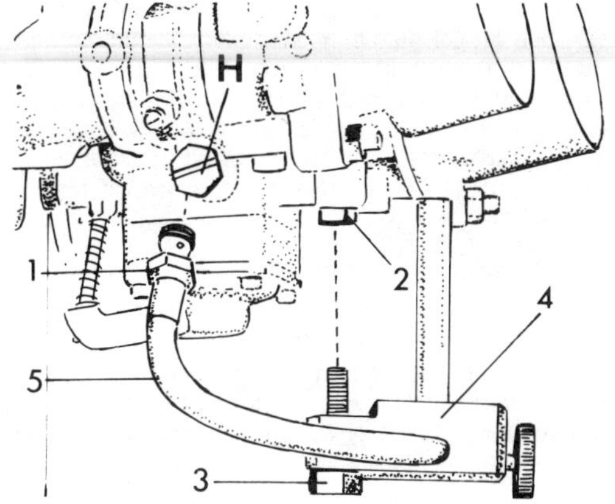

FIG 2:19 Fuel level check

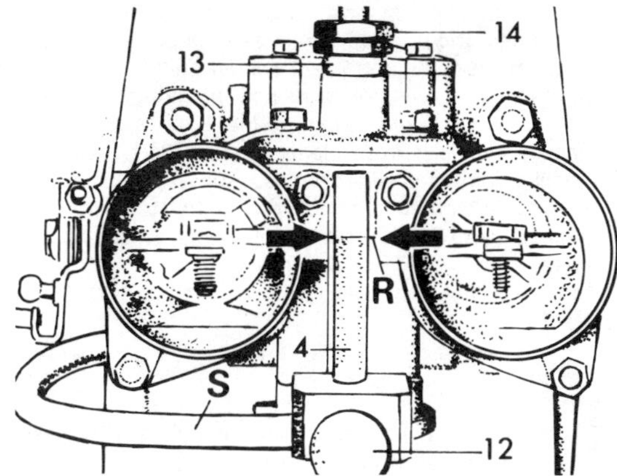

FIG 2:20 Fuel level adjustment

this operation may be completed with, if necessary, a little improvization of standard workshop equipment. To complete the check proceed as follows:

1 A fuel container fitted with a hose as shown in **FIG 2:18** must be set to a height (A) of 8 ft—which should be measured from the centre of the carburetter venturi tube to the centre of the fuel container. **FIG 2:18** shows the BMW 6023 test rig and it is necessary when using this particular rig for the expansion chamber (W) to be sealed off with a correctly fitting plug.

2 Remove both carburetters from the engine and referring to **FIG 2:19,** release the main jet mounting (H) from the carburetter and replace by adaptor (1).

3 Carefully unscrew the ball valve brackets 2 and attach the level testing adaptor by brackets 4 to the carburetter by means of the special hexagonal bolt brackets 3. Connect the adaptor to the level testing equipment using the transparent plastic tube.

4 Attach the carburetter to the test rig and adjust so that it is exactly in the horizontal position indicated by a spirit level or other suitable means.

5 Bleed the entire fuel system by opening and closing the knurled bleed screw (12) until no air bubbles are visible in the transparent hose (S) (see **FIG 2:20**). This procedure must be repeated before each measurement is taken. It should be noted that the fuel level in the gauge glass must be exactly opposite the marking (R) on the carburetter housing. Should this not be evident, loosen the locknut (13) and turn the level regulation screw (14) either in or out until the fuel level in the gauge glass (4) coincides with the carburetter marking (R).

6 This operation must be repeated on both carburetter installations.

Injection volume check and adjustment:

To check and adjust the injection volume proceed as follows:

1 Screw the ball valve and main jet carrier into the carburetter and operate the throttle butterfly shaft approximately ten times to its maximum limit. The pressure stroke must be performed quickly and smoothly with sufficient pause in between each individual stroke to allow a supply of fuel to be drawn in.

2 From the measuring glass on the test rig read off the injected volume of petrol which has been used and divide the result by ten. When the injection volume has been correctly regulated between .6 and .8 cc of premium grade fuel should be injected per stroke.

3 Adjust the injection volume by loosening the locknut (15) on the connection linkage (16) as shown in **FIG 2:21**. Should the injection quantity be too great

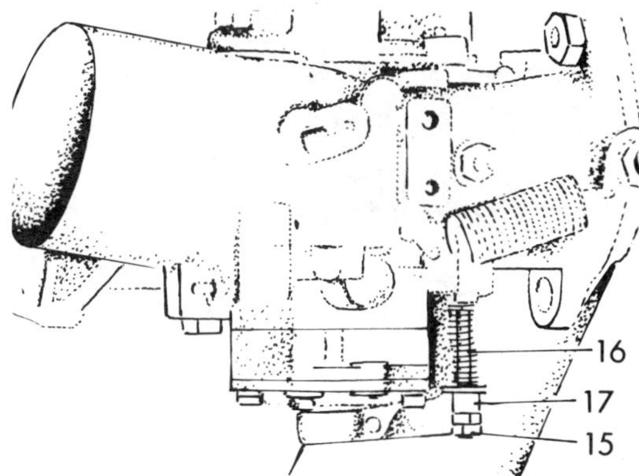

FIG 2:21 Injection volume adjustment

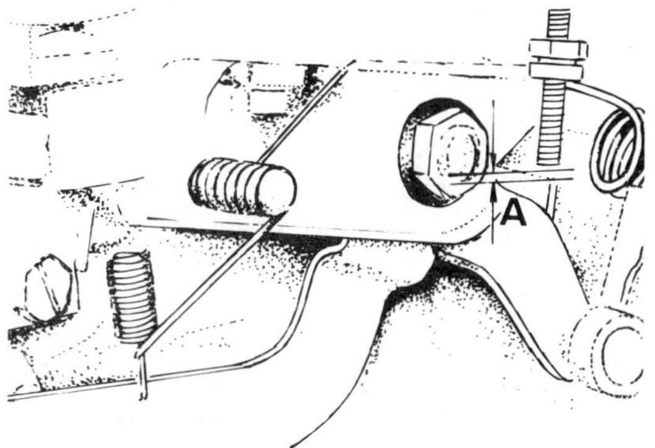

FIG 2:22 Choke butterfly adjustment

unscrew the nut (17), conversely if the quantity is too small the nut should be screwed inwards.

4 Refit the carburetters and synchronize as previously described. If necessary adjust the air fuel mixture.

Choke butterfly adjustment:

Refer to **FIG 2:22** where it will be seen that a set gap A of .0079 inch must be evident between the threaded rod and the choke operating lever. Adjust the threaded rod until the required gap is obtained. Finally adjust the pullrod B (see **FIG 2:23**), until it is a length of 1.614 inch.

2:10 Air cleaner

Fit a new element periodically, depending on operating conditions. Do not unnecessarily disturb the air cleaner cover at any other time or dirt may find its way to the clean side of the intake.

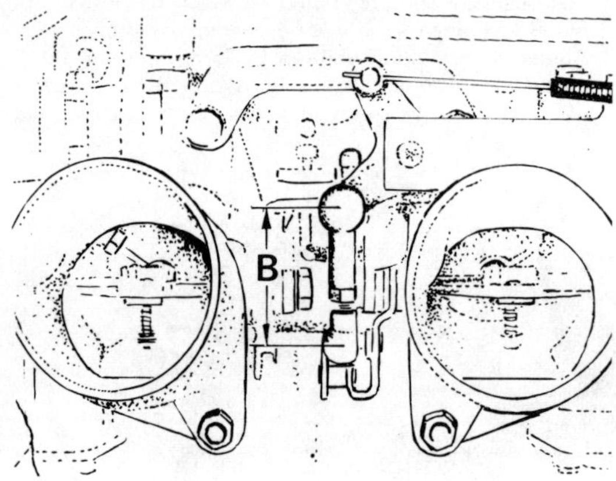

FIG 2:23 Pullrod adjustment

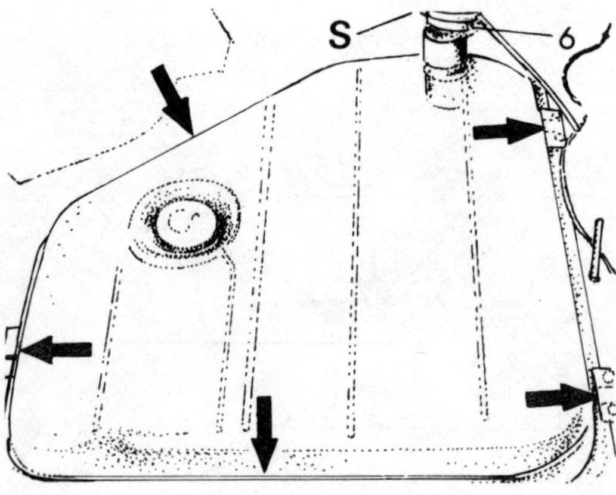

FIG 2:24 Petrol tank mountings

To remove the element open the air filter cover snap retainers and lift off the air cleaner cover, withdraw and discard the old element, wipe the inside of the body with a non-fluffy rag and reassemble, fitting a new element.

The dual carburetter installation has an element fitted at either end of the air cleaner and these must be renewed in pairs.

2:11 Petrol tank

The petrol tank is located in the rear section of the car under the floor panel. It has a capacity of approximately 12.1 Imp gallons (1600) or 10 Imp gallons (1600-2 and TI).

Removal:

To remove the petrol tank proceed as follows:

1 Disconnect the positive terminal of the battery and the two leads from the petrol tank sender unit.
2 Carefully ease away the rubber connection connecting the fuel tank supply pipe to the main supply line. Slacken the filler hose clamp S (see **FIG 2:24**), on the filler union and slide the hose 6 upwards.
3 Release the fuel tank fastening bolts as shown arrowed in **FIG 2:24** and carefully lift away the fuel tank.

To replace the petrol tank is the reverse procedure to removal.

Cleaning:

The tank must be thoroughly checked for leaks especially at the joint seams. Should a leak be found, it is advisable for a garage to attend to this as it is very dangerous to apply heat to a petrol tank without first taking strict precautions, and the garage will be in a better position to do this.

To clean the tank interior, remove the drain pipe and spray in a jet of petrol so that all sediment and dirt deposits can be loosened. Then vigorously shake the tank. Flush the tank with petrol and blow the tank dry. Repeat this procedure until the tank is clean. Refit the drain plug.

Whilst the petrol tank is away from the car it is advisable to disconnect the fuel feed pipe at the pump and carburetter installation and ensure that these are clear by using an air jet to one end of the pipe.

2:12 Fault diagnosis

(a) Leakage or insufficient fuel delivered

1 Air vent in tank restricted
2 Petrol pipes blocked
3 Air leaks at pipe connections
4 Pump or carburetter filters blocked
5 Pump gaskets faulty
6 Pump diaphragm defective
7 Pump valves sticking or seating badly
8 Fuel vapourizing in pipelines due to heat

(b) Excessive fuel consumption

1 Carburetter(s) need adjusting
2 Fuel leakage
3 Sticking controls or choke device
4 Dirty air cleaner(s)
5 Excessive engine temperature
6 Brakes binding
7 Tyres under-inflated
8 Idling speed too high
9 Car overloaded

(c) Idling speed too high

1 Rich fuel mixture
2 Carburetter controls sticking
3 Slow-running screws incorrectly adjusted
4 Worn carburetter butterfly valve

(d) Noisy fuel pump

1 Loose mountings
2 Air leaks on suction side and at diaphragm
3 Obstruction in fuel pipe
4 Clogged pump filter

(e) No fuel delivery

1 Float needle stuck
2 Vent in tank blocked
3 Pipeline obstructed
4 Pump diaphragm stiff or damaged
5 Inlet valve in pump stuck open
6 Bad air leak on suction side of pump

NOTES

CHAPTER 3

THE IGNITION SYSTEM

3:1 Description
3:2 Routine maintenance
3:3 Ignition faults
3:4 Removing and dismantling distributor
3:5 Retiming the ignition
3:6 Sparking plugs
3:7 The distributor spindle
3:8 Fault diagnosis

3:1 Description

All the cars covered by this manual use the Bosch distributor which incorporates automatic timing control by the centrifugal mechanism and a vacuum operated unit.

The weights of the centrifugal device fly out against the tension of small springs as engine speed rises. This movement advances the contact breaker cams relative to the distributor driving shaft to give advance ignition. The vacuum unit is connected by small bore pipe to the induction manifold. Depression in the manifold operates the vacuum unit, the suction varying with engine load. At small throttle openings, with no load on the engine, there is a high degree of vacuum in the induction manifold causing the vacuum unit to advance the ignition. When hill climbing on large throttle openings, the much reduced vacuum ensures that the unit will retard the ignition. The distributor unit as mounted to the front of the cylinder head can be seen in **FIG 3:1**.

3:2 Routine maintenance

Refer to **FIG 3:2** and remove the distributor cap. Carefully pull up the rotor squarely off the end of the cam spindle. Squirt a few drops of oil between the cam spindle and the contact breaker base plate to lubricate the centrifugal advance mechanism but take great care to avoid letting any oil onto the contact breaker base plate or the points themselves. Smear a little grease or engine oil on the cam and apply the tiniest drop of oil to the contact breaker pivot.

Contact breaker points:

1 Release the distributor cap retaining clips and lift away the cap. Carefully lift upwards the rotor arm. Remove the plugs.

2 Using the fan belt to turn the engine in the normal direction of rotation, turn the engine till the contact breaker arm has reached its fully open position on the apex of one of the cams. Using a set of feeler gauges

check the contact breaker point gap. The correct gap should be .015 inch or if metric feeler gauges are available .4 mm.

3 Inspect the contact breaker points whilst they are open and if they show signs of excessive wear, pitting or corrosion on either or both of the contact breaker points they will have to be renewed.

4 Refer to **FIG 3 : 2** and loosen the nut 1 and carefully pull upwards the cable 2. Release the hairpin clip 3 and lift away the washer 4. Carefully push out the spring support 5 on the fixed contact plate 6 and remove the moving contact.

5 Refer to **FIG 3 : 3** and remove the fixed contact locking screw 7 using a screwdriver of suitable width blade. Lift away the fixed contact 6.

6 Reassembly is the reverse procedure to dismantling.

Cleaning the contact points:

If the contact breaker points are dirty or only very slightly pitted they must be cleaned by polishing them with a fine carborundum stone, taking care to keep the faces flat and square. Afterwards wipe away all dust with a clean cloth moistened in fuel. The contacts may be dismantled to assist cleaning as previously described in this section. If the moving contact is removed from its pivot, check that it is not sluggish. If it is tight polish the pivot pin with a strip of fine emerycloth, clean off all dust and apply a tiny spot of oil to the top of the pin. If a spring testing gauge is available the contact breaker spring should have a tension of 15.9 to 19.5 oz measured at the points.

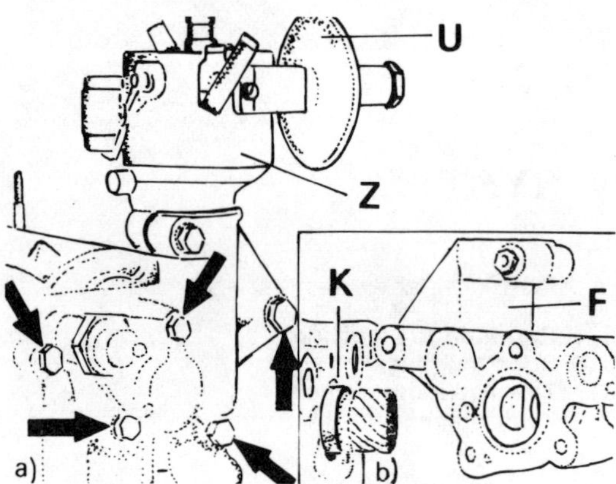

FIG 3 : 1 Distributor location

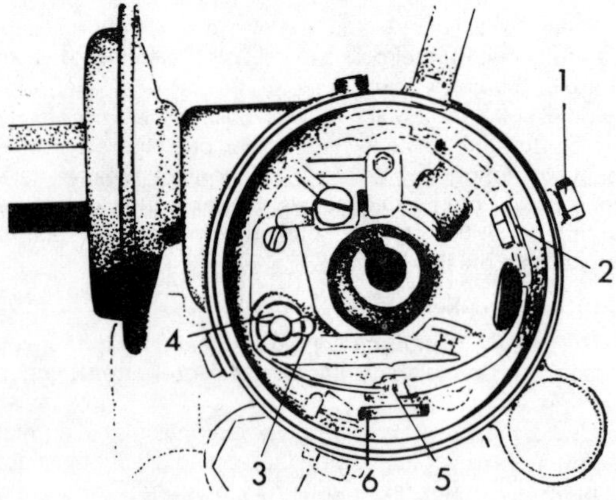

FIG 3 : 2 The contact breaker points

3 : 3 Ignition faults

If the engine runs unevenly set it to idle at a fast speed. Taking care not to touch any metal part of the sparking plug leads pull up the insulator sleeves and short each plug in turn, using a screwdriver with an insulated handle, connect the screwdriver blade between the plug top and the cylinder head. Shorting a plug which is firing properly will make the uneven running more pronounced. Shorting a plug in a cylinder which is not firing will make no difference.

Having located the faulty cylinder, stop the engine and remove the plug lead. Start the engine and hold the lead carefully to avoid shocks so that the metal end is about $\frac{3}{16}$ inch away from the cylinder head. A strong regular spark shows that the fault might lie with the sparking plug. Remove and clean it according to the instructions in **Section 3 : 6.** Alternatively, substitute it with a new plug.

If the spark is weak and irregular, check that the lead is not perished or cracked. If it appears to be defective, renew it and try another test. If there is no improvement remove the distributor cap and wipe the inside clean and dry. Check that the main central carbon brush is free and that it protrudes from the moulding and moves correctly against the pressure of the internal spring. Examine the surface inside the cap for signs of 'tracking', which can be seen as a thin black line between the electrodes or some metal part in contact with the cap. This is caused by a break down in electrical insulation and the only cure is to fit a new distributor cap.

Testing the low-tension circuit:

Before carrying out electrical tests, confirm that the contact breaker points are clean and correctly set. Then proceed as follows:

1 Disconnect the thin black cable from the contact breaker point terminal on the side of the coil marked 1 and also the other end of the cable from the side of the distributor body. Connect a test lamp between the two terminals. Turn the engine over slowly. If the lamp lights when the contacts close and go out when they open, the low-tension circuit is in order. If the lamp fails to light, the contacts are dirty or there is a break or loose connection in the low-tension wiring.

2 If the fault lies in the low-tension circuit, switch on the ignition and turn the crankshaft until the contact breaker points are fully open. Refer to the wiring diagrams in Technical Data and check the circuit with a 0-15 voltmeter. If the circuit is in order the meter should read approximately 6 or 12 volts depending on the electrical system used.

3 Battery to ignition switch terminal 30. Connect the voltmeter between terminal 30 on the back of the ignition switch and earth. No reading indicates a faulty cable or loose connection.

4 Ignition switch. Connect the meter between number 15 switch terminal and earth. Switch on the ignition when no reading indicates an internal fault within the switch.
5 Ignition switch to ignition coil. Connect the meter between terminal 15 on the ignition coil and earth. No reading indicates a damaged cable or loose connection.
6 Ignition coil. Disconnect the cable from the terminal 1 on the side of the ignition coil and connect the meter between this terminal and earth. No reading indicates a fault in the primary winding of the coil and a replacement coil must be fitted. If the reading is correct, remake the connections to the coil.
7 Contact breaker points and capacitor. Connect the meter across the contact breaker points. No reading indicates a fault in the capacitor.

Capacitor:

The best method of testing a capacitor (condenser) is by substitution. Disconnect the original capacitor and connect a new one between the low-tension terminal on the side of the distributor body and to earth.

If a new capacitor is needed, fit one complete with brackets, but if necessary unsolder the original bracket and solder it onto the new capacitor using as little heat as possible.

3:4 Removing and dismantling the distributor

Use **FIG 3:2** for reference. Before removing the distributor turn the crankshaft until the rotor arm is pointing to the brass segment in the cap which is connected to No. 1 cylinder plug lead at the fan end of the engine. This will supply a datum for replacement. Do not turn the crankshaft after this.

1 Remove the distributor cap and disconnect the cable from the low-tension terminal. Disconnect the vacuum pipe from the vacuum unit.
2 Release the distributor body clamp located at the top of the mounting bracket F (see **FIG 3:1**), and very carefully lift upwards the distributor body.
3 Carefully pull upwards the rotor arm.
4 Remove the nut 1 and dismantle the terminal assembly from the side of the distributor body. Remove the hairpin clip 3 together with the washer 4 (see **FIG 3:2**). Carefully push out the spring support 5 on the fixed contact plate 6 and lift away the moving contact.
5 Remove the fixed contact locking screw 7 (see **FIG 3:3**), with a screwdriver and lift away the fixed contact.
6 Remove the contact breaker base plate screws and carefully withdraw the base assembly from the distributor housing. Care must be taken in releasing the vacuum control unit.
7 The location of the rotor arm driving slot and centrifugal weights must be noted to assist with retiming once the distributor is assembled. Remove other parts as necessary.

Inspection:

1 Thoroughly clean all the metal parts in fuel.
2 Thoroughly inspect the weight springs and if found to be weak in operation or signs of cracking, these must be renewed.
3 Examine the contact breaker points for wear and replace as necessary.
4 By the addition of shims eliminate any excessive end play in the distributor shaft or cam.

Reassembly:

Reassembly is the reverse procedure to dismantling but the following points should be noted:

1 Lubricate the parts of the centrifugal advance mechanism, the distributor shaft and that part of the shaft which accepts the cam, with thin engine oil.
2 When reassembling the distributor insert it so that the vacuum chamber is on the righthand side when viewed from the front of the engine as shown in **FIG 3:1**.

3:5 Retiming the ignition

It is important that before the ignition timing is reset the distributor points are checked to ensure that they are in good condition and that the gap is correctly adjusted. To retime the ignition with the engine stationary proceed as follows:

1 Remove the distributor cap and rotor arm.

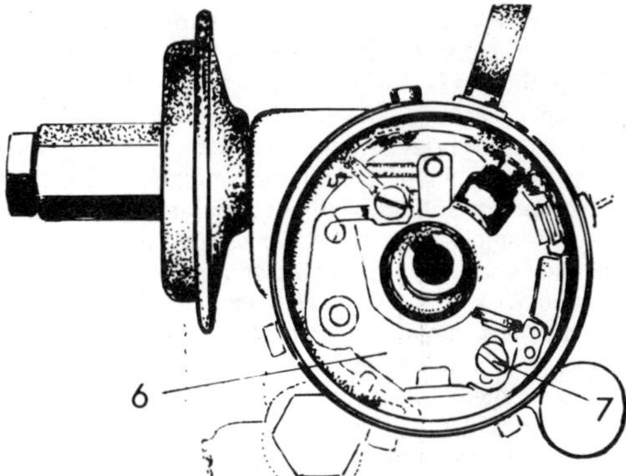

FIG 3:3 Contact breaker earth point locking screw

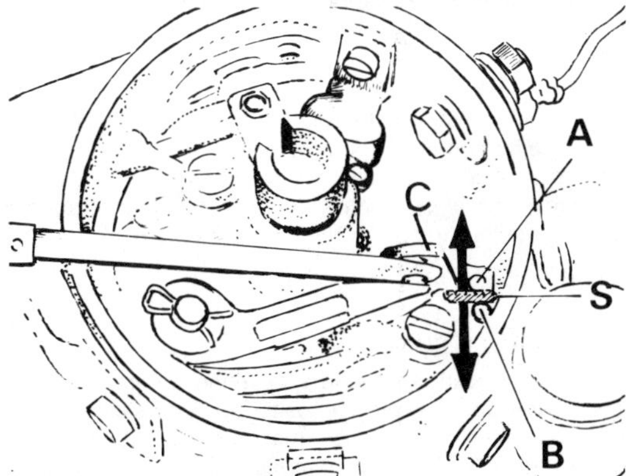

FIG 3:4 Contact beaker point adjustment

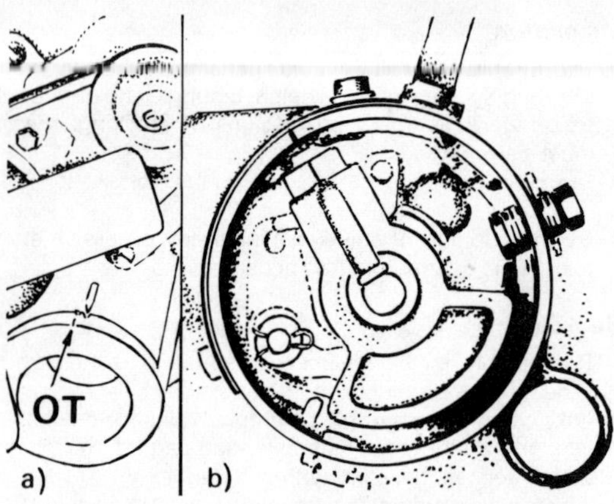

FIG 3:5 Ignition timing marks location

2 Carefully turn the engine in its normal direction of rotation until the contact breaker arm is fully open. Recheck the contact breaker point gap. This should be .0157 inch or .4 mm.
3 Position No. 1 cylinder at 3 deg. BTDC (first notch) or TDC for the 1600TI engine. The pointer on the gear-case cover as shown in **FIG 3:5** should point towards the notch on the belt pulley. Read off in the normal direction of rotation. The notch marked on the distributor rotor should coincide with the marking cut into the top face of the side of the distributor body.
4 Connect a test lamp between the terminal on the side of the distributor body and earth. Switch on the ignition. If the ignition timing is correctly adjusted the contact breaker points should have just separated at this point. The test lamp will be alight. To check the setting turn the crankshaft through approximately 45 deg. in an anticlockwise direction. The test light should be extinguished. Turn the crankshaft back again in a clockwise direction and the test lamp should light at the moment when the pointer on the gear case cover is opposite to the appropriate notch in the belt pulley, seen from the normal direction of rotation.
5 To adjust the ignition timing or reset it as required loosen the clamping screw on the distributor flange and rotate the distributor as necessary.

Stroboscopic timing:

With this method do not let the engine speed rise above approximately 600 rev/min or the centrifugal advance plate will start to operate. If the vacuum advance pipe is connected direct to the inlet manifold, disconnect this first or the timing will be retarded.

3:6 Sparking plugs

Inspect, clean and adjust sparking plugs regularly. The inspection of the deposits on the electrodes is particularly useful because the type of colour of the deposit gives a clue to conditions inside the combustion chamber and is therefore most helpful when tuning.

Remove the sparking plugs by loosening them a couple of turns and then blowing away loose dirt from the plug recesses with compressed air or a tyre pump. Store them in the order of removal.

Examine the gaskets. If they are about half their original thickness they may be used again.

Examine the firing end of the plugs to note the type of deposit. Normally, it should be powdery and ranging from brown to greyish tan in colour. There will also be slight wear of the electrodes, and the general effect is one which comes from mixed periods of high speed and low speed driving. Cleaning and resetting the gap is all that will be required. If the deposits are white or yellowish they indicate long periods of constant speed driving or much low speed driving about town. Again, the treatment is straightforward.

Black, wet deposits are caused by oil entering the combustion chamber past worn pistons, rings or down valve stems. Sparking plugs of a type which run hotter may be of assistance in alleviating the problem. The cure of course, is an overhaul.

Dry, black fluffy deposits are usually the result of running with a rich mixture. Incomplete combustion may also be a cause and this might be traced to defective ignition or excessive idling.

Overheated sparking plugs have a white, blistered look about the centre electrode and the side electrode may be erroded. This may be caused by poor cooling, wrong ignition, or sustained high speeds with heavy loads.

Have the sparking plugs cleaned on an abrasive blasting machine and tested under pressure after attention to the electrodes. File these till they are clean, bright and parallel. Set the electrode gap to .024 to .027 inch (.014 inch platinum tipped plugs). **Do not try to bend the centre electrode.**

Before replacing the plugs clean the threads with a hand wire brush. Do not use a wire brush on the electrodes. If it is found that the plugs cannot be screwed in by hand, run a tap down the threads in the cylinder head. Failing a tap, use an old sparking plug with cross cuts down the threads. Tighten the spark plugs using a normal box spanner through half a turn.

Sparking plug leads:

The high-tension cables must be examined carefully and any which have the insulation cracked, perished, or damaged in any way must be renewed. Fitting new plug leads is a straightforward operation but it is recommended that the lead sockets in the distributor cap are smeared with a silicone grease before the cable is inserted to prevent water from entering. Ensure that the lead is pushed home as far as it will go and then secure firmly.

3:7 The distributor driving spindle

If for any reason the distributor has been removed from the mounting in the cylinder head it must be correctly meshed with camshaft gear with the rotor arm pointing in the right direction once the timing marks have been realigned. This operation is fully described in **Section 3:5.**

3:8 Fault diagnosis

(a) Engine will not fire

1 Battery discharged
2 Distributor contact points dirty, pitted or maladjusted
3 Distributor cap dirty, cracked or 'tracking'
4 Carbon brush inside distributor cap not touching rotor
5 Faulty cable or loose connection in low-tension circuit
6 Distributor rotor arm cracked
7 Faulty coil
8 Broken contact breaker spring
9 Contact points stuck open

(b) Engine misfires

1 Check 2, 3, 5 and 7 in (a)
2 Weak contact breaker spring
3 High-tension plug and coil leads cracked or perished
4 Sparking plug(s) loose
5 Sparking plug insulation cracked
6 Sparking plug gap incorrectly set
7 Ignition timing too far advanced

NOTES

CHAPTER 4

THE COOLING SYSTEM

4:1 Description
4:2 Protective maintenance
4:3 Testing cooling system and radiator pressure cap
4:4 Removing the radiator
4:6 The water pump
4:7 Thermostat removal and replacement
4:8 Frost precautions
4:9 Fault diagnosis
4:5 Adjusting and removing the fan belt

4:1 Description

All models which are covered by this manual have the same type of pressurized cooling system. The natural thermo-syphon action of the water is assisted by a centrifugal impeller mounted at the cylinder block end of the fan spindle, driven from the crankshaft by a V-belt.

A thermostat is fitted into the cooling system to enable the engine to quickly warm up to normal operating temperature by restricting the water circulation.

The induction manifold has waterways cast into it, so enabling good fuel vaporisation at ambient temperatures thus enabling the engine to give good performance during all normal climatic condition changes. A spring-loaded valve in the radiator filler cap pressurizes the system and so increases the temperature at which the coolant boils.

4:2 Protective maintenance

There is only one lubrication point and this is a plug in the water pump casing. At approximately every 12,000 miles, remove the plug and introduce some recommended grade of grease into the pump. Do not force the lubricant in under pressure or it may pass through the bearings and get onto the pump seal, impairing the efficiency of the seal.

The cooling system should be drained, flushed through and refilled with clean water at regular intervals. Antifreeze may be used for two years providing that its concentration is checked during the cold weather. When draining the system filled with antifreeze, it should be collected for re-use during that period. Take care to separate any sediment in the bottom of the container and do not allow it to enter the radiator.

Draining:

Open both the radiator and cylinder block drain taps as shown in **FIG 4:1**. Remove the radiator pressure cap and set the heater control to 'hot'. Allow the system to completely drain into a clean container of a suitable size. Inspect the coolant for traces of oil or signs of excessive corrosion.

Flushing:

Introduce water from a hose into the top tank of the radiator and let it continue to run through the system and out through the draining plug holes until it runs clear.

If the radiator is blocked, remove it as detailed in **Section 4:4** and turn upside down. Reverse flush by inserting a hose into the bottom tank and allow water to flow through the radiator and out through the pressure cap neck.

Filling:

Before refilling the cooling system, the heater control lever must be set to the 'hot' position. Carefully fill with water through the radiator pressure cap neck and screw down the radiator cap until it is engaged on the second retaining notch. Start the engine and allow to warm up to normal operating temperature thus ensuring the thermostat has fully opened. Place a rag over the radiator pressure cap and release slowly to the first notch position. This will release the pressure. Finally remove the cap, check the water level and top up as necessary using hot water. Refit the radiator pressure cap firmly.

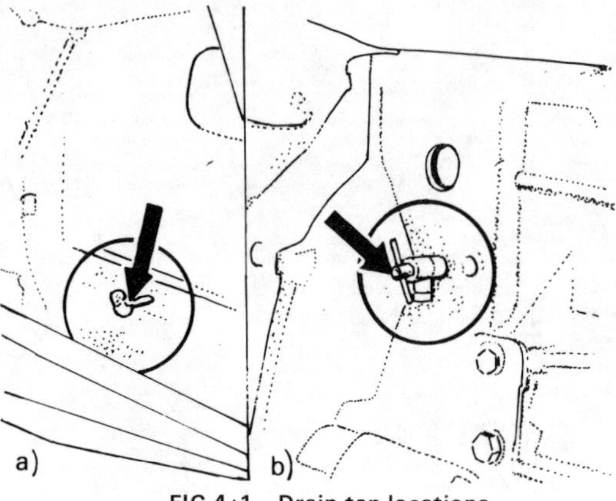

FIG 4:1 Drain tap locations

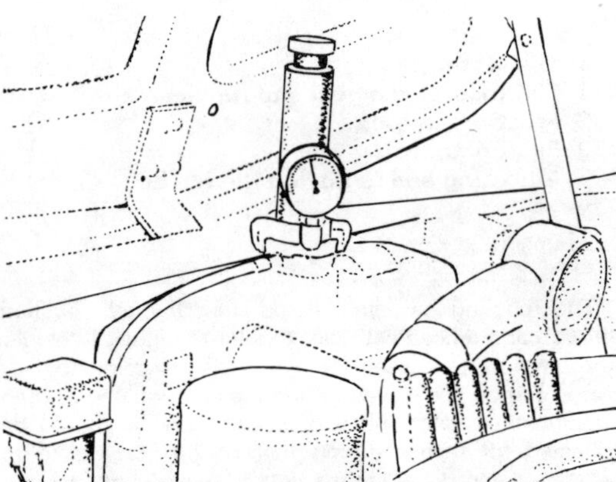
FIG 4:2 Pressure testing cooling system

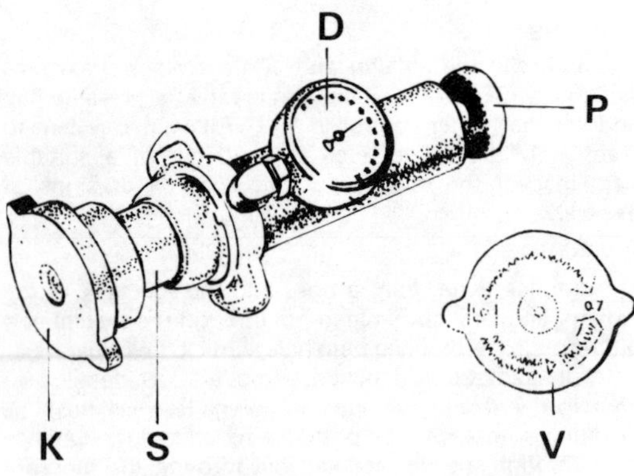

FIG 4:3 Pressure tester

4:3 Testing cooling system and radiator pressure cap

The object of this test is to ensure that the pressure cap is seating correctly and that the spring rating has not changed with use over a period of time. Also it is designed to ensure that no coolant leaks from the system whilst it is operating under normal running pressure. The test requires special pressure testing equipment which is available at most service stations.

1 Fix the test equipment to the radiator pressure cap neck as shown in **FIG 4:2**, and pressurize the cooling system to 14.22 lb/sq in using the hand pump.
2 The gauge should be watched for a minimum period of two minutes during which time the gauge reading should not alter thus indicating complete watertightness. Should the pressure fall, the cause must be investigated and rectified accordingly.
3 Remove the test gauge and fit the union S as shown in **FIG 4:3**. Screw the radiator pressure cap K to the union and using the hand pump P pressurize the tester. The opening pressure as indicated by the tester gauge should be compared with the opening pressure which is marked on the top of the radiator pressure cap under test. If the cap does not come to the required specifications a new one must be fitted.

4:4 Removing the radiator

To remove the radiator from the car proceed as follows:

1 Drain the coolant from the cooling system by opening the two drain taps as shown in **FIG 4:1**, and collect in a clean container of suitable size.
2 Remove the air filter and lift away together with the air pre-heater regulator housing.
3 Remove the radiator hose K from the thermostat housing T (see **FIG 4:4**), and also the radiator hose S from the water pump elbow W.
4 Release and unscrew the four radiator fixing bolts and very carefully lift the radiator upwards ensuring that the fan blades do not damage the radiator matrix.

FIG 4:4 Cooling system parts identification

5 Reassembly is the reverse procedure to dismantling. Refill the cooling system as described in **Section 4:2**.

4:5 Adjusting and removing the fan belt

1 Slacken the three tension bolts from the generator end plates and push the generator down towards the cylinder block.
2 Carefully lift the V-belt from the generator pulley, followed by the water pump pulley and the crankshaft pulley.
3 Upon reassembly the V-belt should be suitably adjusted by pulling upwards on the generator body. When correctly adjusted it should be possible to depress the V-belt between .179 and .394 inch on the longest run.

4:6 The water pump

This is shown in **FIG 4:5**, where the water impeller is on the lefthand end of the spindle and the pulley on the right. The bearing assembly can be seen and also the seal pressing against the inner face of the impeller boss. The face of the seal is spring-loaded thus ensuring a good quality seal between the shaft and pump body.

Removing the water pump:

1 Drain the coolant from the cooling system as described in **Section 4:2**.
2 Release hose clip 3 (see **FIG 4:6**), and carefully ease the breather pipe from the cylinder head top cover. Carefully pull the air filter housing together with its hose 6 from the air pre-heater regulator housing.
3 Remove the radiator hose K (see **FIG 4:4**), from the thermostat housing T and the radiator hose S from the water pump elbow W.

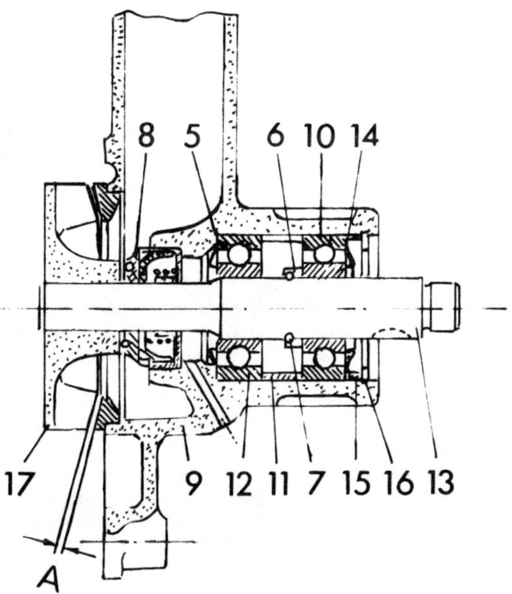

FIG 4:5 Water pump—sectional view

4 Remove the radiator fixing bolts and carefully lift out the radiator ensuring that the fan blades do not damage the radiator matrix.
5 Using the hand, increase the V-belt tension so locking the water pump spindle and unscrew the fixing nut 1 (see **FIG 1:25**). Open the lock plates 2 and 3 and release the four fixing bolts 4 to 7.

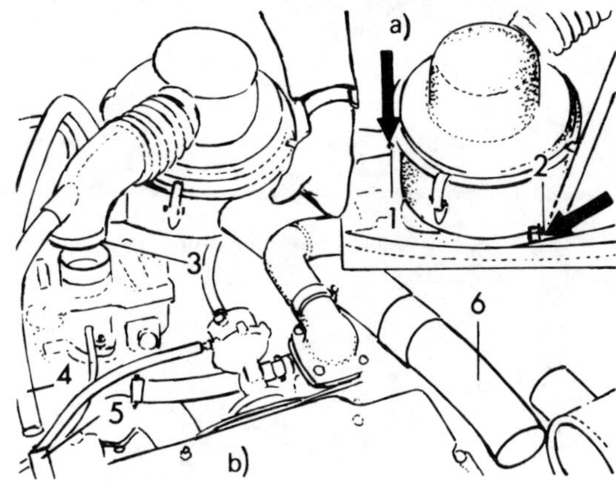

FIG 4:6 Air filter parts identification

FIG 4:7 Generator mounting bolts

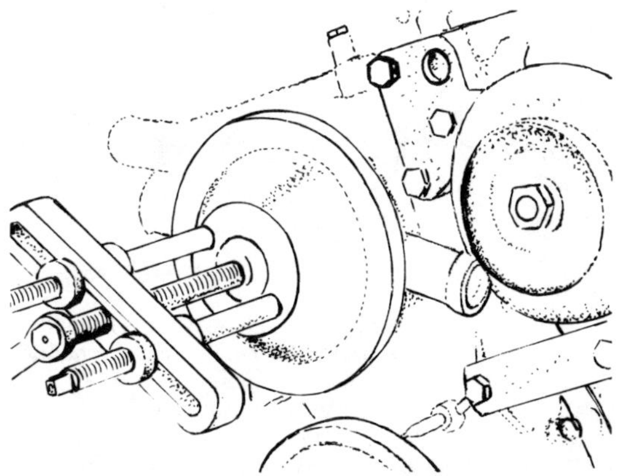

FIG 4:8 Water pump pulley removal

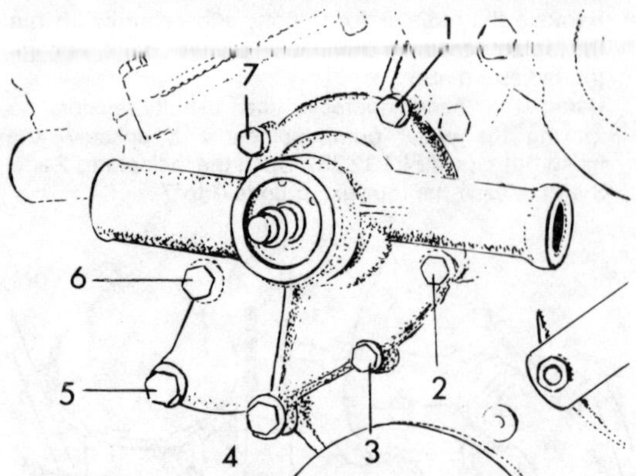

FIG 4:9 Water pump retaining bolts

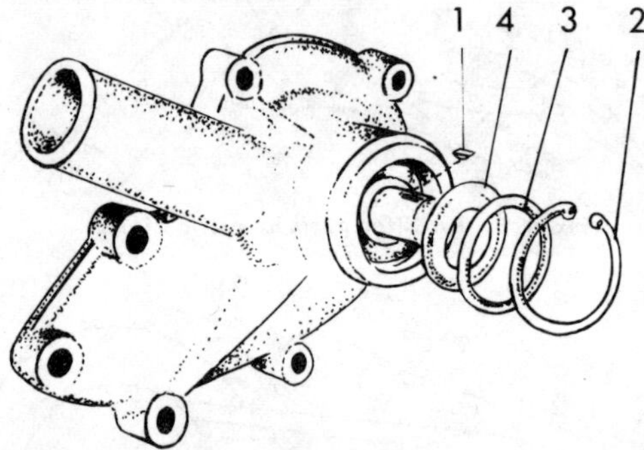

FIG 4:10 Water pump front end components

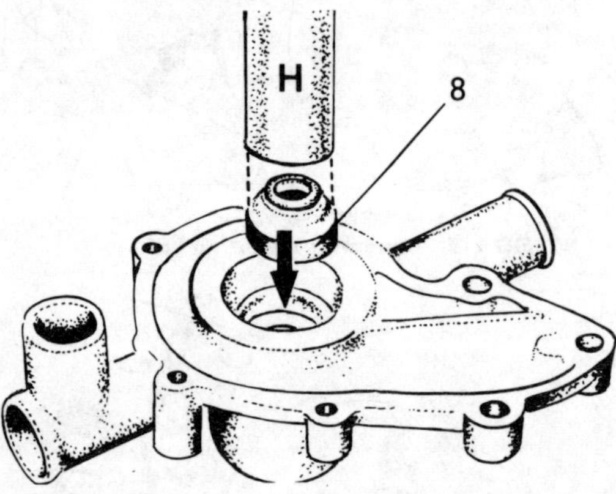

FIG 4:11 Water pump seal

6 Remove the fan blades and release the generator mounting bolts. Lift away the V-belt. Slacken the hose clip S on the return pipe as shown in **FIG 4:7**.
7 Using a universal puller with suitably tapped legs remove the pulley from the water pump as shown in **FIG 4:8.** Remove the seven fixing bolts as shown in **FIG 4:9** and carefully lift away the water pump.

Reassembly:

Reassembly is the reverse procedure to dismantling but the following points should be noted:
1 When refitting the water pump the copper gaskets must be renewed.
2 Refer to **Section 4:5** for the correct procedure for adjustment of the V-belt.
3 When tightening the fixing nut 1 as shown in **FIG 1:25** the V-belt tension must be increased by depressing it and the nut tightened to a torque wrench setting of 28.9 lb ft.

4:6 Water pump dismantling and reassembly

Two types of water pump are fitted to the 1600 power unit. One has a flange pressed onto the main spindle and it is onto this that the fan blades and pulley are bolted. The second type of pump fitted has a detachable flange which is retained in place by a Woodruffe key and locked by a nut screwed onto the end of the shaft.

Water pump type 1—model without flange fitted:

1 Using a suitably pointed tool remove the Woodruffe key 1 (see **FIG 4:10**) from the shaft. Release the circlip 2 using a pair of circlip pliers with pointed ends fitted. Carefully extract the spacing ring 3 and the seal ring 4.
2 Using a press and suitably sized drift carefully press the shaft with the grooved ballbearings from the impeller. Use a suitably sized drift and drive the seal ring 8 from its housing 9. Refer to **FIG 4:11** for seal location.
3 Carefully withdraw the grooved ballbearing races from the shaft 13 together with the securing ring 6 (see **FIG 4:5**).

Inspection:

Inspect the bearing races for discolouration or excessive wear and fit new as necessary. Ensure that the seals are in good condition although it is considered advisable to fit new if available. Inspect the impeller seal assembly if it shows signs of wear, excessive corrosion or damage. If there have been signs of water leakage from the water pump itself, new impeller seals must be fitted.

Reassembly:

To reassemble the water pump proceed as follows:
1 Carefully insert the snap ring 7 into the groove and slide in the securing ring 6 over the top of it.
2 Carefully pack the grooved ballbearing race 10 with multi-purpose high melting point grease and press onto the spindle. Fit the spacer ring 11 and pack with grease. It should be noted that both the notches should be facing towards the grooved ballbearing race 10. Pack the grooved ballbearing race 12 with grease and also press onto shaft.
3 Carefully insert the sealing ring 5 into the housing and assemble the complete shaft into its housing. This operation must be carried out with care as the spacer ring must be in correct alignment. Insert the sealing ring 14 and spacer ring 15. Using circlip pliers insert the circlips 16 and ensure that it is correctly located.
4 Using a press carefully replace the impeller 17 ensuring that clearance A (.039 $\pm$ .008) is available between the housing 9 and impeller 17 as shown in **FIG 4:5**.

Water pump type 2—model with flange fitted:

1 Using a heavy duty universal puller or hydraulic press remove the boss from the shaft. Release the circlip (see **FIG 4:12**), using a pair of circlip pliers with pointed ends and carefully remove the spacer ring.
2 Using a press and suitably sized drift remove the impeller from the shaft and the water pump bearing from its housing.
3 Remove the axial friction seal from its housing using a hammer and suitably sized drift. The assembly is shown in **FIG 4:13.**

Inspection:

Inspect the bearing races for discolouration or excessive wear and fit new as necessary. Ensure that the seals are in good condition although it is considered advisable to fit new if available. Inspect the impeller seal assembly if it shows signs of wear, excessive corrosion or damage. If there have been signs of water leakage from the water pump itself a new impeller seal assembly must be fitted.

Reassembly:

Reassembly is the reverse procedure to dismantling but the following points must be noted:

1 Using a press and suitably sized drift, press in the water pump bearing 1 until it is up against its seating. Follow by inserting the axial friction seal 2 with a suitably sized drift (see **FIG 4 :13**).
2 Insert the spacer ring and refit the circlip ensuring that it is correctly seated in the pump body. Using a press carefully replace the flange ensuring that dimension A (see **FIG 4:14**) is 2.965±.008 inch.
3 Turn over the pump body and using Locktight AAV carefully press on the impeller until clearance B (see **FIG 4:15**), is .039 ± .008 inch. It is recommended that this clearance be set using feeler gauges. As this assembly is an interference fit a press suitable for exerting a pressure of at least 1100 lb is required.

4:7 Thermostat removal and replacement

The thermostat is located towards the forward end of the cylinder head. To remove the thermostat proceed as follows:

1 Unscrew the radiator cap and also open the water drain tap on the radiator.
2 Referring to **FIG 4:16,** release the four bolts retaining the thermostat housing cover 1 and lift away the thermostat housing cover. Remove the thermostat 2 from its housing together with its gasket 3.
3 The thermostat can be tested by immersing it in water so that it does not touch the sides or bottom of the

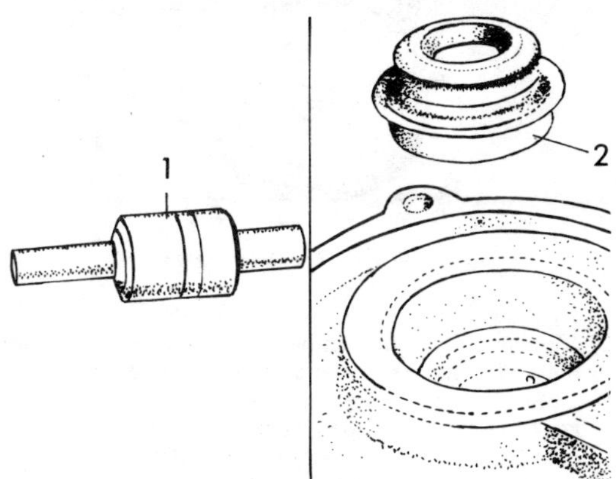

FIG 4:13 Water pump seal

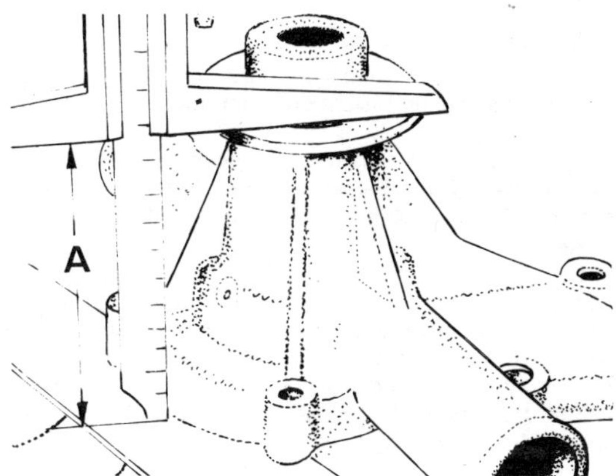

FIG 4:14 Flange location

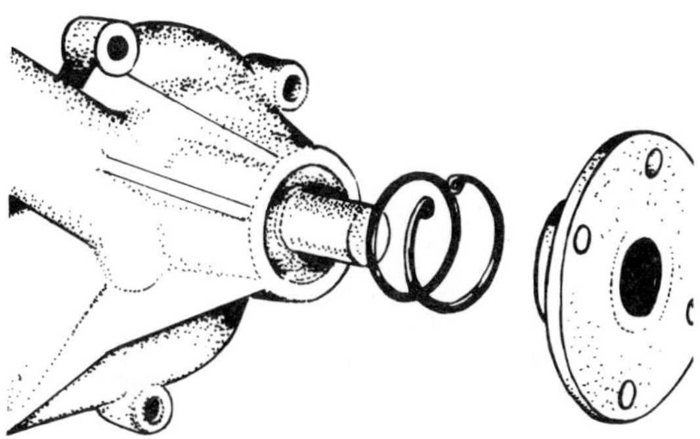

FIG 4:12 Water pump front end components

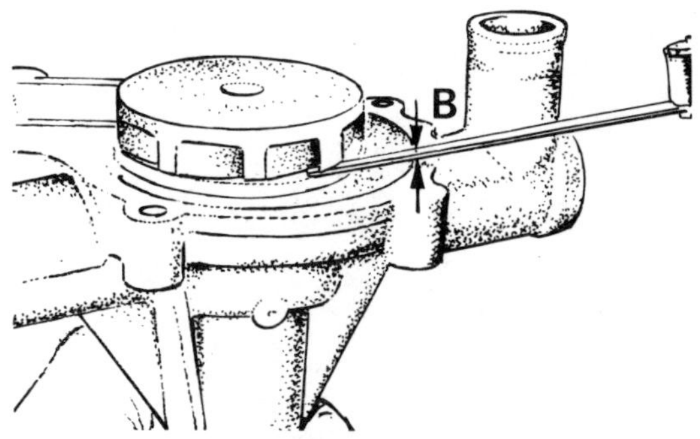

FIG 4:15 Impellor location

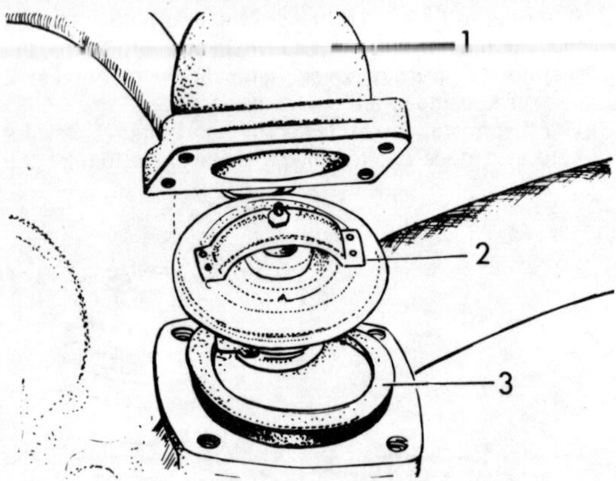

FIG 4:16 Thermostat

container. The temperature of the water is raised until the thermostat valve starts to open at the temperature given in Technical Data. If the valve does not open or sticks in the fully open position, renew it. It is impossible to repair a defective thermostat.

4 Refitting is the reverse procedure to dismantling. It is recommended that a new joint gasket be fitted whenever the original one is disturbed.

4:8 Frost precautions

When a heater is fitted antifreeze must be used, as draining the cooling system does not automatically drain the heater.

To add antifreeze mixture the cooling system should first be drained and flushed through with water until it runs out clean. Pour in antifreeze first, followed by the water.

Use only antifreeze of the ethylen-glycol type which conforms to British Standards Specification BS.3151 or BS.3152. The mixture can remain in the system for two years providing that the SG is checked periodically and fresh antifreeze is added as required. After the second winter drain the system, flush out using water and refill with new antifreeze solution.

Do not use antifreeze in the windscreen washer container. Special additives are available for this purpose. The recommended quantities of antifreeze for different degrees of frost are:

Antifreeze	*Starts freezing at*	*Absolute safe limit*
$1\frac{3}{4}$ pints	—9°C or 15°F	—19°C or —3°F
2 pints	—13°C or 9°F	—26°C or —15°F
$2\frac{1}{4}$ pints	—16°C or 3°F	—33°C or —28°F

4:9 Fault diagnosis

(a) Internal water leakage

1 Cracked cylinder wall
2 Loose cylinder head nuts
3 Cracked cylinder head
4 Faulty head gasket
5 Cracked tappet chest wall

(b) Poor circulation

1 Radiator core blocked
2 Engine water passages restricted
3 Low water level
4 Loose fan belt
5 Defective thermostat
6 Perished or collapsed radiator hoses

(c) Corrosion

1 Impurities in the water
2 Infrequent draining and flushing

(d) Overheating

1 Check (b)
2 Sludge in crankcase
3 Faulty ignition timing
4 Low oil level in sump
5 Tight engine
6 Choked exhaust system
7 Binding brakes
8 Slipping clutch
9 Incorrect valve timing
10 Retarded ignition
11 Mixture too weak

CHAPTER 5

THE CLUTCH

5:1 Description
5:2 Removal and refitting
5:3 Clutch inspection
5:4 Servicing the hydraulic system—all models except the 1600-2
5:5 Bleeding the hydraulic system—all models except the 1600-2
5:6 The clutch pedal—all models except the 1600-2
5:7 The clutch pedal—1600-2
5:8 Self-adjusting clutch
5:9 Fault diagnosis

5:1 Description

The BMW 1600-2 model is fitted with a mechanically-operated clutch whilst the remainder of the 1600 models are fitted with a hydraulic system.

The two main driving members of the clutch assembly comprise the flywheel and pressure plate assembly as shown in **FIG 5:1**, hydraulic operation, or **FIG 5:2** mechanical operation. The pressure plate is caused to rotate with the flywheel by a projection on the pressure plate engaging with slots in the cover which is bolted to the back of the flywheel. A series of nine springs are located between the clutch cover and the pressure plate and these force the pressure plate towards the flywheel face, so trapping the friction-lined driven plate between the two machined surfaces.

The drive shaft sometimes called first motion shaft, is supported in front of the gearbox by a journal bearing and in the flywheel by a ballbearing race. It is splined so enabling the hub of the clutch disc to have longitudinal movements and yet be able to transmit the torque from the clutch disc to the gearbox. The clutch disc incorporates a spring cushioned hub so minimizing transmission vibration being transmitted to the engine and car body.

The clutch is disengaged by withdrawing the pressure plate assembly from the clutch disc against the tension of the nine clutch springs. This is accomplished by three specially-shaped release levers which pivot at their centres on the clutch cover and engage with the pressure plate at one end and the clutch withdrawal bearing at the other end. The clutch pedal operates the withdrawal bearing by using a pivoted fork lever which is operated by a simple hydraulic system. The withdrawal bearing comprises a special ball thrust race which bears onto a hardened steel plate that is carried by the outer track of the release bearing.

5:2 Removal and refitting clutch

To remove the clutch from the car proceed as follows:

1 Remove the gearbox assembly as detailed in **Chapter 6**.

2 Carefully slacken the clutch cover retaining bolts in a diagonal pattern as shown in **FIG 5:3.** Carefully ease the cover assembly from the dowels located in the back of the flywheel and lift away the complete assembly.

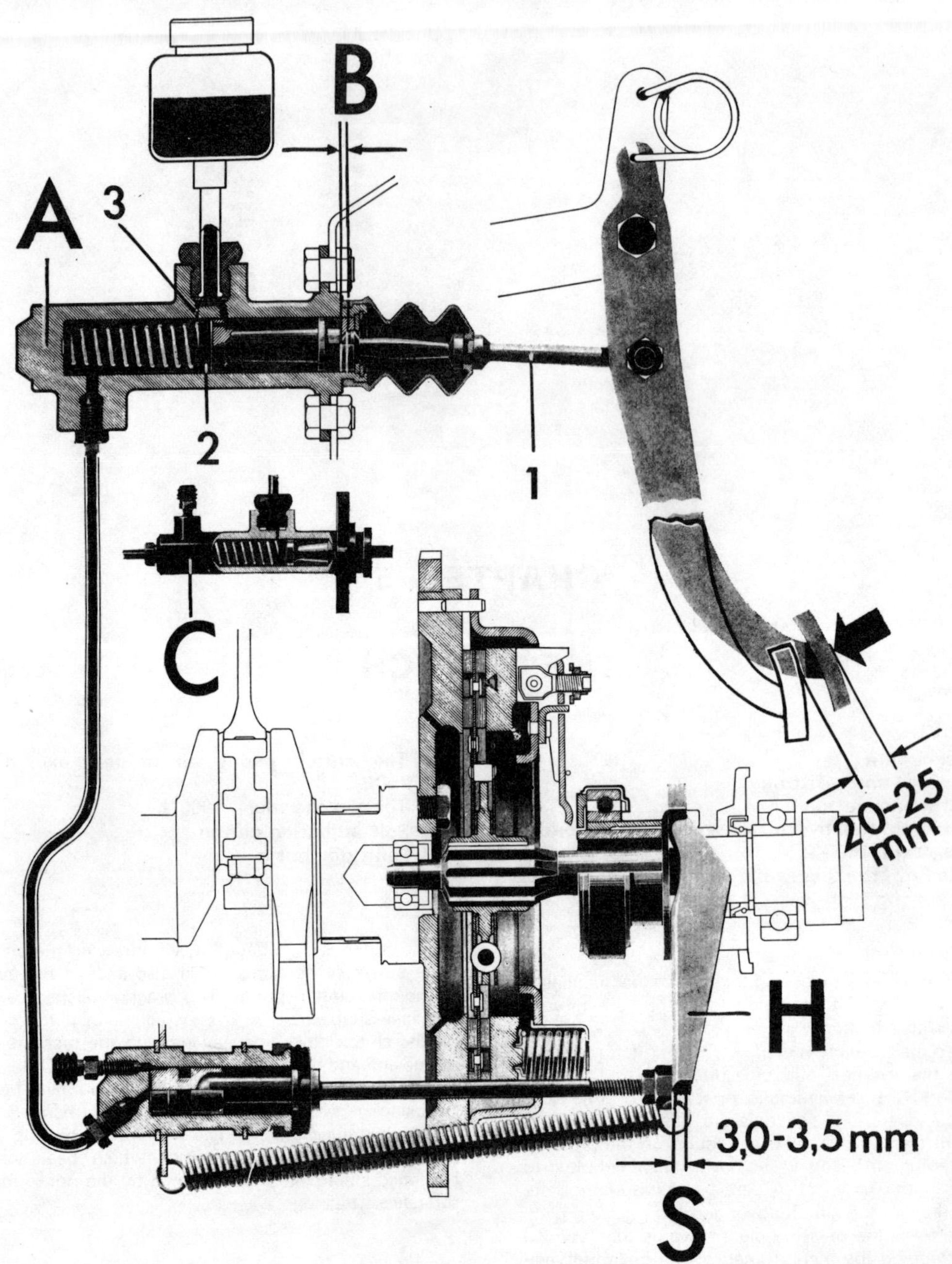

FIG 5:1 The clutch system—hydraulic

Refitting:

Reassembly of the clutch unit is the reverse procedure to dismantling but the following points should be noted:

1 Refer to **FIG 5:4** and identify the correct lining location so that the driven plate may be assembled the correct way round to the flywheel. The T.450.W lining faces the engine denoted by the letter 'M'. The T.50.S lining faces the gearbox denoted by the letter 'G'.

2 Before securing the clutch cover to the flywheel the driven plate should be centred to the flywheel (see **FIG 5:5**) by means of a dummy shaft BMW.603 which, if not available, can easily be made out of wood or scrap metal rod. The clutch mounting screws should be

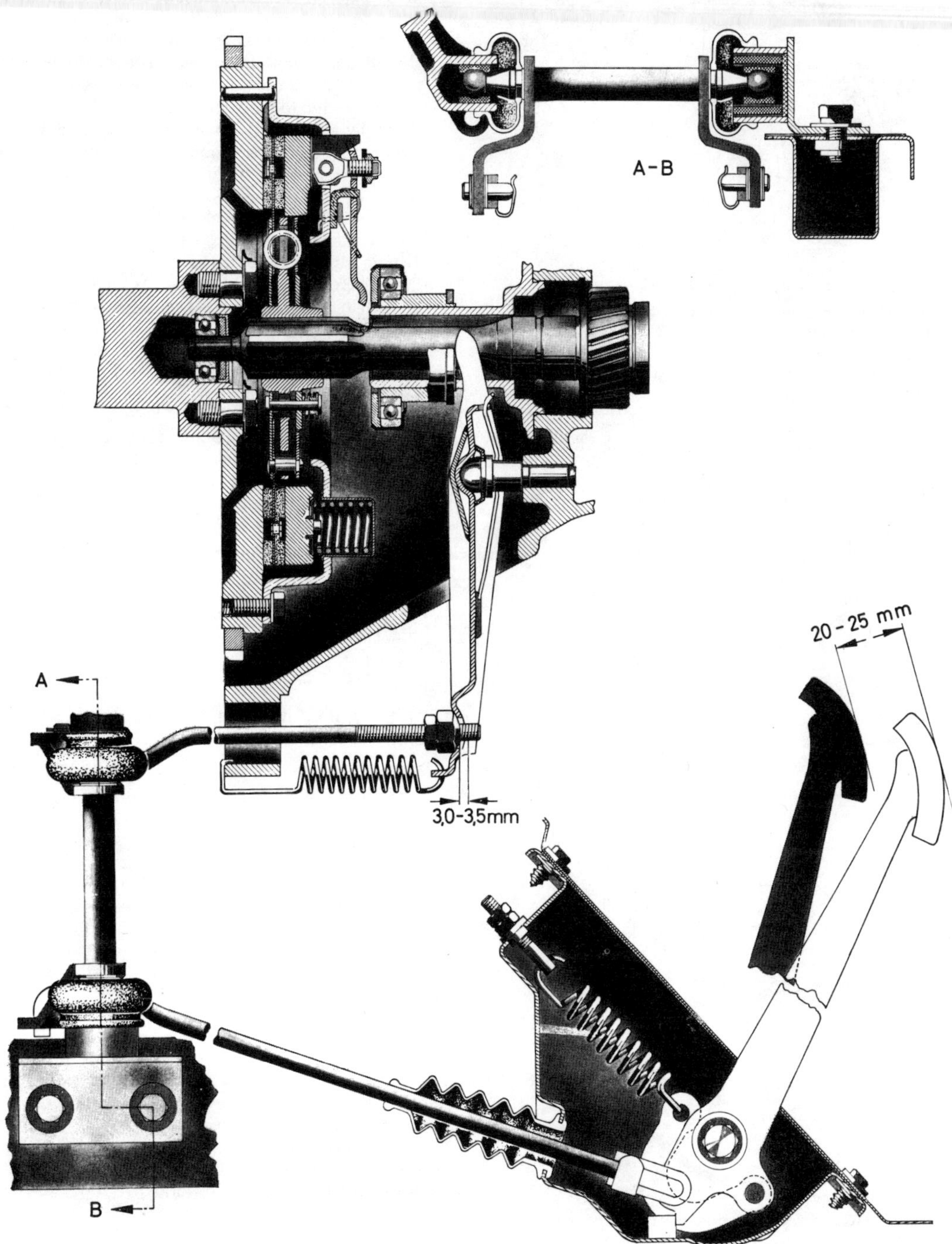

FIG 5 : 2 The clutch system—mechanical

tightened in the same diagonal pattern as previously described and tightened to a torque wrench setting of 12.3 ± 1.4 lb ft.

3 Lubricate the clutch shaft spigot bearing with a high melting point multi-purpose grease.

4 Adjust the clutch play on the withdrawal arm as indicated in **FIG 5 : 6.** The clearance 'S' should be between .1181 and .1378 inch.

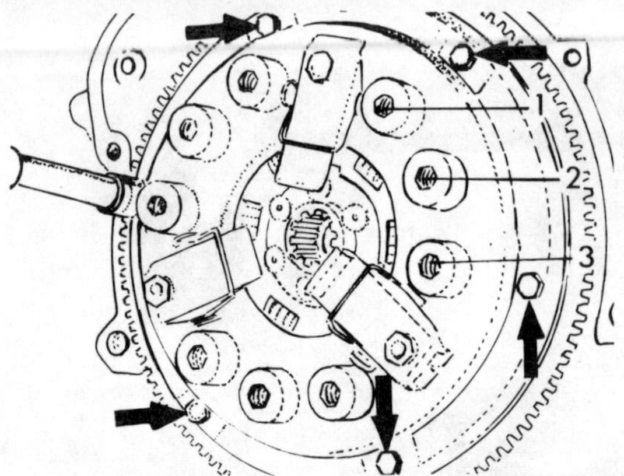

FIG 5 : 3 Clutch cover bolt location

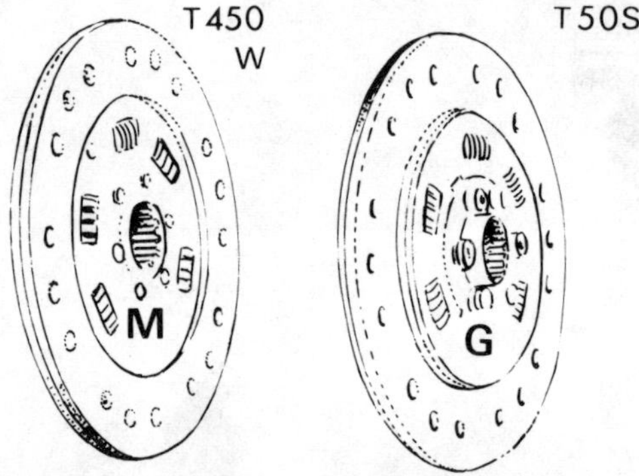

FIG 5 : 4 Friction lining faces

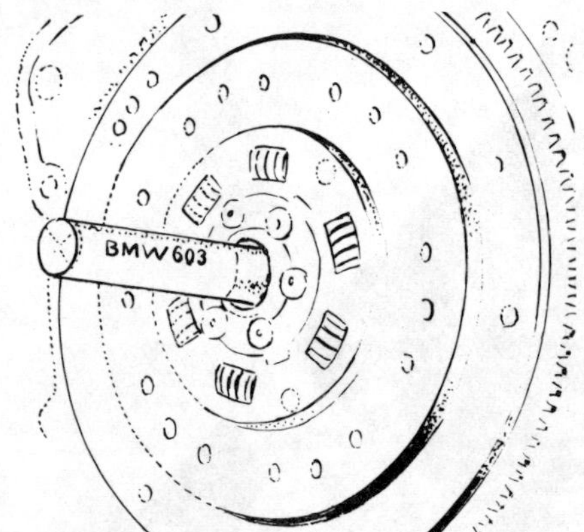

FIG 5 : 5 Clutch disc centralization

5 : 3 Clutch inspection

1 Thoroughly clean all parts of the clutch assembly ensuring that no cleaning fluid comes into contact with the lining if the clutch disc is to be re-used.
2 Measure the total thickness of the friction linings and plate and if it is thinner than the minimum requirement of .315 inch (8.0 mm) it must be renewed. Examine the lining for uneven wear or loose rivets and also ensure that the driven plate splines have not worn, distorted or show signs of fatigue cracks. It is considered essential to install a complete driven plate assembly when renewal of the friction surfaces is necessary.
3 Carefully examine the machined face of the pressure plate and if this shows signs of grooving or roughness the surface may be carefully reground until the grooves disappear.
4 Check the tips of the release levers which bear onto the release bearing. A small amount of worn flat surface is permissible but if this is excessive the levers must be renewed. Check for excessive wear in the groove in which the fulcrum action of the release levers operates. If the metal here has worn thin the lever must be renewed as it may break under load.
5 Examine the release bearing for cracks, pitting, signs of overheating or excessive wear and it should be renewed as necessary.
6 Examine the pressure springs for weakness, distortion or signs of cracks which, if evident, the springs must be renewed as a complete set. The correct spring rating is indicated by paint marks on the springs which are marked with blue/white/blue paint with a yellow stripe on the outer edge. The contact pressure should be approximately 1075 ± 33 lb.
7 Examine the clutch withdrawal fork for signs of wear at the contact point between the release bearing and the fork and also for signs of distortion or fatigue cracks. Renew as necessary.

5 : 4 Servicing the hydraulic system—all models except 1600-2

Description:

The clutch is operated hydraulically, the clutch pedal being connected to pushrod 1 as shown in **FIG 5 : 1**. The pushrod will press the piston and seal down the master cylinder bore when the pedal is depressed. Fluid in front of the piston will then be forced along the pipes until it reaches the slave cylinder. Here the piston will move down the bore in the body pushing the rod in front of it. This rod is connected to the clutch operating lever. Fluid leakage passed the pistons in both the master cylinder and slave cylinder is prevented by rubber seals or cups. When the master cylinder piston is fully retracted a small hole 3 in the master cylinder is uncovered. This communicates with the supply tank shown above the master cylinder in **FIG 5 : 1** and provides replenishing fluid to the system if there has been any loss. The hole is covered as soon as the piston starts to move.

Servicing operations must be carried out in conditions of great cleanliness as dirt will score the highly-finished bores and prevent the rubber cups from sealing properly.

Removing the master cylinder:

Remove the stud bolt 3 (see **FIG 5 : 7**), out of the clutch pedal 4 and the piston rod 5. Carefully lift away the bushes 6 and 7. Plug the reservoir outlet hole using a piece of tapered wood and release the connection pipe between the reservoir and master cylinder. Release the hydraulic pipe that connects the master cylinder to the slave cylinder at the master cylinder union. Remove the two retaining bolts holding the master cylinder to the body panel and carefully lift away.

Dismantling the master cylinder:

Refer to **FIG 5:1**. Carefully pull back the rubber boot and remove the circlip. Withdraw the pushrod 1 together with the dished washer. Extract all the internal parts. Gentle air pressure at the hydraulic line connection to slave cylinder may be used to blow out the parts taking extreme care in doing so. Remove the secondary cup washer from the piston using fingers only.

Reassembling the master cylinder:

Clean all the rubber parts in the correct grade of hydraulic fluid. Any solvents such as petrol, paraffin or trichlorethylene which may be used to clean the metal parts must be dried off completely before reassembling. Examine the rubber cups for damage or distortion, particularly to the knife-edges. The cups are available in kits of replacement parts and if they have seen considerable service it is wise to renew them even though they may seem to be satisfactory. Take care never to turn the cups inside out othrwise irreparable damage will be caused.

Start by dipping all internal parts in hydraulic brake fluid of the correct grade and assemble them wet. Stretch the secondary cup over the piston flange and work it about with the fingers until it is correctly seated. Insert the spring small end first, making sure that the retainer is in place. Insert the main cup lip first, taking great care not to damage or turn back the lip. Press it down the bore onto the spring retainer. Fit the washer followed by the piston. Refit the pushrod dished washer and circlip, followed by the rubber boot.

Before refitting the assembly to the car, test it by refitting the supply tank to the master cylinder and pushing the piston up and down the bore several times letting it return on its own. After a few strokes, fluid should flow from the main outlet orifice.

Refitting the master cylinder:

Fit the master cylinder to the front panel and connect the pressure pipeline to the outlet from the cylinder. Line up the pushrod yoke with the end of the pedal lever and connect up with the shouldered bolt, bushes and nut. Refit the supply reservoir and bleed the hydraulic system as detailed in **Section 5:5.**

Removing the slave cylinder:

Fit the length of rubber tube to the nipple on the body of the slave cylinder and open the nipple screw three-quarters of a turn. Pump the clutch pedal until all the fluid has been transferred into a clean container.

Unscrew the pressure pipe from the cylinder taking care that the pipe does not turn otherwise it will either kink or fracture.

Release the adjustment nut and locknut from the control rod, disconnect the draw spring 36 (see **FIG 5:8**) from the withdrawal arm 37. Carefully ease back the rubber cap 38 (see **FIG 5:9**) and remove the circlip 39 from the slave cylinder 40 using a pair of pointed circlip

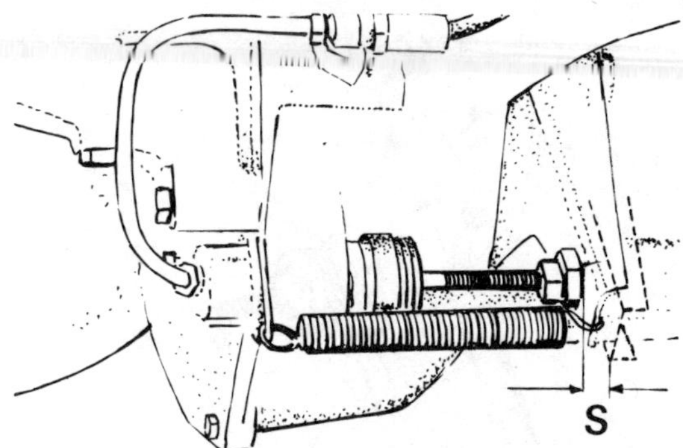

FIG 5:6 Clutch fork free play

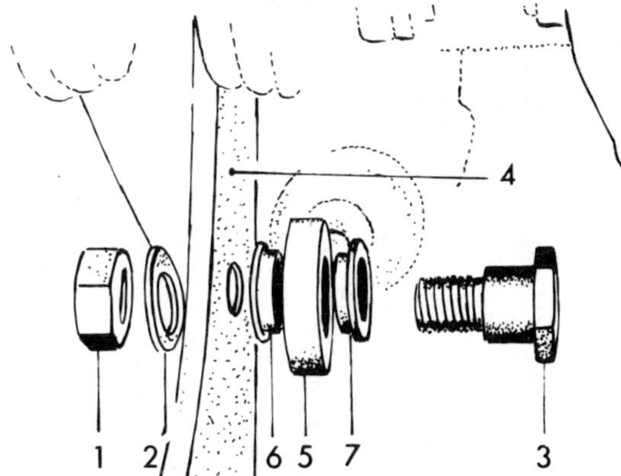

FIG 5:7 Slave cylinder pushrod to pedal mounting

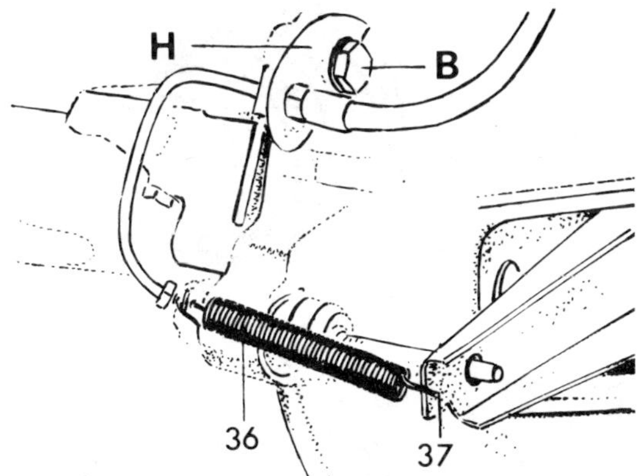

FIG 5:8 Slave cylinder retraction spring

pliers. Ease the slave cylinder forwards away from the withdrawal lever and take out the pushrod, followed by the slave cylinder itself.

Dismantling the slave cylinder:

Clean the exterior thoroughly and remove the rubber boot, using only the fingers to displace the boot retaining

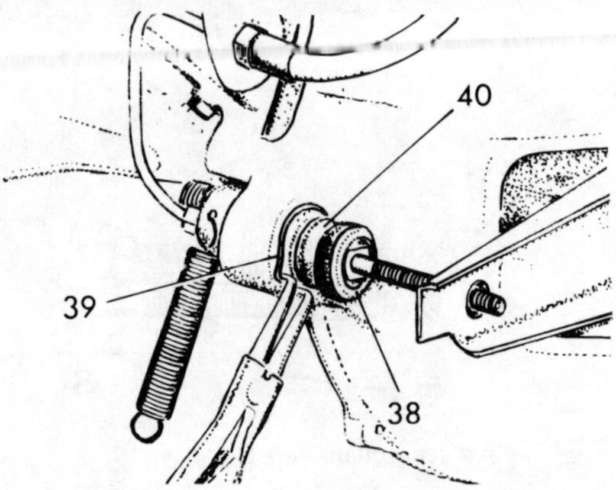

FIG 5:9 Slave cylinder retaining circlip removal

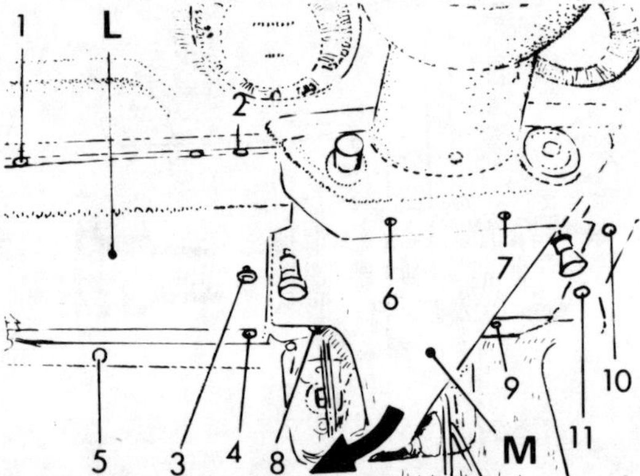

FIG 5:10 Under lining mounting screws

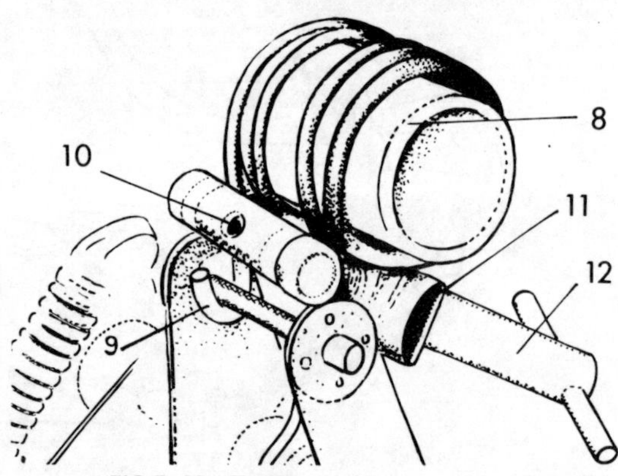

FIG 5:11 Torsion spring clamp location

ring. Withdraw the parts from the interior of the slave cylinder or carefully blow them out with gentle air pressure.

Clean the internal parts with hydraulic fluid of the required specification and assemble the parts wet. It is always considered advisable to renew all the rubber parts particularly the piston sealing cup. Any solvents used for cleaning the metal parts must be completely dried off before reassembly.

Reassembly of the slave cylinder:

Carefully ease the rubber seal onto the piston and carefully insert the assembly into the bore. Take extra care to ensure that the seal is not damaged or turned back. Push the piston down the bore and refit the boot to the body ensuring that the lip of the boot is correctly located in its seating. Carefully replace the pushrod.

Refitting the slave cylinder to the hydraulic system is the reverse procedure to dismantling. Refill the hydraulic fluid reservoir and bleed the system as directed in **Section 5:5.** It will also be necessary to adjust the clutch slave cylinder pushrod details of this operation being described in **Section 5:6.**

5:5 Bleeding the system—all models except the 1600-2

Fill the master cylinder reservoir with the correct grade of hydraulic fluid and attach a rubber tube to the bleed screw on the end of the slave cylinder. Immerse the open end of the tube in a small amount of the same brake fluid in a clean glass container. A second operator is needed to pump the clutch pedal after the bleed screw has been opened about threequarters of a turn. At the end of each down stroke of the clutch pedal close the bleed screw and let the pedal return to the 'off' position. At first, air bubbles will emerge from the immersed end of the tube. When clear fluid free from bubbles is delivered into the container, tighten the bleed screw on a down stroke of the pedal. The operation of bleeding the system is necessary whenever the pipelines are disconnected or when the fluid in the supply tank has fallen so low that air has entered the system.

It is not advisable to use again, hydraulic fluid which has been collected in the container unless it is clean beyond all doubt. Even then it must be allowed to stand for 24 hours to allow the air bubbles carried in the fluid to be released.

5:6 The clutch pedal—all models except the 1600-2

To remove the clutch pedal assembly from the car proceed as follows:

1 Refer to **FIG 5:10** and release the clamping screws 1 to 5 holding the lefthand cover 'L' in place. Also release the clamp screws 6 to 11 for the centre cover 'M'. Remove the heater booster motor switch plug connection and lift away the covering from below twisting it towards the left as shown in the arrow in **FIG 5:10.**

2 Remove the retaining nut 1 (see **FIG 5:7**) together with its spring washer and push the specially shaped stud bolt 3 from the clutch pedal and piston rod taking care not to misplace the bushes 6 and 7.

3 Using BMW clamping attachment 6021 comprising the clamp and sleeve, push the sleeve 8 (see **FIG 5:11**), into the torsion spring 9. Depress the clutch pedal to its maximum limit and insert the threaded part of the tool 10 through the torsion spring 9. Fit the thrust member 11 and washer onto the threaded

member 10. Using the clamp handle 12 compress the torsion spring 9.

4 With the torsion spring compressed turn the torsion spring 9 (see **FIG 5:12**) with its plastic insert 14 upwards out of the clutch pedal assembly 4.

5 Remove the locknut 15 (see **FIG 5:13**) and carefully pull the screw 16 out of the bearing support 17. Lift away the clutch pedal. Push the spacing sleeve 18 and bearing bush 19 from the clutch pedal arm 4. Release the BMW clamp attachment and remove the swivel spring.

Reassembly:

Reassembly is the reverse procedure to dismantling. The following points should however be noted:

1 Always fit the swivel spring 20 and sleeve 21 onto the shaft as shown in **FIG 5:14**, before the spring compressor is fitted.

2 Always compress the swivel spring 20 until the plastic insert slips into its special recess in the clutch pedal arm (see **FIG 5:12**).

Clutch adjustment:

1 Refer to **FIG 5:1**. When the clutch unit is in its disengaged position the clutch pedal must abut the special limit stop on the pivot assembly.

2 The clearance should be between 5.7 to 5.9 inch between the clutch pedal face and the lower horn ring assembly. Care must be taken to ensure that any obstruction in the form of carpets or sound deadening media placed underneath the clutch pedal do not affect its movement. Should the clearance be less than 5.3 inches a piston rod 1 (see **FIG 5:1**) having a length of 4.37 inches is to be fitted in place of the original. Should the clearance be between 5.3 and 5.5 inches a piston rod of 4.29 inches should be fitted. It is highly undesirable for the maximum clearance of 5.9 inches to be exceeded.

3 Free travel of the piston rod to piston of the hydraulic master cylinder, dimension B (see **FIG 5:1**), should be .0394 inch.

Should a piston rod of the wrong length be fitted the oil seal 2 will press into the compensation bore 3 whilst in its rest position, causing irreparable damage to the seal.

4 Inset 'C' shows the older type of master cylinder fitted with a bleed valve. Later models do not have a bleed valve fitted. Whenever the clutch hydraulic system is being bled it should be done so from the slave cylinder position.

5 From Chassis No. 976909 and 986061 on all models except the 1600-2 the diameter of the master and slave cylinders was altered to .75 inch. Should repair or new units be fitted it is important that only master and slave cylinders of the same specification are fitted so making a matched pair.

5:7 The clutch pedal—1600-2

To remove the clutch pedal assembly from the car proceed as follows:

1 Refer to **FIG 5:15** and release the retaining clip 1 holding the tension rod 3 to the intermediate shaft. Remove the tension rod from the intermediate shaft.

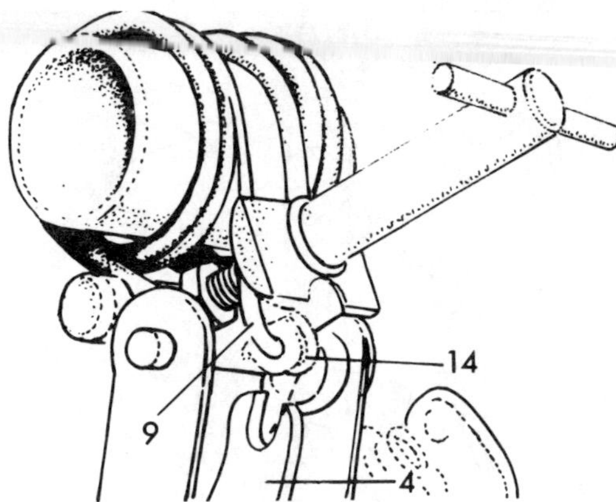

FIG 5:12 Torsion spring removal

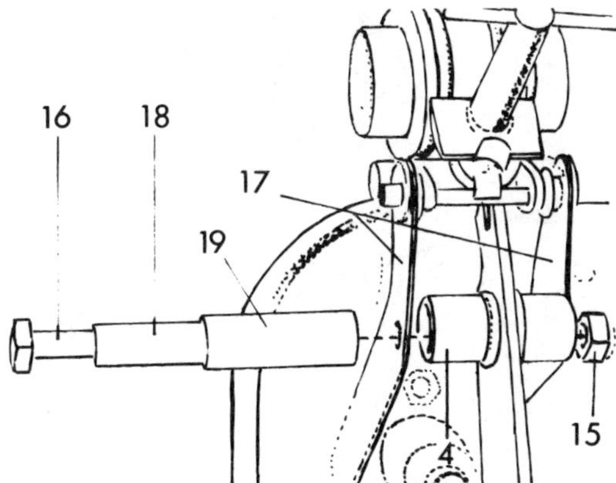

FIG 5:13 Pedal pivot assembly

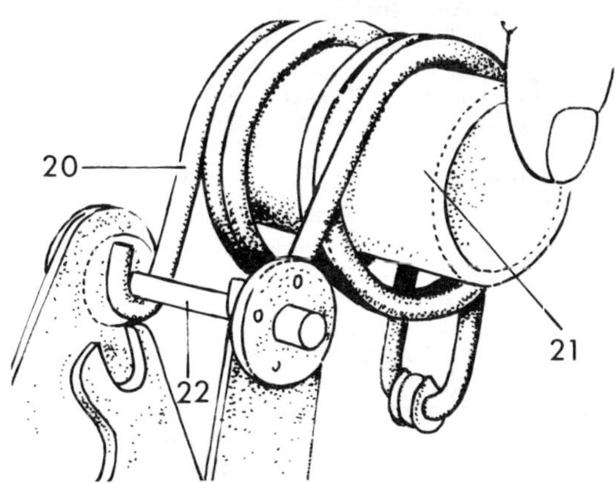

FIG 5:14 Torsion spring reassembly

2 Remove the interior floor covering and referring to **FIG 5:16** release the retaining clip 2 from the tension rod 3 at the clutch pedal. Remove the tension rod from the clutch pedal.

3 Depress the clutch pedal fully and the spring eye bolt securing nuts 4. Detach the tensioning spring from the eye bolt.

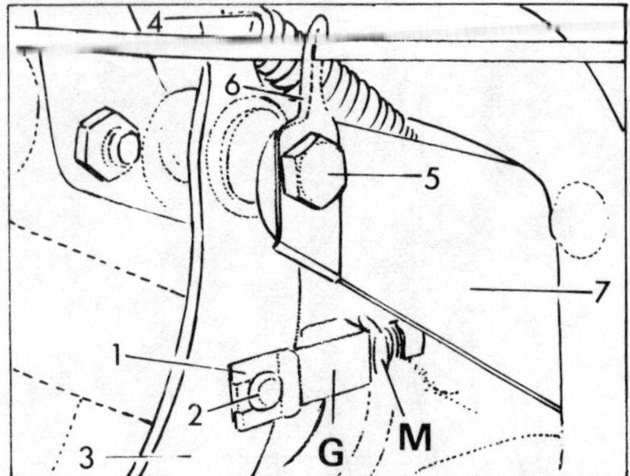

FIG 5:15 Clutch pedal pivot assembly

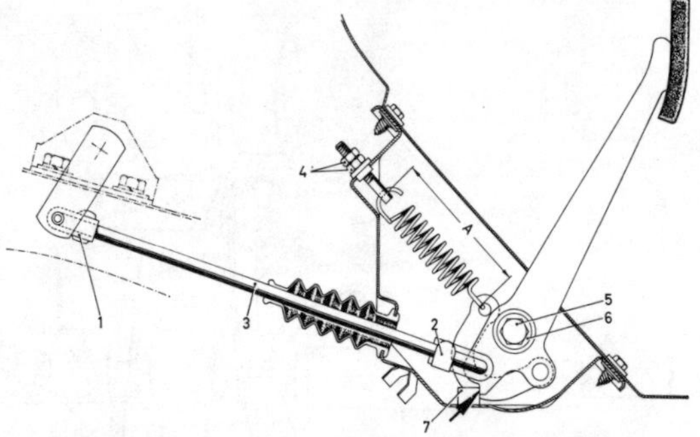
FIG 5:16 Mechanical clutch operating linkage

4 Remove the rubber closure plug from the bearing bracket by pressing outwards towards the left to the engine compartment. Release the locknut on the bolt 5. Remove the bolt, and washer through the opening in the bearing bracket towards the engine compartment.
5 Carefully lift away the clutch pedal. Referring to **FIG 5:17** press out the spacer sleeve 8 and bearing bush 9.

Reassembly:

Reassembly is the reverse procedure to dismantling but the following points should be noted:
1 Refer to **FIG 5:18.** The drilled bolt 'A' has now been replaced by a ring bolt 'B'. It is important that the spring is correctly tensioned to a length of 3.62 inch by shortening the spacing sleeve from .28 to .18 inch (7 to 4.5mm).
2 Before refitting the bearing bush coat with Molykote Longterm 2 to ensure long life lubrication.
3 Refer to **FIG 5:16** for the correct position of the pedal lever relative to the stop 7.
4 Tighten the pedal lever bolt to a torque wrench setting of 31.1 lb ft.
5 The tension spring length 'A' (see **FIG 5:16**) should be adjusted to a length of 3.62 inch.

Clutch adjustment:

The correct operating clearance is adjusted at the pedal connection and should be .12 to .14 inch at the point denoted by the arrow in **FIG 5:16**.

5:8 Self-adjusting clutch

On later cars, after 1969, a self-adjusting clutch mechanism is incorporated on which no attention is required other than an inspection every 8000 miles to measure the amount of wear on the clutch friction surfaces.

Push the clutch withdrawal lever forwards with the hand as shown in **FIG 5:19** until it contacts the slave cylinder, then measure the travel of the operating arm at **A**. On a new clutch this will be between 17 and 19mm but will steadily decrease as the surfaces wear down.

When the dimension **A** is reduced to 5mm the clutch plate must be renewed.

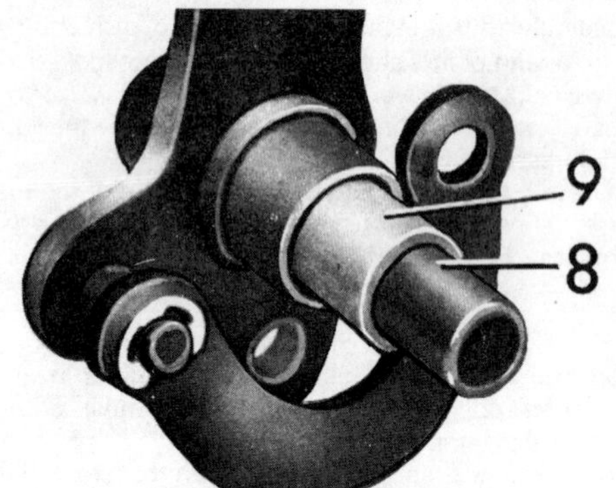

FIG 5:17 Pivot bearing bush

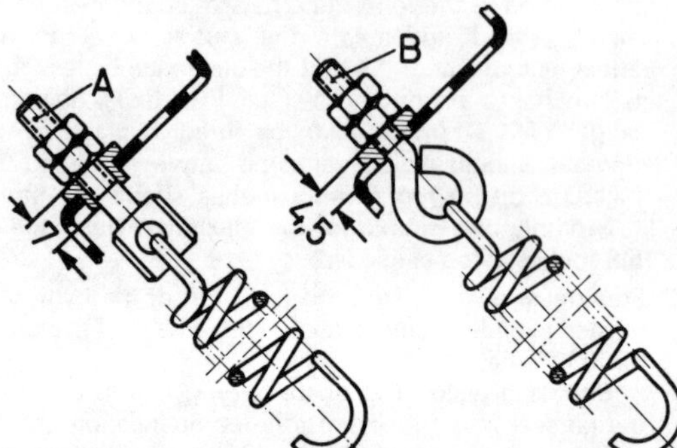

FIG 5:18 Clutch pedal return spring mountings

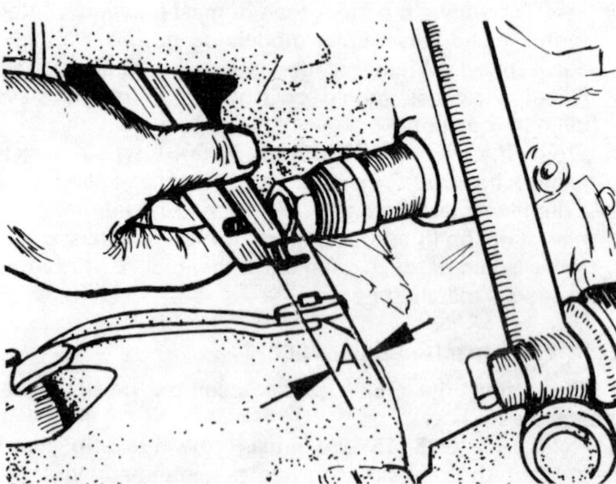

FIG 5:19 Measuring wear on self-adjusting clutch

5:9 Fault diagnosis

(a) Drag or spin

1 Oil or grease on driven plate linings
2 Leaking master cylinder, slave cylinder or piping
3 Driven plate hub binding on splines
4 Distorted driven plate
5 Warped or damaged pressure plate
6 Broken driven plate linings
7 Air in the clutch hydraulic system

(b) Fierceness or snatch

1 Check 1, 2, 4 and 5 in (a)
2 Worn clutch linings

(c) Slip

1 Check 1 in (a) and 2 in (b)
2 Weak pressure spring(s)
3 Seized piston in clutch slave cylinder
4 Operating lever stop has no clearance

(d) Judder

1 Check 1 and 4 in (a)
2 Pressure plate incorrectly fitted to spring housing
3 Contact area of driven plate linings not evenly distributed
4 Faulty rubber mountings

(e) Tick or knock

1 Badly worn driven plate hub splines
2 Worn release bearing
3 Faulty drive pinion on starter
4 Elongated holes in spring housing
5 Defective driven plate springs.

NOTES

CHAPTER 6

THE GEARBOX

6:1 Description
6:2 Gearbox removal and replacement
6:3 Gearbox dismantling
6:4 Synchromesh assembly
6:5 Output shaft and speedometer drive
6:6 The layshaft
6:7 Third- and fourth-speed pinion sets
6:8 Output shaft groove bearing
6:9 Refitting selector shafts and selector forks
6:10 Input shaft refitting
6:11 Fault diagnosis

6:1 Description

The gearbox provides four forward speeds and one reverse. First, second, third and fourth gears are silent and equipped with the Porsche type synchromesh devices. All the forward gears are of constant mesh helical type to ensure maximum quiet running.

The gearbox is in a single unit connected to the engine backplate. It consists of two detachable parts, (a) a front bell-mouthed housing and central body, (b) a rear end cover. The clutch shaft is supported by a ballbearing race located at the front of the gearbox housing whilst the constant mesh shaft is supported by a spigot bearing located on the inside of the clutch shaft and a ballrace located at the rear of the central section of the gearbox casing. A front and rear ballbearing race supports the layshaft located at the bottom of the gearbox.

6:2 Gearbox removal and replacement

To remove the gearbox from the vehicle proceed as follows:

1 Jack up the front of the vehicle so that the front wheels are well clear of the ground and place on firmly based stands. Refer to **FIG 6:1** and remove the attachment bolts on the triangular flange (1 to 3). Also remove the attachment bolts 4 and 5 from the exhaust bracket to gearbox support bracket. Remove the centre exhaust bracket mounting bolt and tie back the bracket. Remove the exhaust pipe to manifold mounting nuts.

2 Remove the four propeller shaft front flange to gearbox flange bolts and carefully ease back the propeller shaft.

3 Disconnect the battery positive terminal. Detach the reversing light switch plug connection 13 (see **FIG 6:2**), and slacken the bolt clamping the speedometer drive cable to the gearbox casing. Withdraw the cable.

4 Refer to **FIG 6:3** and slacken the fixing bolt 11 using an Allen key. Gently push out the kingpin 12.

5 Gently ease up the gaiter 1 (see **FIG 6:4**), the foam rubber ring 2 and using a pair of circlip pliers release circlip 3. Lift upwards the gearchange lever making a note of any shims present.

6 Disconnect the starter motor cables and remove the two retaining bolts. Lift away the motor.

7 Remove the clutch hydraulic pipe bracket from the gearbox cover and release the clutch withdrawal lever tension spring as shown in **FIG 6:5.** Carefully pull back the protective cap 20 and lift away the circlip

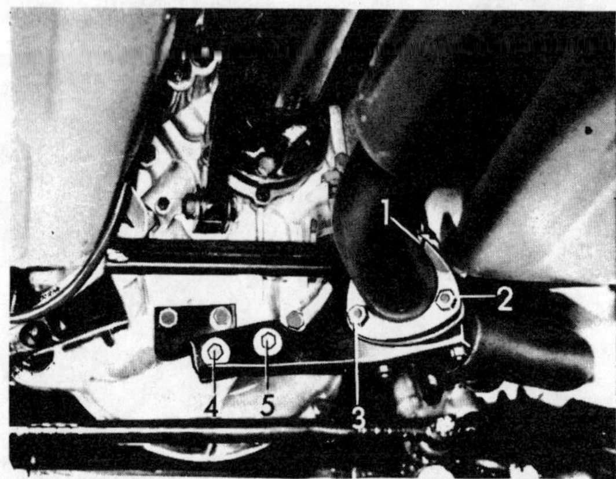

FIG 6:1 Exhaust system front mounting

FIG 6:2 Rear view of gearbox in position

21. Remove the slave cylinder forwards and also push out the pushrod at the same time.
8 Remove the steering control lever bracket retaining bolts, the location being shown in **FIG 9:17.** Turn the steering wheel to full righthand lock and rotate the bearing support towards the bulkhead. Gently turn the steering wheel back on the lefthand lock and at the same time lay the drop arm down and to the right onto the track arm.
9 Remove the three gearbox cover fixing bolts and lift away the coverplate.
10 Using an overhead hoist or garage crane support the engine from above, moving forward as far as is permitted by the silentbloc engine mountings.
11 Release the engine and gearbox mounting bolts and carefully withdraw the gearbox away from the engine downwards and towards the rear taking very great care that no load is put on the clutch shaft otherwise it will distort.

Refitting:

To refit the gearbox is the reverse procedure to dismantling but the following points should be noted:
1 When assembling the gearbox bellhousing to the engine back face, tighten the size M8 clamp bolts to a torque wrench setting of 18 lb ft, and the size M10 clamp bolts to a torque wrench setting of 34 lb ft.
2 The steering control lever bracket retaining bolts should be tightened to a torque wrench setting of 18 lb ft.
3 Tighten the starter motor retaining bolts to a torque wrench of 34 lb ft.
4 Upon reassembling the gearchange lever always replace any shims fitted or fit further shims to ensure all play from the ball sockets is removed.
5 When assembling the gearchange lever the pivot pin must be inserted from the righthand side only. It is advisable to check the plastic bushes for wear and renew if necessary.
6 The propeller shaft to gearbox drive flange retaining bolts must be tightened to a torque wrench setting of 34 lb ft.

6:3 Gearbox dismantling

1 Remove the oil drain pipe and allow all oil to drain out into a suitably sized container. Refer to **FIG 6:6** and remove the fixing bolts 1 to 3 on the bracket and stay. Lift away the bracket together with the stay. Engage second gear and push back the spacer sleeve 4 with a screwdriver.

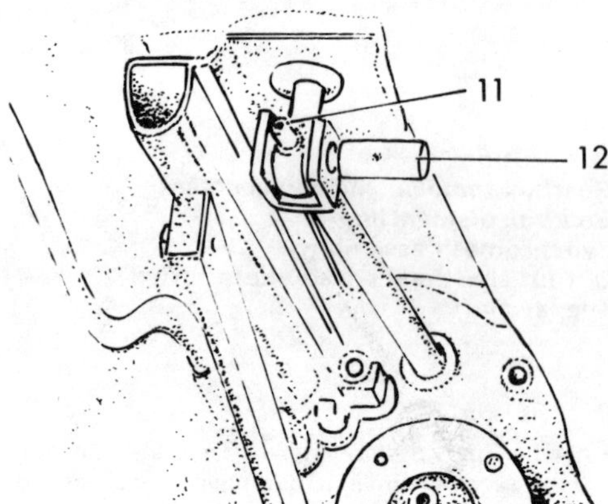

FIG 6:3 Gearchange lever lower linkage

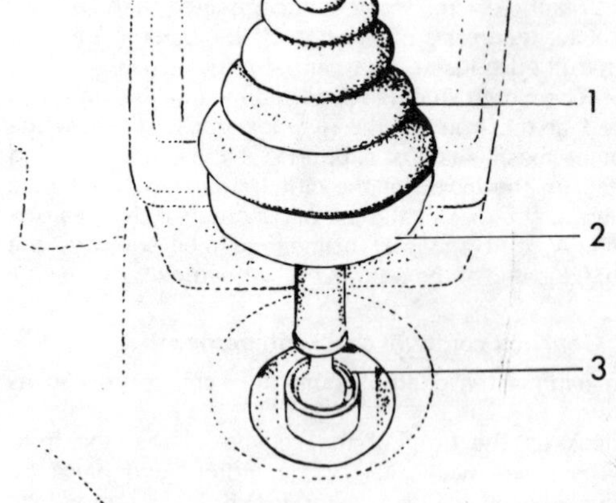

FIG 6:4 Gearchange lever retaining circlip location

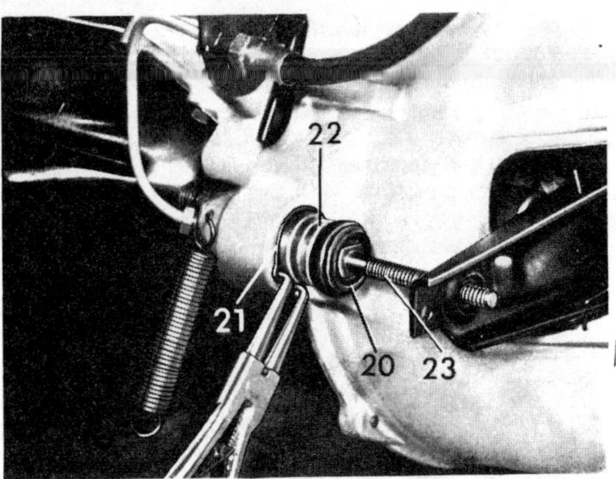

FIG 6:5 Clutch slave cylinder

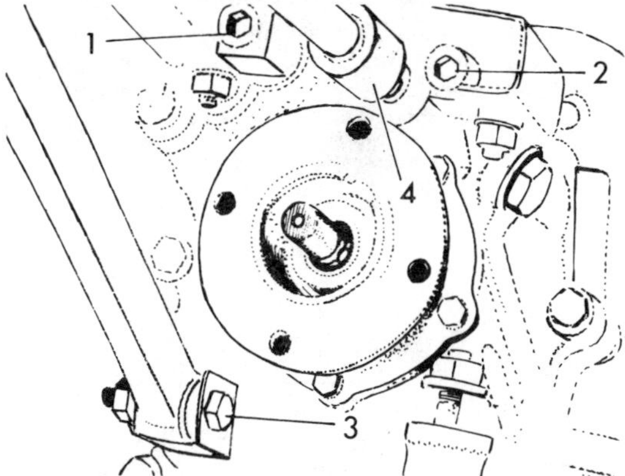

FIG 6:6 Rear view of gearbox

2 Using a pin punch drive out the cylindrical pin from the selector shaft joint. Remove the selector shaft and joint from the rear of the gearbox.
3 Remove the two exhaust support bracket retaining bolts and lift away the bracket. Using a screwdriver remove the locking strip on the flanged nut of the output flange and remove the flanged nut on the output flange using a socket wrench whilst the flange is held tight.
4 Compress and lift away the spring for the clutch withdrawal lever and carefully lift away the withdrawal lever. Unscrew the three securing nuts for the guide sleeve and gently tap the side of the guide sleeve to loosen it from its seating. Lift away together with the gasket taking care to make a note of any shims that might be in place. Using a pair of circlip pliers remove the circlip together with any shims in place between the circlip and the ballrace.
5 Using a special ballrace extractor or Rillex 6206 tool as shown in **FIG 6:7** carefully withdraw the clutch shaft bearing. Note the location of any shims released.
6 Remove the gearbox housing cover retaining bolts and referring to **FIG 6:8** carefully heat up the gearbox housing around the sealing cover 'D' so that the grooved bearing on the layshaft slides out easily. Using a plastic faced hammer gently tap the gearbox housing and pull off. Remove the seal if it shows signs of wear.
7 Refer to **FIG 6:9** and slacken the screw plug 8 on the locking pin 9 and withdraw the locking pin and spring 10.
8 Using a pair of side cutters remove the locking wire for the selector fork retaining bolts and slacken these. Carefully withdraw the gearchange shaft 14 forwards as shown in **FIG 6:10.**
9 Set the selector shaft 15 (see **FIG 6:11**) to the fourth gear position and turn the guide sleeve until the locating pin 16 can be driven out using a suitably sized drift. Carefully pull the selector shaft 15 forwards until the selector fork 17 can be withdrawn from the selector sleeve. Take care not to loose any of the ballbearings.
10 Set the selector sleeve 19 (see **FIG 6:12**), to the neutral position and carefully push the selector shaft 18 to the second gear position and drive out the locating pin on the selector fork 20 using a suitably sized drift. Carefully withdraw the selector shaft 18 forwards until the selector fork 20 can be withdrawn from the selector sleeve. Take great care to note the location of any ballbearings that will be released during this operation.

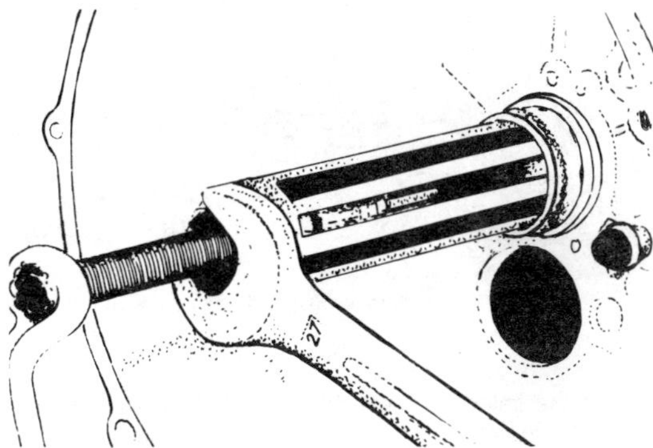

FIG 6:7 Clutch shaft bearing removal

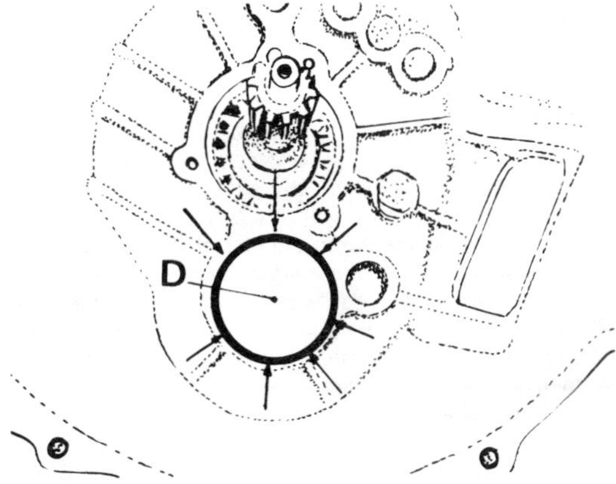

FIG 6:8 Front view of gearbox housing

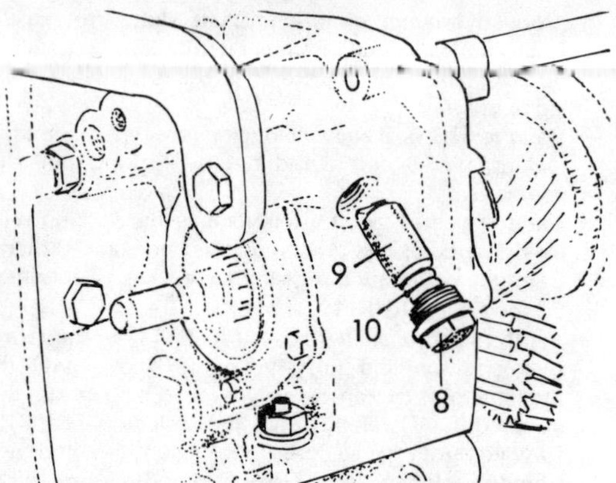

FIG 6:9 Locking pin and spring removal

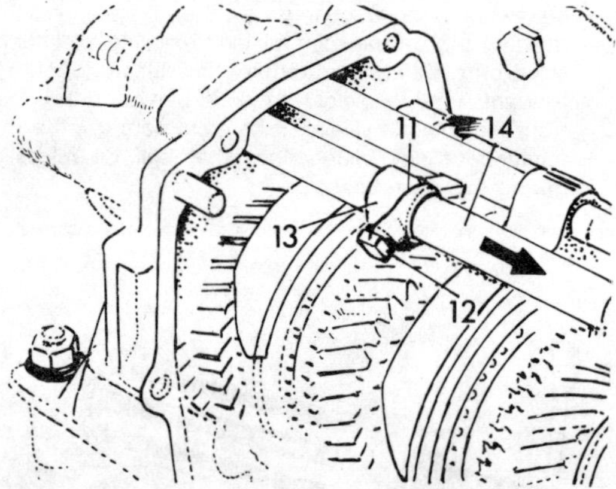

FIG 6:10 Gearchange shaft removal

11 Set the selector sleeve 21 (see **FIG 6:13**), to the neutral position and using a suitably sized drift drive out the locating pin 22 on the selector fork 23. To ensure that this is driven out correctly turn the guide sleeve until the locating pin is in a good working position. Carefully withdraw the selector shaft 24 forwards until the selector fork can be withdrawn from the reverse pinion. Again take great care to note the location of any ballbearings that will be released during this operation. Remove the five retaining bolts on the sealing cover and lift away the cover making a note of any shims. Using a special ballrace extractor or Rillex 6206 tool remove the grooved ballbearing from the rear of the output shaft. Carefully lift away the complete main shaft manipulating forwards and twisting slightly to the right.

12 Carefully heat the gearbox cover and pull off the layshaft and idler pinion from the gearbox housing cover taking care to note the location of any ballbearings that will be released during this operation.

13 Carefully pull off the drive shaft, the selector sleeve and needle roller bearing from the drive shaft. Using a pair of circlip pliers remove the circlip and carefully ease away the support disc from the guide sleeve. Pull off the guide sleeve and third gear pinion with the synchromesh unit. Extract the needle roller cage.

14 Using a press and suitably sized drift remove the speedometer drive 39 (see **FIG 6:14**), from the output shaft 38 together with the reverse gear pinion 40, first gear pinion 41 with the synchromesh unit, the selector sleeve 42 and the second gear pinion together with the synchromesh unit 43. Note the location of the shim between the speedometer drive and the reverse gear pinion.

6:4 Synchromesh assembly

The synchromesh assembly must be thoroughly inspected for signs of misuse which will show in the form of chipped teeth, hairline cracks and the tooth edges of the selector sleeve must have sharp edges and show no signs of chamfer.

Internal inspection and reassembly:

1 Using a pair of circlip pliers lift away the circlip 1 and lift off the synchromesh ring 2 as shown in **FIG 6:15.** Push the selector sleeve into the synchromesh ring 2. It should be noted that the front face of the selector

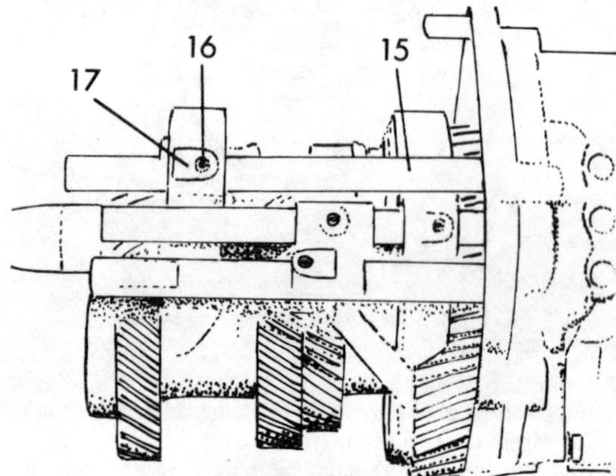

FIG 6:11 Selector shaft removal

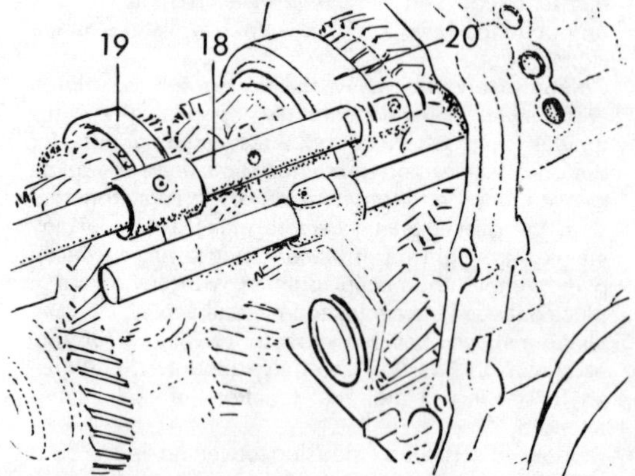

FIG 6:12 Selector shaft removal

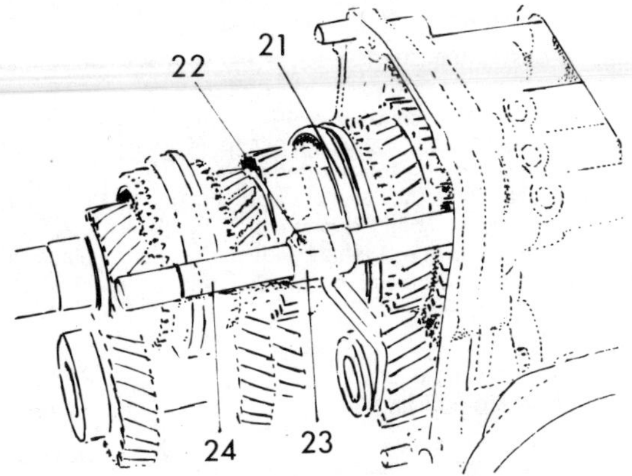

FIG 6:13 Selector shaft removal

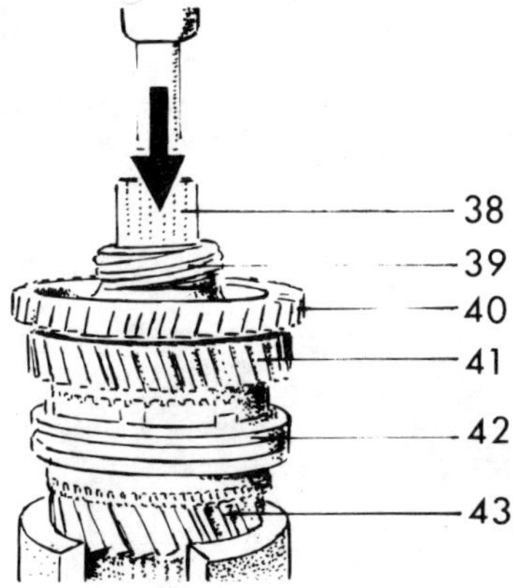

FIG 6:14 Speedometer drive gear removal

sleeve be correctly aligned with the face of the synchromesh ring as shown in **FIG 6:16.** The synchromesh ring contact surface should be distributed as evenly as possible. It is important that at least 50 per cent of the circumference of the synchromesh ring must be in contact. The outer diameter of the unbiased synchromesh ring should measure 3.020±.006 inch.

2 Faulty synchromesh can be caused by a damaged locking band. The first gear is distinguishable by the block, in addition to which, it only contains one locking band whereas gears on second, third and fourth speeds are fitted with two locking bands.

3 Once the synchronizing ring has been reassembled to the synchromesh unit it must be easily turned by hand otherwise difficult gear changing will result.

6:5 Output shaft and speedometer drive

1 Carefully hold the output shaft between soft faces in a firm bench vice and place the needle roller cage 37 (see **FIG 6:17**), the third gear pinion 36 and the guide sleeve 35 onto the output shaft.

2 Place a .079 inch thick thrust washer 4 (see **FIG 6:18**), onto the guide sleeve 35 and spring the circlip into its groove using a pair of suitably sized circlip pliers.

3 Reverse the position of the output shaft in the vice and push the needle roller cage 6 (see **FIG 6:19**), the second gear pinion 7 and the guide sleeve 8 onto the output shaft.

4 Carefully push the spacer sleeve 9 (see **FIG 6:20**), onto the output shaft whilst it is cold with the aid of a suitably sized sleeve in conjunction with a spindle press. Place the needle roller cage 10, the selector sleeve 11 and the first gear pinion 12 into position. Place the reverse gear pinion 13 (see **FIG 6:21**), in position on the output shaft with the polished surface side towards the first gear pinion. Refer to **FIG 6:21** and check the overall dimension of the gear train. It should be noted that the overall dimension 'A' is measured from the surface ground face of the guide sleeve 35 up to the front face of the boss of the reverse gear pinion 13. This should be 5.433 ± .004 inch (138 ± .1 mm) Shims may be fitted to the front face of the boss of the reverse gear pinion 13 using shims of suitable thickness.

Example:

'A' Theoretical	=	5.433 inch
'A' Actual	=	5.394 inch
Shim	=	.039 inch

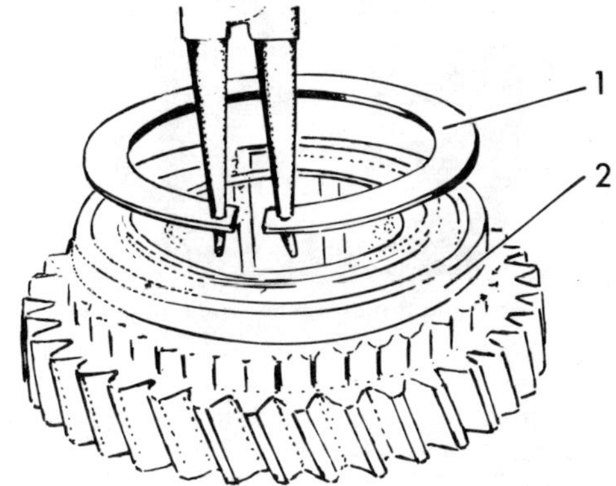

FIG 6:15 Synchromesh ring removal

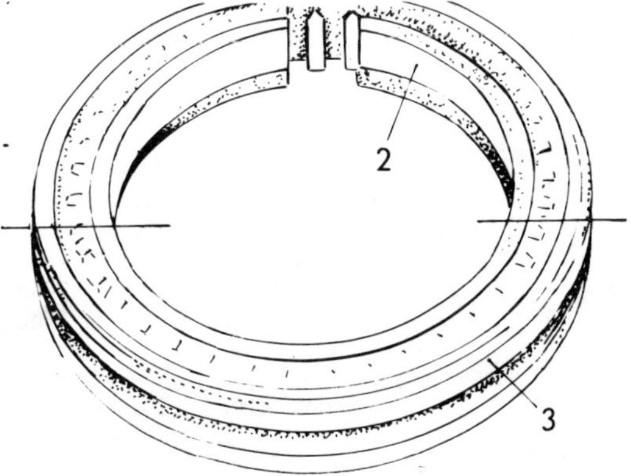

FIG 6:16 Synchromesh ring alignment

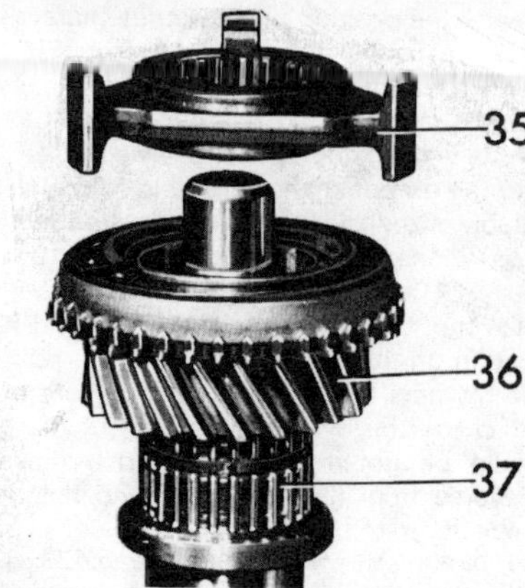

FIG 6:17 Third gear pinion reassembly

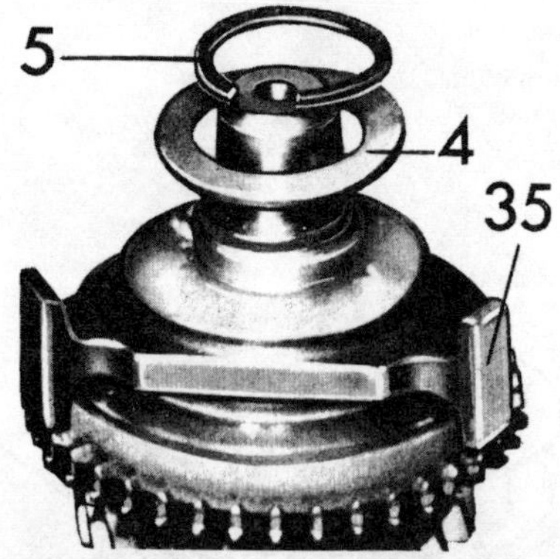

FIG 6:18 Refitting thrust washer and circlip to output shaft

5 Using an accurate vernier check the thickness of the speedometer pinion and make a note of its thickness. Press the speedometer pinion onto the output shaft using a suitably sized sleeve and a spindle press. Carefully drive the groove bearing of the output shaft into the gearbox housing cover as far as it will go using a suitably sized sleeve on the outer track. Using a vernier depth gauge measure the distance 'C' from the gearbox housing cover with a gasket in place up to the grooved bearing outer race. This is shown in **FIG 6:22**. To determine the thickness of the shim calculate as in the following example:

'A' Theoretical	=5.433 inch
+ Speedometer pinion thickness	= .583 inch
	6.116 inch
—(C)	=1.457 inch
Actual selector sleeve	=4.559 inch
Theoretical gearbox housing cover	=4.567 inch
'X' Shim thickness (see **FIG 6:23**)	= .008 inch

6 Remove the grooved bearing fit the shims of required thickness and refit the bearing.

6:6 Layshaft

To ensure that the layshaft is correctly located within the gearbox housing proceed as follows:

1 Using a depth gauge measure the dimension from the housing sealing face to the circlip. Make a note of this dimension 'F' for future reference.

2 Correctly refit the layshaft into the gearbox housing cover and establish dimension 'E' which is equal to the height of the layshaft with the gasket in place on the gearbox housing cover. Determine the thickness of the shim required 'G'.

Example:

F housing depth	= 6.496 inch
—E height of layshaft	= 6,480 inch
	.016 inch
Subtract .2 mm permissible axial play	= .008 inch
G shim thickness	= .008 inch

3 Remove the layshaft and seal from the gearbox housing cover and insert the shim 'G' as previously calculated into the gearbox housing cover. Refit the idler pinion with the layshaft into the gearbox housing cover.

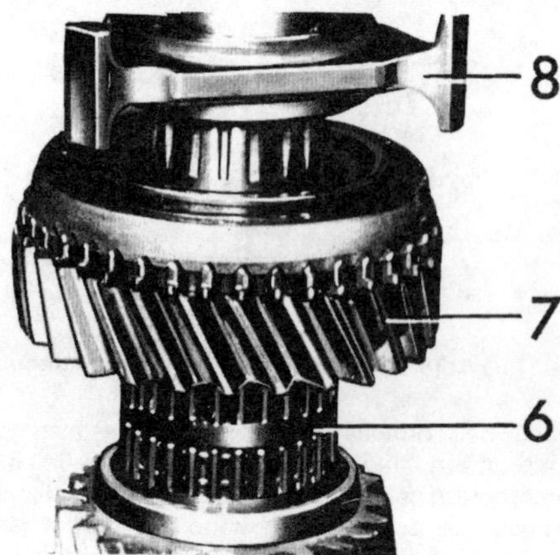

FIG 6:19 Second gear pinion reassembly

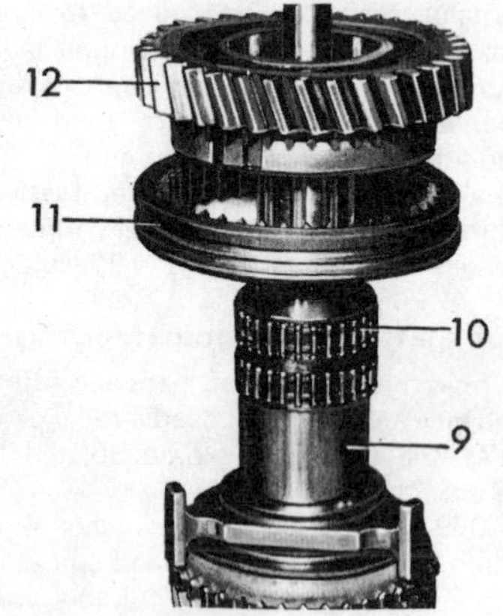

FIG 6:20 First gear pinion reassembly

FIG 6:21 Gear train overall measurement

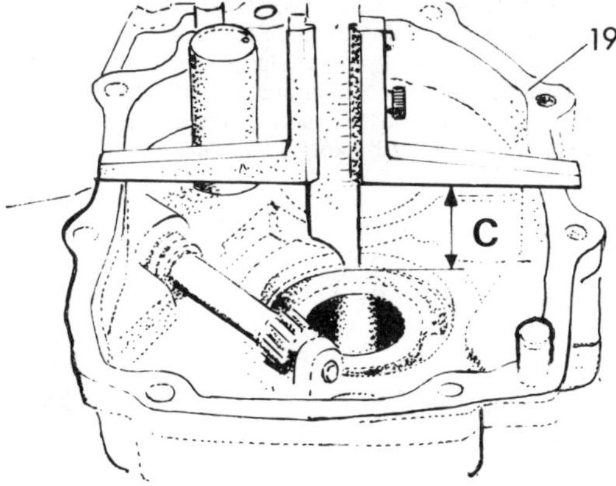

FIG 6:22 Gearbox housing cover groove bearing measurement

4 Carefully position the selector sleeve, the needle roller bearing and the drive shaft onto the output shaft. Carefully insert the drive and output shaft into the gearbox housing cover. Position the shim 'X' as previously calculated in the position shown in **FIG 6:23.** Carefully drive the groove bearing 18 onto the output shaft using a suitably sized sleeve.
5 Using engineers 'Blue' check the tooth engagement which, of course, may be altered by the shim 'G' which, if necessary, may be inserted on the side in front of the grooved bearing of the layshaft.
6 Should the gearbox be dismantled to trace the cause of noisy operation check the reverse gear pinion and shim on layshaft for traces of wear and if necessary grind the reverse gear pinion down on the teeth on the driven side by .0551 ± .0118 inch and taper by 30 deg. (A) and shim on the layshaft by .051 to .0118 inch and taper by 30 deg. (B) (see **FIG 6:24**).

6:7 Third- and fourth-speed pinion sets:

Should the fourth gear pinion (drive shaft) and third gear pinion (driven shaft) be renewed this must be carried out together with operations described in **Sections 6:3, 6:4, 6:5** and **6:6.** Then proceed as follows:

1 Using a universal grooved bearing puller remove the grooved bearing and press off the fourth gear pinion from the layshaft.
2 Remove the circlip and then press the third gear pinion from the layshaft. Inspect the pinions and using emerypaper smooth any grooves that may be apparent.
3 Before the pinions are pressed into place measure the overlap when cold and referring to **FIG 6:25** ensure that the third gear pinion dimension A is to a tolerance of .0031 to .00457 inch. The fourth gear pinion B should be within the tolerance of .00343 to .00508 inch.
4 Using a light machine oil coat the surfaces to be contacted on the layshaft and heat the pinions to between 120 to 150°C and using a hydraulic press capable of exerting a force of at least 8820 lb press the pinions into position. Finally check the toothed engagement and adjust as necessary.

6:8 Output shaft grooved bearing

1 Refer to **FIG 6:26** and using a depth gauge measure dimension A from the gearbox housing cover to the grooved bearing outer race.

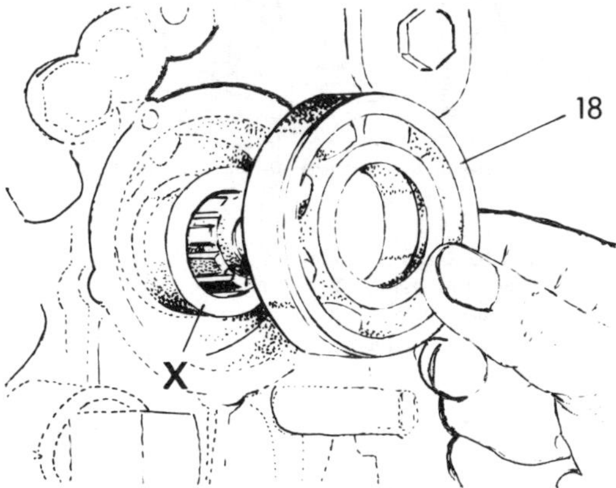

FIG 6:23 Groove bearing shim location

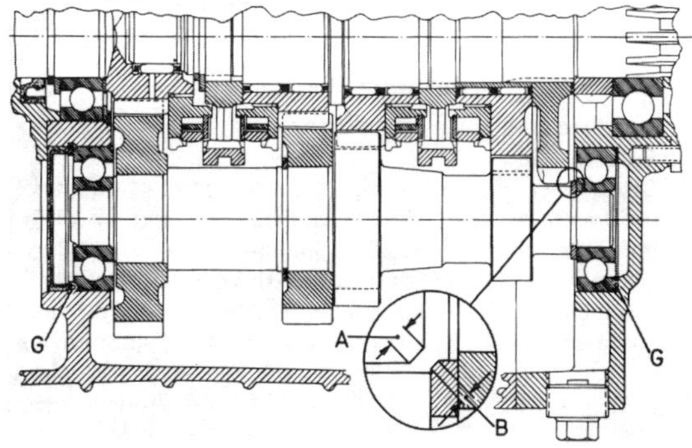

FIG 6:24 Reverse gear pinion and shim angle adjustment

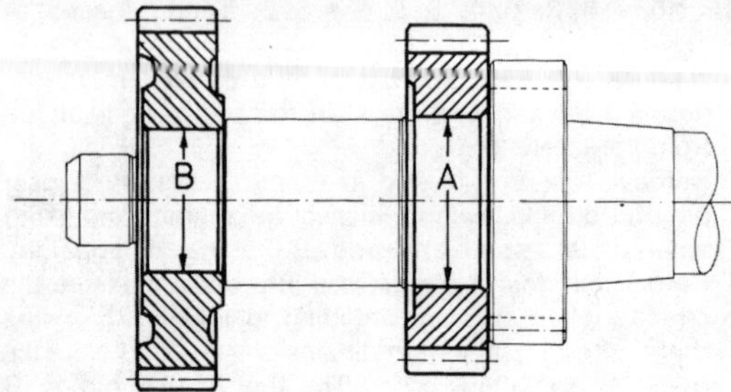

FIG 6:25 Third- and fourth-speed pinion internal measurements

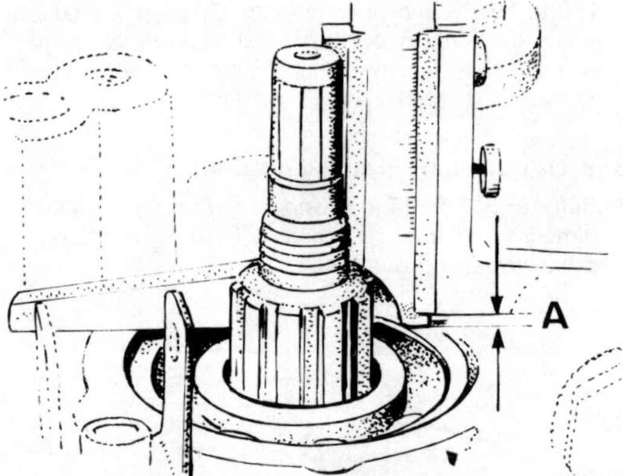

FIG 6:26 Qutput shaft grooved bearing measurement

2 Refer to **FIG 6:27** and using the vernier depth gauge determine dimension 'B' being the height of the sealing cover with the seal in position.
3 Calculate the thickness of the shim required.
Example:

A	=	.008 inch
—B	=	.110 inch
D shim thickness	=	.008 inch

4 Once the shim thickness D has been calculated place this in front of the grooved bearing and secure the sealing cover together with the seal to the gearbox housing cover.

6:9 Selector shafts and selector forks

To service the selector shaft and selector forks proceed as follows:

1 Disconnect the cables from the reversing light switch, the location being shown in **FIG 6:2** and unscrew the switch from the gearbox housing.
2 Using a suitably shaped punch drive out the sealing cap located next to the reversing light switch. The ballbearings should be pushed down with a screwdriver through the drillings exposed and also drilling next to reversing light switch drilling. Insert the arrester ballbearings and also the selector fork 27 (see **FIG 6:28**), into the guide slot in the idler pinion 28. Carefully push the selector shaft 29 through the selector fork 27 and into the gearbox housing cover. Correctly align the slot in the locating pin so that it is along the longitudinal axis of the selector shaft and knock in the locating pin 30.
3 Refer to **FIG 6:29** and insert the locking and arrester ballbearing. Correctly position the selector fork 31 in the selector sleeve and push the selector shaft 32 through the selector fork 31 and into the gearbox housing cover. Ensure that the slot in the locating pin points along the longitudinal axis of the selector shaft and carefully knock in the locating pin 33.
4 Refer to **FIG 6:30** and insert the locking and arrester ballbearing and also the selector fork 34 into the selector sleeve. Carefully push the selector shaft 35 through the selector fork 34 and into the gearbox housing cover. Ensure that the slot in the locating pin points along the longitudinal axis of the selector shaft and carefully knock in the locating pin 36.
5 Refit the gearchange shaft 37 (see **FIG 6:31**), and tighten the square head tapered bolt and secure with soft iron wire. Refer to the **FIG 6:31** and note the fitting position of the gearchange shaft 37, the taper bush K, the locking pin S and the selector finger 38. Refit the locking pin, the spring and screw plug.
6 Screw in the reversing light switch and finally drive the sealing cap into the gearbox housing cover.

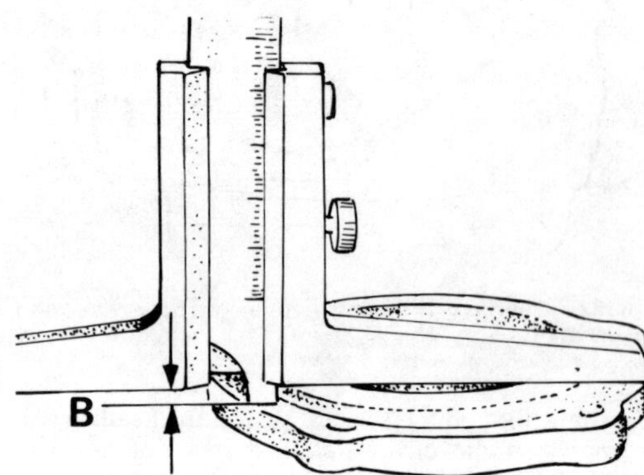

FIG 6:27 Gearbox housing cover measurement

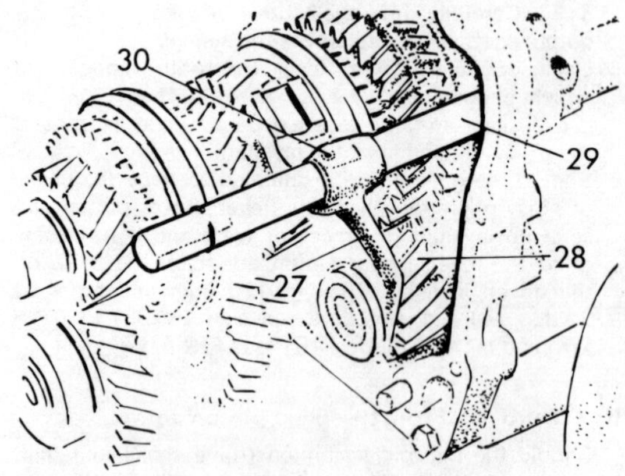

FIG 6:28 Idler pinion reassembly

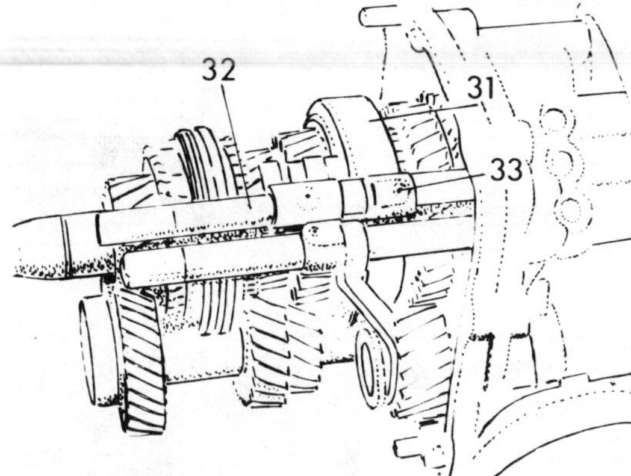

FIG 6:29 Selector fork and shaft reassembly

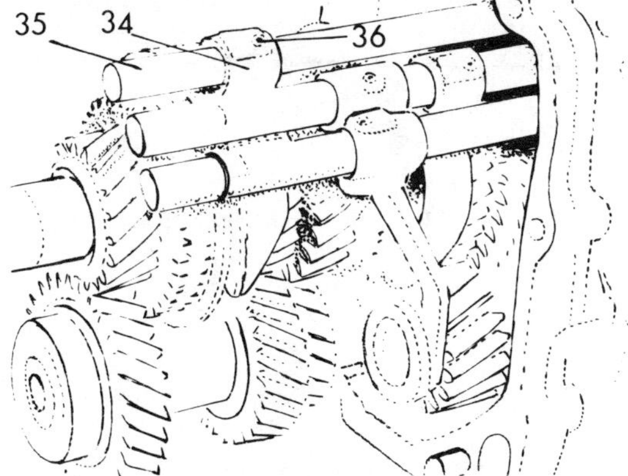

FIG 6:30 Selector fork and shaft reassembly

6:10 Input shaft refitting

1 Refer to **FIG 6:32** and with a packing washer .039 inch thick lay the packing washer 39 on the circlip 40 in the input shaft bearing seat.

2 Carefully drive the ballbearing 41 using a suitably sized sleeve into the gearbox housing until a tight fit is obtained.

3 Using a vernier depth gauge and referring to **FIG 6:33** determine dimension 'A' from the housing seal surface to the inner ballbearing race. Dimension 'B' is engraved on the input shaft and is to be read off on the shaft. The figures stated refer at all times to the dimension below the line.

4 Once dimensions 'A' and 'B' have been determined read off from column 'C' of the table the required thickness of the shim to be positioned as shown in **FIG 6:34**. Place the shim on the input shaft and lay the gasket 42 onto the gearbox housing cover. Carefully lower the gearbox housing over the gear assembly which if it is a tight fit, preheat the gearbox housings slightly.

5 Carefully press the input shaft into the ballbearing and the gearbox housing onto the gearbox housing cover and tighten the retaining bolts to a torque wrench setting of 18 lb ft.

6 Refer to **FIG 6:35** and using a pair of engineer's calipers determine dimension E, which is the thickness of the circlip. Secure the circlip in the input shaft groove and determine dimension D which is the distance from the circlip to the ballbearing inner race. This may be done by using a vernier depth gauge.

A	*ins* B	*ins* C
6.059	(.9252)	(.0196)
	(.9212)	(.0236)
	(.9173)	(.0276)
6.055	(.9252)	(.0157)
	(.9212)	(.0196)
	(.9173)	(.0236)
6.051	(.9252)	(.0118)
	(.9212)	(.0157)
	(.9173)	(.0196)
6.047	(.9252)	(.0078)
	(.9212)	(.0118)
	(.9173)	(.0157)

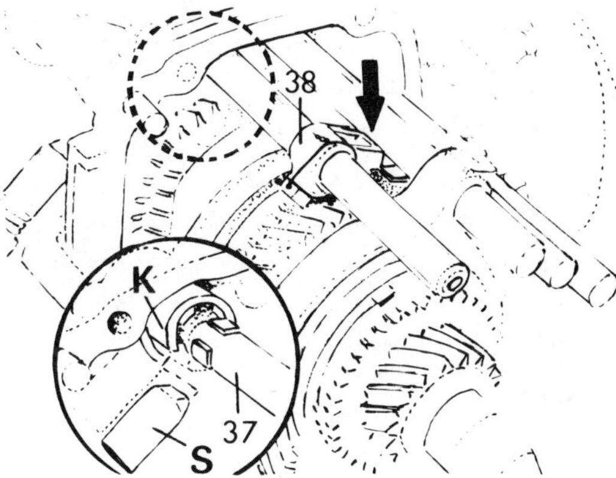

FIG 6:31 Gearchange shaft refitting

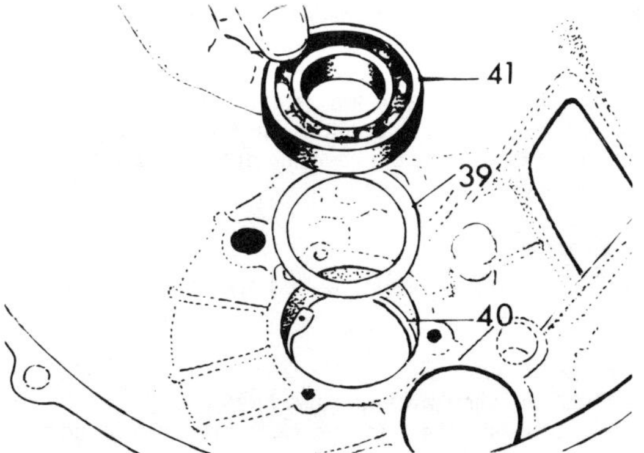

FIG 6:32 Input shaft bearing shim location

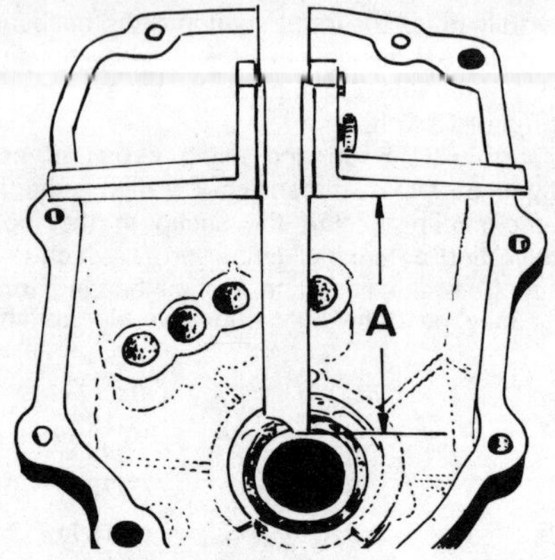

FIG 6:33 Inner ballbearing race measurement

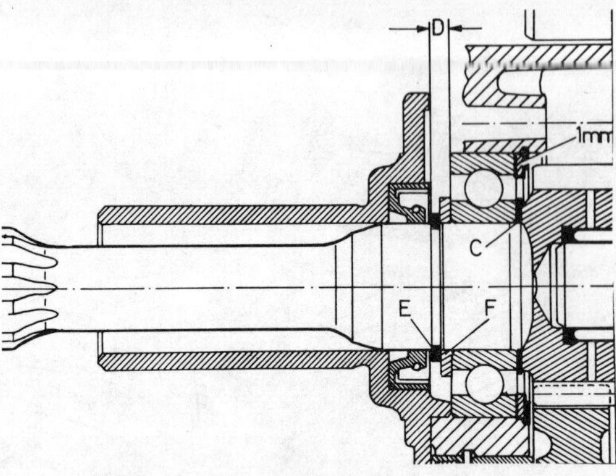

FIG 6:35 Input shaft circlip location

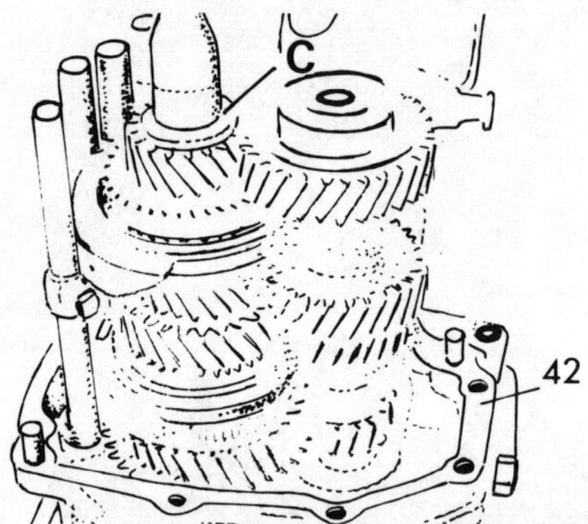

FIG 6:34 Input shaft shim location

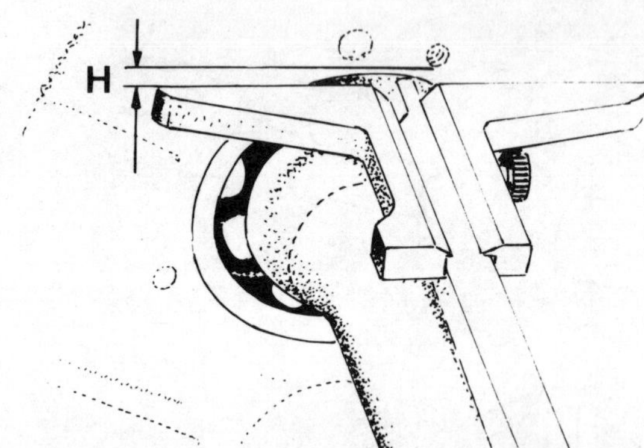

FIG 6:36 Outer ballbearing track to housing measurement

Calculate the thickness of the shim F as shown by the following example.

Example:

D	=	.157 inch
—E	=	.078 inch
F shim thickness	=	.079 inch

7 Take out the circlip and fit the appropriate shim F.

8 Carefully measure the distance 'H' between the gearbox housing and the outer ballbearing track using a vernier depth gauge as shown in **FIG 6:36** and determine the height K of the gearbox extension with the gasket seal in place again using a depth gauge. There should be no play between the outer ballbearing track and the gearbox extension.

Example:

H Housing/bearing outer track	=	.204 inch
—K Rim height	=	.196 inch
Shim thickness	=	.008 inch

9 Once the shim thickness has been ascertained fit the gearbox extension to the gearbox housing and to reassemble all other parts is the reverse procedure to dismantling.

6:11 Fault diagnosis

(a) Jumping out of gear

1 Broken spring behind locating ball for selector rod
2 Excessively worn locating groove in selector rod
3 Worn coupling dogs

(b) Noisy gearbox

1 Insufficient oil
2 Excessive end play in laygear
3 Worn or damaged bearings
4 Worn or damaged gear teeth

(c) Difficulty in engaging gear

1 Incorrect clutch pedal adjustment
2 Worn synchromesh unit
3 Gearchange linkage wrongly adjusted

(d) Oil leaks

1 Damaged joint washers
2 Worn or damaged oil seals
3 Front guide bush loose or marked

CHAPTER 7

PROPELLER SHAFT, REAR AXLE, REAR SUSPENSION

7:1 Servicing the propeller shaft
7:2 Removing and refitting rear axle assembly
7:3 Rear axle carrier renewal
7:4 Trailing arm servicing
7:5 Halfshaft servicing
7:6 Hydraulic shock absorber removal and replacement
7:7 Universal joint servicing
7:8 Final drive unit removal and replacement
7:9 Differential housing removal and replacement
7:10 Differential overhaul
7:11 Crown wheel and pinion renewal
7:12 Crown wheel and pinion gear meshing
7:13 Fault diagnosis

7:1 Servicing the propeller shaft

1 Using a garage hydraulic jack raise the vehicle and support on firmly based stands.

2 Detach the exhaust system at the three point coupling flange and the central suspension point and tie up the lower drilling in the down pipe flange so that the exhaust system may be swung to one side when necessary. Release the propeller shaft from the gearbox drive flange.

3 Release the rubber coupling from the differential unit leaving the rubber coupling on the propeller shaft. Carefully lift away from the underside of the body.

Propeller shaft self-centring bearing:

1 Refer to **FIG 7:1** and remove the centring bearing sealing cap using a screwdriver. Release the circlip using a pair of suitably pointed circlip pliers and extract the centring ring and ball socket using a Kukko extractor 22/1 or a universal two leg puller.

2 To reassemble the centring ring and ball socket a suitable arbor and press must be used. Pack the centring seating with approximately .28-.35 ounce of multipurpose high melting point grease. Replace the parts in the following order. Referring to **FIG 7:2**. 1 spring, 2 ball socket, 3 centring ring, 4 ball socket, 5 retaining ring, 6 sealing cap.

Refitting propeller shaft assembly:

This operation is the reverse procedure to dismantling. The flexible coupling locknuts must be tightened to a torque wrench setting of 32.5 lb ft.

Propeller shaft centre bearing:

Removal:

1 Refer to **FIG 7:3** and remove the four fixing bolts as arrowed from the propeller shaft.

2 Remove the retaining bolts 2 (see **FIG 7:4**) from the centre bearing block. Carefully withdraw the propeller shaft 3 and the centre bearing block from the front.

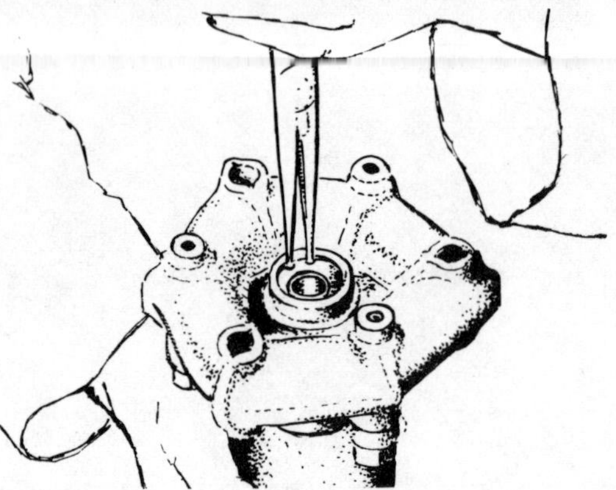

FIG 7:1 Circlip removal

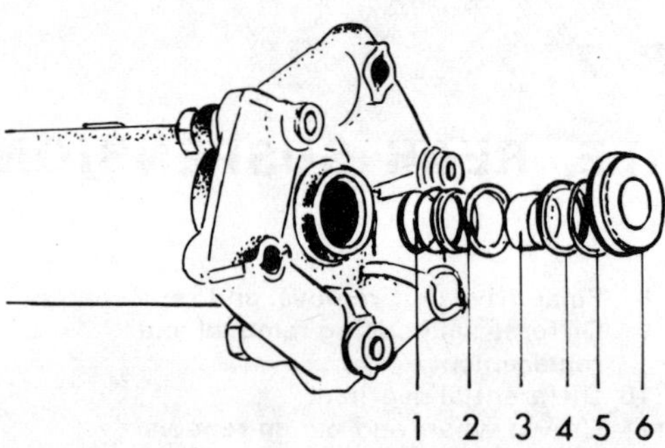

FIG 7:2 Centring bearing

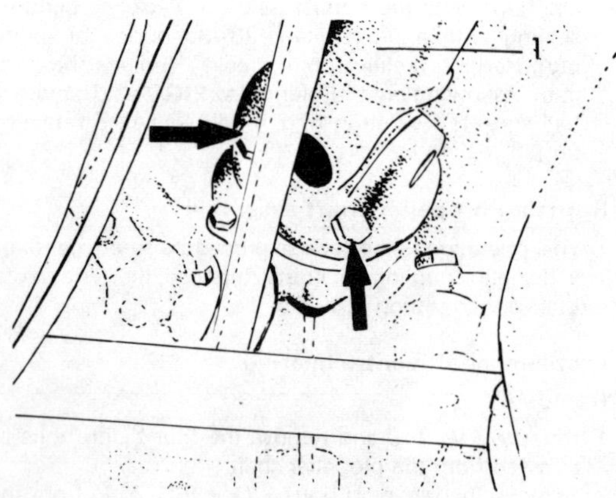

FIG 7:3 Propeller shaft flange bolts

3 Using a pair of pointed circlip pliers remove the circlip from the shaft. Press out the centre bearing block and ballbearing taking care not to press against the dust cap 5 (see **FIG 7:5**).

4 Press out the bearing from the centre bearing block.

Reassembly:

1 Wet the ballbearing reception bore with water and using a suitably sized drift press the new bearing into the centre bearing block. If the dust cap is disturbed it must be set to dimension 'A' (see **FIG 7:5**), which should be .23 inch.

2 Press the ballbearing and centre bearing block 2 (see **FIG 7:6**) tightly onto the propeller shaft flange. Install the distance piece 7, and insert the circlip 4 into the groove ensuring the inner side of the convex circlip faces the distance piece.

3 It should be noted that the propeller shafts and splined joints are matched and balanced together. Should non-matching parts be fitted, the propeller shaft assembly may be out of balance causing vibration at certain speeds.

4 Refitting the propeller shaft is the reverse procedure to removal. Ensure that the centre bearing block is brought forward .08 inch (2mm) as shown in **FIG 7:4**.

7:2 Removing and refitting rear axle assembly

Removal:

1 Carefully ease back the protective rubber cap from the handbrake lever and remove the handbrake cable adjustment nuts.

2 Remove the wheel trims and carefully slacken the rear wheel nuts. Using a garage hydraulic jack raise the vehicle and support on firmly based stands.

3 Detach the exhaust system at the three point coupling flange and the centre suspension point. Release the exhaust silencer by removing the mounting bracket to silencer retaining bolt.

4 It is important that only one trailing suspension arm be supported by a jack at one time. Open the boot lid and remove the upper shock absorber locknut and retaining nut from the floor panel. It should be noted that the shock absorber also acts as a retaining member and if the upper shock absorber mounting on the boot compartment housing is removed before the vehicle is jacked up it is essential to ensure that the driven shafts are separated simultaneously from the halfshafts. Separate the driven shafts from the differential unit by releasing the retaining bolts and suspend the driven shafts from the underside of the car using wire.

5 From the underside of the car withdraw the shock absorber from its upper mounting by retracting the upper half of the shock absorber. Gently lower the trailing arm assembly using the garage hydraulic jack. Lift away the helical spring together with the upper spring plate and damper rings.

6 Release the rubber coupling from the differential unit but not from the propeller shaft.

7 Release the flexible brake hoses from the main brake pipe line as detailed in Chapter 10 and cover the ends of the brake hoses to ensure no dirt ingress into the hydraulic system.

8 Using a garage hydraulic jack together with a suitably

shaped cradle, support the rear axle beam under the differential mounting. Detach the rear axle beam attachments from the body.

9 Remove the rear seat backrest and carefully knock out the bolts from the underside of the car using a soft-faced hammer. Carefully detach the fastening bolt for the rear differential unit mounting and very carefully lower the rear axle assembly and at the same time withdrawing it backwards from the rear of the car (see **FIG 7:7**).

Refitting:

Refitting is the reverse procedure to dismantling but the following points should be noted:

1 Tighten the rear differential mounting retaining bolt to a torque wrench setting of 65.1 lb ft.
2 Tighten the rear axle beam retaining locknut to a torque wrench setting of 86.8 lb ft.
3 Once the rear brake hydraulic system has been refitted the complete system must be bled as described in **Chapter 10.**
4 Tighten the rubber coupling to differential drive flange from the propeller shaft retaining bolts to a torque wrench setting of 32.55 lb ft.
5 Tighten the halfshaft to differential unit universal joint locknuts to a torque wrench setting of 21.7 lb ft.

7:3 Rear axle carrier removal

Removal:

1 Remove the rear axle assembly as detailed in **Section 7:2.**
2 From the rear axle assembly remove the differential unit (see **FIG 7:8**), and also the trailing arm.
3 Detach both the rubber bearings from the rear axle beam by releasing the retaining bolts.

Reassembly:

Reassembly is the reverse procedure to dismantling but the following points should be noted:

1 The rubber bearing fastening holes are elongated so that when fitting always ensure that the rubber bearings are centred otherwise the rear axle will not be correctly aligned to the body and therefore front axle, so causing the vehicle to move along the road in crab wise fashion.
2 Upon reassembly of the trailing arm the retaining bolts must be kept loose so that final tightening to a torque wrench setting of 54.25 lb ft may be performed once the vehicle is in its normal loaded position with all four wheels firmly on the ground.
3 When reassembling the differential unit, fit the distance bushes below the upper retainer plate with the collar towards the top. Tighten the retaining bolts to a torque wrench setting of 65.1 lb ft.
4 The rear axle carrier should always be fitted with both rubber bearing before mounting to the body otherwise the rear axle may become distorted in the three rubber mounting bearings.

7:4 Trailing arm servicing

Removal:

1 Carefully push back the protective rubber cap on the

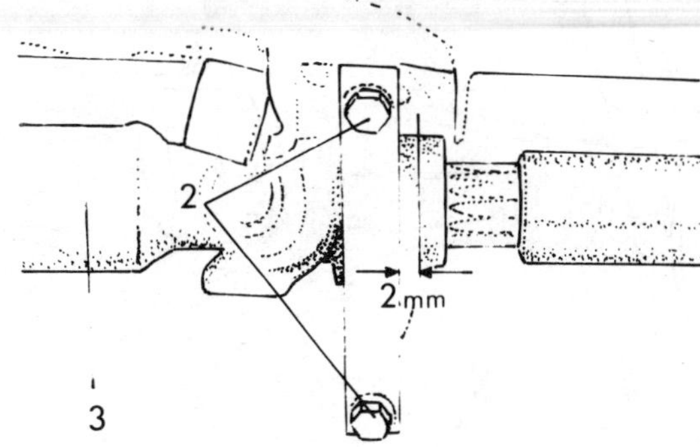

FIG 7:4 Centre bearing block

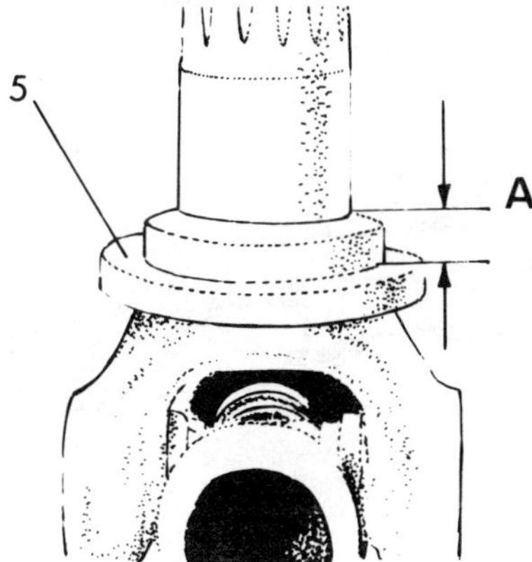

FIG 7:5 Dust cap position

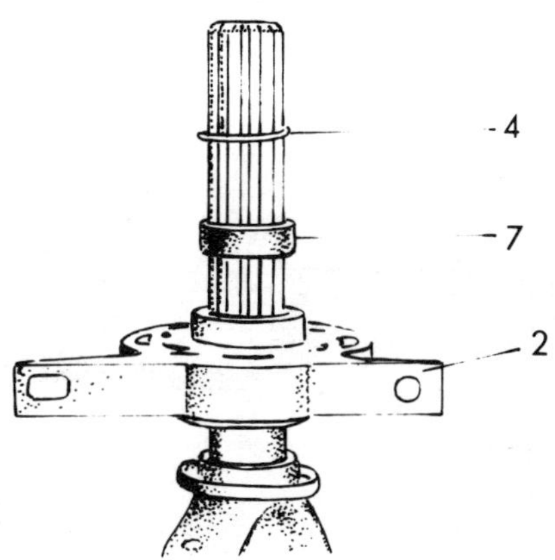

FIG 7:6 Centre bearing spacer and clip

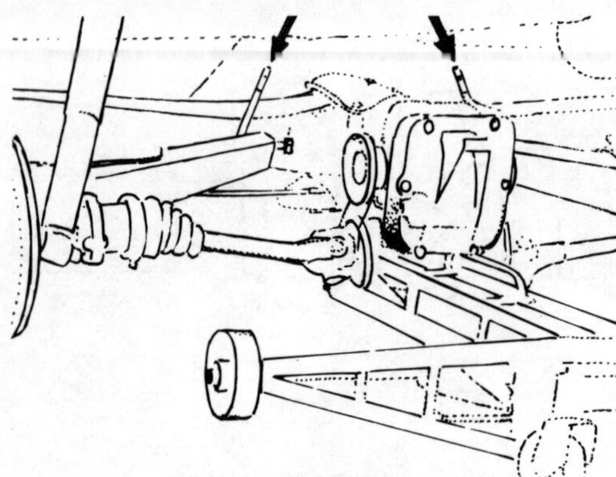

FIG 7 : 7 Rear axle assembly removal

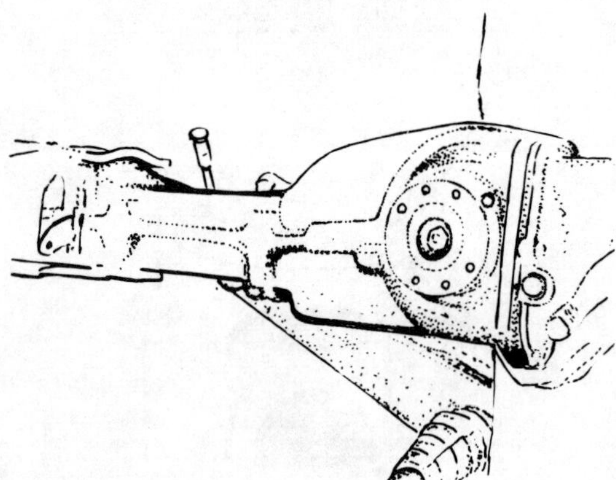

FIG 7 : 8 Differential unit removal

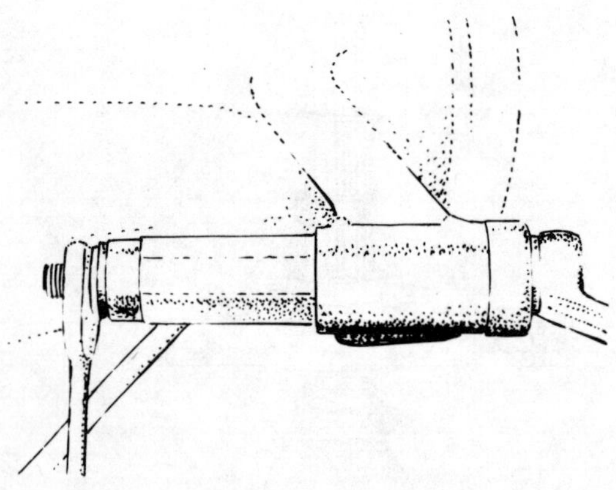

FIG 7 : 9 Silentbloc bush removal

handbrake lever and release the handbrake cable retaining nuts.

2 Remove the wheel trims and slacken the wheel nuts. Jack up the rear of the vehicle and place on firmly based stands. Remove the road wheels.

3 Using a garage hydraulic jack carefully support the trailing arm. Open the boot compartment lid and remove the two nuts holding the shock absorber in position. It should be noted that the shock absorber functions as a support for the rear suspension. The inclination of the sliding universal joint must not exceed 14 deg. otherwise it may be strained.

4 Separate the driven shaft from the halfshaft and tie to the underside of the car with wire. Carefully withdraw the shock absorber from its upper mounting by compressing.

5 Carefully lower the trailing arm using the hydraulic garage jack and lift away the coil spring together with the upper spring plate.

6 Separate the flexible hydraulic brake hose from the main pipeline as detailed in **Chapter 10**, and cover the ends of the hose to ensure that no dirt finds its way into the hydraulic system.

Reassembly:

Reassembly is the reverse procedure to dismantling but the following points should be noted:

1 The trailing arm mounting retaining bolts should be left loose and only tightened to a torque wrench setting of 54.25 lb ft, when all four road wheels are firmly on the ground and the vehicle normally loaded.

2 Upon reassembly of the brake hydraulic system the system must be bled as detailed in **Chapter 10**.

3 When reassembling the coil spring ensure that the smooth ground spring end faces upwards. Rotate the cylindrical coil end of the spring into the channel in the trailing arm.

Trailing arm silentbloc bushes:

1 Remove and refit the trailing arms as previously described.

2 Using BMW tool 6011 extract the silentbloc bushes as shown in **FIG 7 : 9**.

3 Prepare the silentbloc bushes in the tool and coat the outer surface with glycerine.

4 Carefully pull the silentbloc bushes into the trailing arm until they are flush with the chamfered side.

Suspension arm silentbloc bushes:

1 Carefully slacken one bolt for the tie bar fixing and using a garage hydraulic jack carefully lower the suspension arm until the fixing bolts of the silentbloc bush can be slackened.

2 Remove the silentbloc bush. It should be noted that only solid rubber bushes may be fitted and in no circumstances may bushes with cavities be fitted (see **FIG 7 : 10**). Should a trailing arm with recessed spring mountings be encountered only rubber bushes with cavities in the sides should be fitted (see **FIG 7 : 11**).

3 Reassembly is the reverse procedure to dismantling.

7:5 Halfshaft servicing

Removal:

1 It is important that if a halfshaft is to be removed the halfshaft nut should only be released with the handbrake fully applied and before the road wheel is removed. Remove the wheel trim and hub cap. Carefully extract the cotter pin from the shaft end and loosen the castellated nut on the halfshaft.
2 Loosen the wheel nuts and using a garage hydraulic jack raise the vehicle and place on firmly based stands. Remove the wheel and brake drum.
3 Release the retaining bolts from the driven shaft at the wheel hub end and also at the differential end having first marked the respective flange mating positions for correct reassembly.
4 Carefully lift away the drive shaft.
5 Using a soft-faced hammer remove the driving flange and drive halfshaft from the trailing arm as shown in **FIG 7:12**. It is recommended that the castellated nut be screwed onto the threaded end of the halfshaft to ensure protection of the thread.
6 Remove the radial sealing ring and finally drive out the ballbearing races using a suitably sized drift.

Inspection and reassembly:

1 To inspect a ballbearing race first the bearing must be cleaned in petrol or white spirit, revolving it constantly until all impurities have been removed. Generally the bearing may be regarded as still serviceable if a visual inspection shows no traces of damage to the balls, race grooves, running faces or if there is no pronounced general wear. If bearing is defective or if there is any variation in axial play both bearings will have to be renewed. After a service life of 60,000 miles it is advisable to renew the bearings even if visual inspection indicates that they are apparently still serviceable. When installing new components the prescribed bearing play of .002-.004 inch is to be obtained.
2 Replace the rear ballbearing and measure the depth of the front ballbearing contact surface in the hub to the rear outer ballbearing (see **FIG 7:13**).
3 Carefully measure the length of the spacer bush using a vernier. Determine whether the unit can be assembled as it is or whether it is necessary to compensate to achieve the prescribed amount of bearing play. Any adjustment necessary should be performed by the use of shims.
4 Before finally inserting the bearings into the hub check the seating areas of the ballbearings on sliding tracks in the hub for any trace of slipping by the outer ballbearing race.
5 When refitting the hub it should be packed with approximately 2.47 oz per wheel bearing of a multipurpose high melting point grease.
6 Before refitting the halfshaft to the trailing arm, pack the sealing groove for the sealing ring with a graphite grease.
7 When tightening the halfshaft castellated nut it should be tightened to a torque wrench setting of 217.36 lb ft with the road wheel assembled and the handbrake fully on.

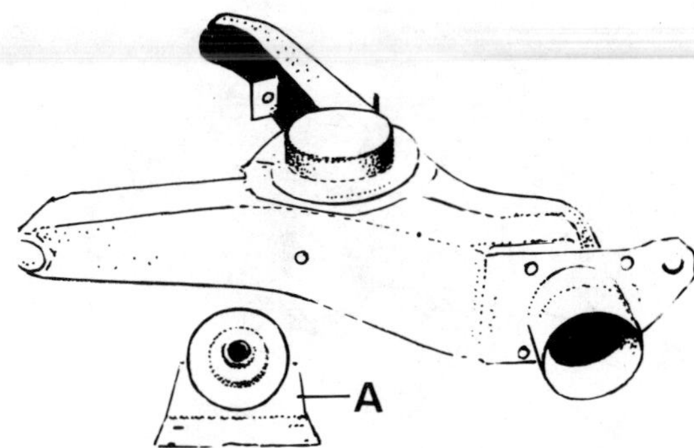

FIG 7:10 Silentbloc bush identification

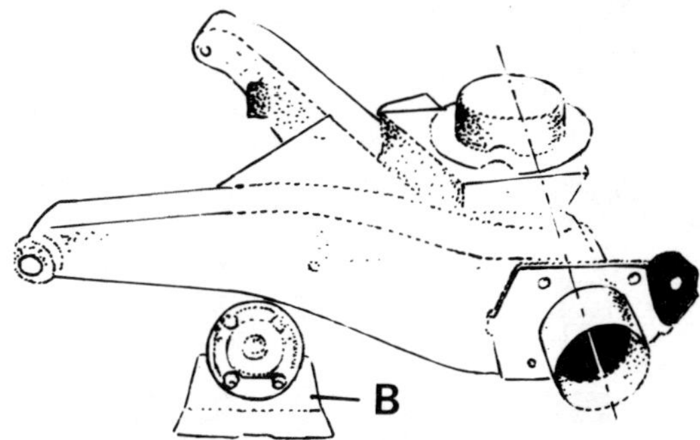

FIG 7:11 Silentbloc bush identification

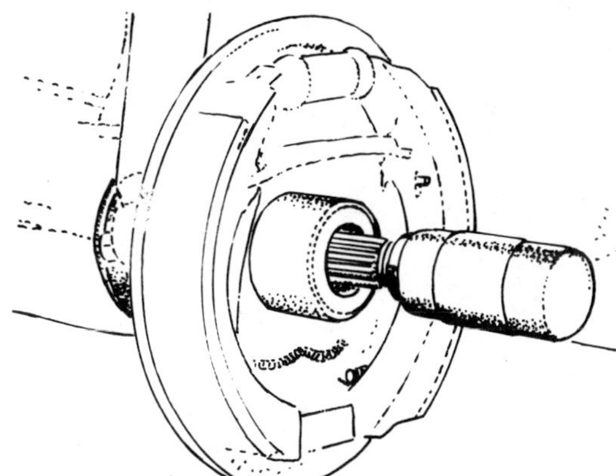

FIG 7:12 Removal of halfshaft from trailing arm

7:6 Hydraulic shock absorber removal and replacement

Removal:

1 Using a garage hydraulic jack raise the vehicle and place on firmly based stands. Support the trailing arm with a garage hydraulic jack.

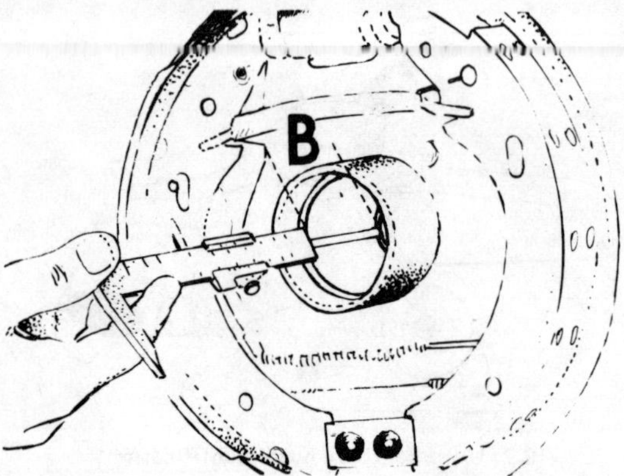

FIG 7:13 Measurement for bearing shim thickness

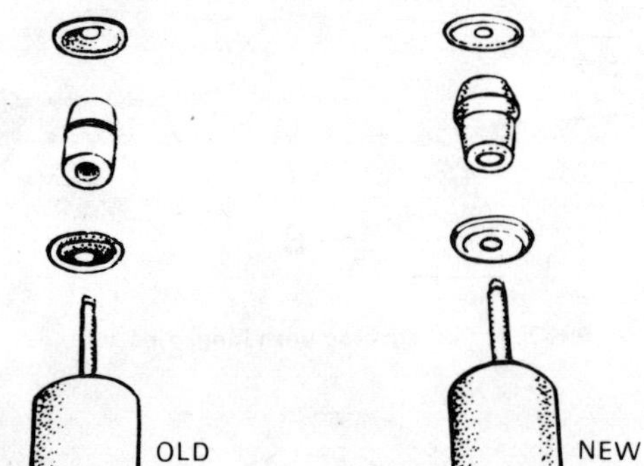

FIG 7:14 Shock absorber upper mounting bushes early type on the left

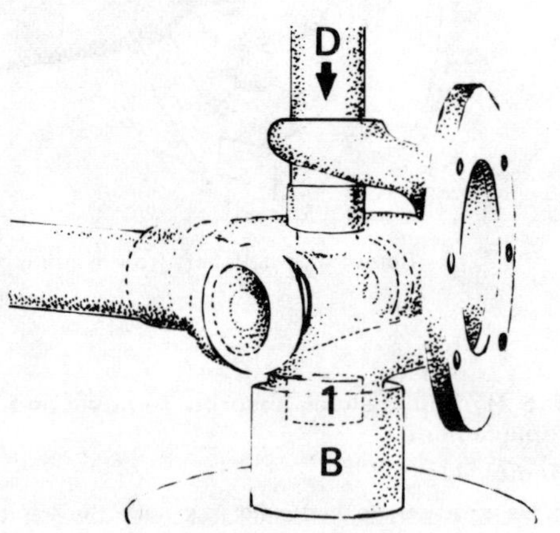

FIG 7:15 Needle bearing bush removal

2 Open the boot compartment lid and detach the upper shock absorber fastening nuts.
3 Release the lower shock absorber retaining nut. Compress the shock absorber and lift away from the underside of the vehicle.

Reassembly:

Reassembly is the reverse procedure to dismantling but the following points should be noted:

1 From Chassis No. 969552 shock absorbers are installed with a special comfort adjustment. This is indicated by a green spot on the sleeve in the vicinity of the shock absorber number. Shock absorbers should only be installed in matched pairs otherwise the road holding qualities of the car will be altered.
2 When refitting the lower shock absorber retaining nut the locknut should be tightened to a torque wrench setting of 54.25 lb ft when the vehicle's road wheels are firmly on the ground and the vehicle normally loaded.
3 Modifications have been made to the top shock absorber mounting rubbers and it should be noted that if an old type rubber bearing is replaced by one of the newer type it is necessary to fit the appropriate larger washers (see **FIG 7:14**).

7:7 Universal joint servicing

Removal:

1 Mark the position of the two pairs of flanges relative to each other so that they may be correctly assembled.
2 Release the retaining bolt at both the differential drive flange and also the halfshaft flange and carefully lift away the halfshaft.

Refitting:

Refitting is the reverse procedure to dismantling, but care should be taken to ensure that both pairs of flanges correctly line up and that the locknuts are tightened to a torque wrench setting of 22 lb ft.

Universal joint:

To overhaul the universal joint proceed as follows:

1 Lift out the circlip and lay the yoke of the universal flange on a sleeve suitably dimensioned so that the needle bearing bush may be pressed out.
2 With a suitably sized drift 'D' push down the needle bearing bush so pressing the needle bearing bush 1 out as far as it will move (see **FIG 7:15**).
3 Lay the halfshaft on a suitable firm base and press the needle bearing bush 2 with sleeve 'H' out to limit stop (see **FIG 7:16**).
4 Lift away the halfshaft flange. Lay the yoke of the driven shaft on sleeve 'B' and push the lower needle bearing bush 3 out as far as possible using the drift 'D' (see **FIG 7:17**).
5 Lay both bearing trunnions of the universal joint yoke on a suitable firm base and with the aid of sleeve 'H' carefully push out the needle bearing bush 4 to its limit (see **FIG 7:18**).
6 Insert the universal joint yoke ensuring that the grease nipple points towards the universal shaft flange. The needle bearing bush seals must be carefully checked for damage and renewed as necessary, otherwise rapid wear will occur due to lubrication failure.
7 Carefully press the needle bearing bush further in and insert the circlip with the aid of circlip pliers. Press

inwards the opposing needle bearing bush and insert circlip with circlip pliers. Fit the remaining two needle bearing bushes in the same manner and lower the universal yoke on a suitable base and release any offset by one firm blow from a soft-faced hammer. When the coupling is correctly aligned it should drop slowly under its own weight.

8 Finally fit driven shaft.

7:8 Final drive unit removal and replacement

Removal:

1 Using a garage hydraulic jack raise the vehicle and place on firmly based stands.

2 Detach the exhaust system at the three point coupling flange and also at its centre suspension. Release the exhaust silencer box from its two outside mounting brackets.

3 Disconnect the universal shaft from the final drive unit ensuring that the rubber coupling remains on the universal shaft. It should be noted that the universal shaft is not secured on the gearbox by the gearbox flange which means therefore that the shaft could slip out from the gearbox neck. It is therefore necessary to tie up the universal shaft.

4 Detach the halfshaft couplings at the final drive unit having first marked the two pairs of flanges for correct reassembly. Tie the halfshaft to the underside of the car ensuring that they are not angled in excess of 14 deg.

5 Release the retaining bolts from the rear axle carrier and also the fastening bolt for the final drive mounting.

6 Carefully lift the final drive unit rearwards and down. Care must be taken to ensure that the three arm flange is so turned so that one arm of the flange is pointing vertically upwards as shown in **FIG 7:19**.

Reassembly:

Reassembly is the reverse procedure to dismantling but the following points should be noted:

1 Ensure that the three arm flange is turned so that one arm of the flange is pointing vertically upwards as shown in **FIG 7:19**.

2 Tighten the final drive mounting retaining bolt to a torque wrench setting of 65 lb ft.

3 When refitting the rear axle carrier retaining bolts always fit the spacer sleeve below the upper mounting plate with the collar facing upwards. Tighten the retaining bolts to a torque wrench setting of 65 lb ft.

4 Tighten the universal shaft locknuts to a torque wrench setting of 32.55 lb ft.

7:9 Differential housing removal and replacement

Removal:

1 Remove the final drive unit as detailed in **Section 7:8** and thoroughly clean the exterior of the unit. Drain the oil into a suitably sized container.

2 Remove the six rear cover retaining bolts and also the two driving flange retaining bolts on either side of the final drive unit.

3 Mark the bearing caps and final drive unit casing to

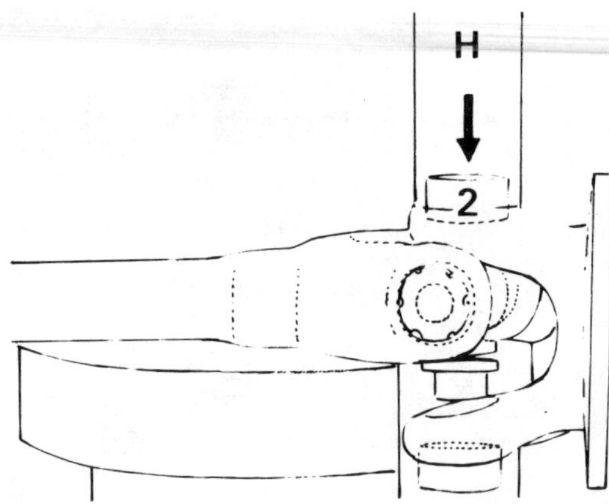

FIG 7:16 Needle bearing bush removal

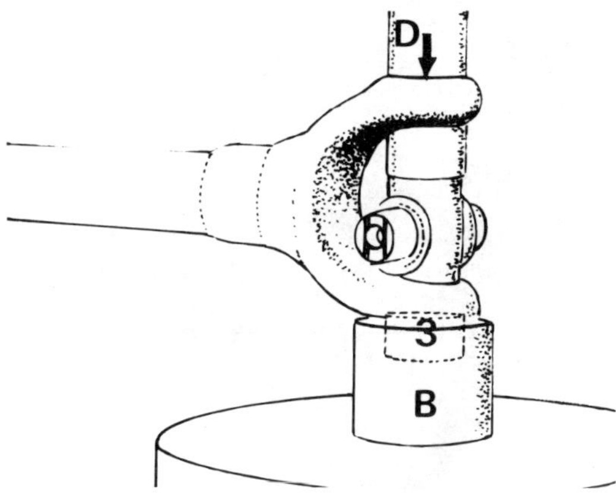

FIG 7:17 Needle bearing bush reassembly

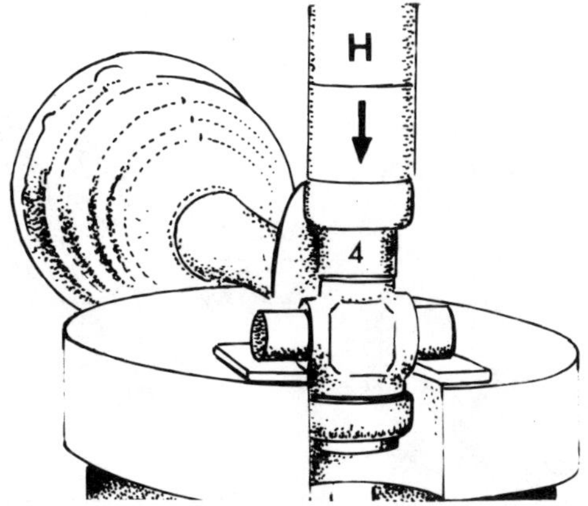

FIG 7:18 Needle bearing bush reassembly

ensure correct reassembly and remove the four retaining bolts for each cap. Lift away the bearing cap.

4 Turn the differential housing until it is in the vertical position and to remove lift the righthand bearing out through the aperture in the bearing cap as far as is possible and turn the pinion set clockwise to remove. This operation is shown in **FIG 7:20**.

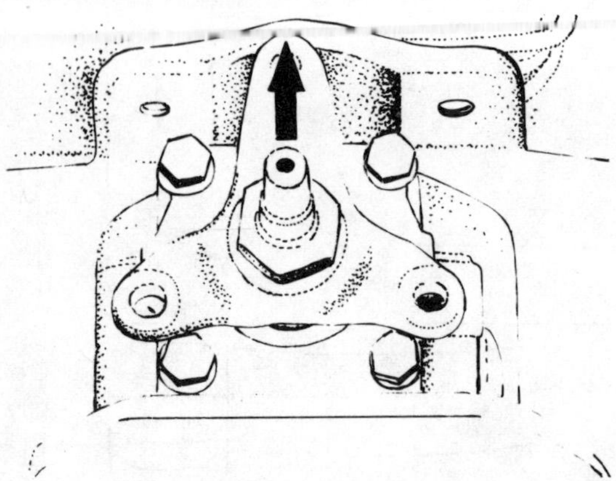

FIG 7:19 Three arm flange location for final drive unit removal

Reassembly:

Reassembly is the reverse procedure to dismantling but the following points should be noted:

1 Should the differential unit taper roller bearings need renewing the cap must be heated to approximately 75°C before removing or replacing the new outer track. Once this operation has been completed the crownwheel and pinion mesh will have to be re-adjusted as detailed in **Section 7:12**. Ensure that the oil groove in the cap is facing downwards on re-assembly.

2 Refit the driving flange bearing caps in their correct location as previously marked and tighten the retaining bolts to a torque wrench setting of 18 lb ft.

3 Tighten the driving flange bolts to a torque wrench setting of 72 lb ft.

4 Tighten the final drive unit rear cover bolts to a torque wrench setting of 36 lb ft.

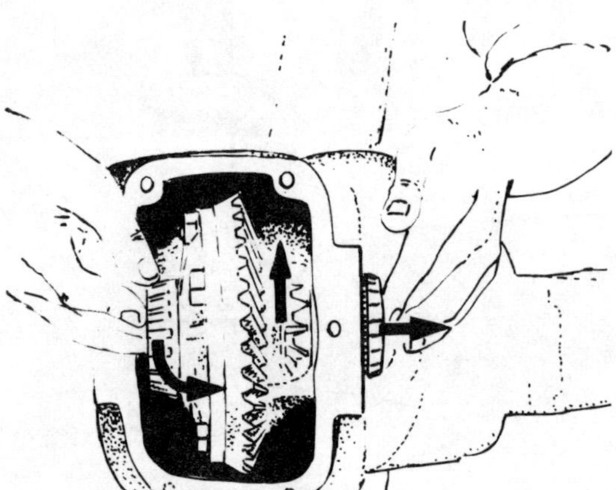

FIG 7:20 Differential removal

7:10 Differential overhaul

1 Remove the final drive unit from the car as detailed in **Section 7:8.**

2 Remove the differential housing as detailed in **Section 7:9.**

3 Removing the securing bolts from the crownwheel to differential housing in a diagonal pattern and to separate the two strike the crownwheel with a soft-faced hammer.

4 Using a hammer and suitably sized drift remove the differential shaft retaining pin (see **FIG 7:21**). Drive the differential shaft out of the differential housing using a suitably sized drift.

5 Lift away the halfshaft pinions and differential pinions through the opening in the differential housing.

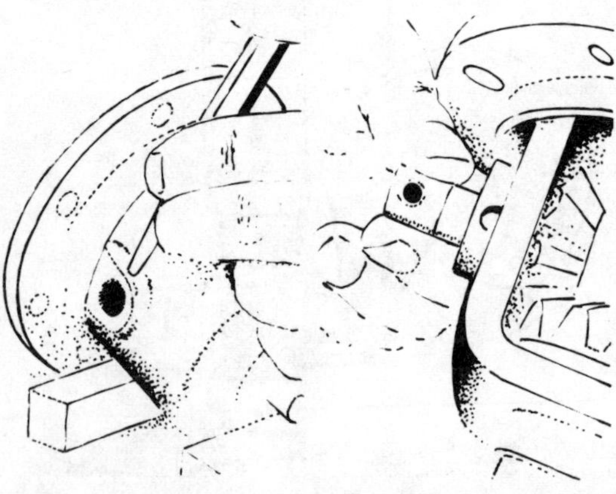

FIG 7:21 Differential shaft removal

Inspection and reassembly:

Reassembly is the reverse procedure to dismantling but the following points should be noted:

1 Check the bronze thrust washers for wear and these should be renewed if necessary. There should be no play between the differential pinions. The lubricating groove machined in the bronze washers must face towards the contact surface of the pinions. Should new pinions be fitted they must be correctly paired and must always carry the same colour identification mark. Upon reassembly of the differential unit check the torque required to rotate the differential gears by fitting a driving flange and rotating using a torque wrench. After initial fitting the torque may reach 7.2 lb ft up to a maximum of 29 lb ft.

2 When reassembling the crownwheel to the differential housing always heat the crownwheel in an electric oven to a temperature of 75°C. Allow the crownwheel with the two guide bolts to drop onto the differential housing. It is recommended that two or three threads

of each of the securing bolts are coated with Loctite for additional security.

7:11 Crownwheel and pinion renewal

Removal:

1 Remove the final drive unit as detailed in **Section 7:8.**
2 Remove the differential housing as detailed in **Section 7:9.**
3 Remove the nut from the three arm drive input flange and using a two leg universal puller remove the flange.
4 Remove the bearing cap retaining bolts on the front of the final drive casing and using a universal two leg puller pull off the bearing cap. Lift away the shim.
5 Place BMW tool 6046 socket wrench onto the elastic stop nut and push the three arm flange back onto the splines. Hold the assembly with BMW tool 604 locking spanner to prevent from rotating and loosen the elastic stop nut.
6 Using a press remove the pinion from the final drive housing.
7 Carefully press the large taper roller bearing from the pinion. Using a long drift and hammer remove the bearing outer tracks from the final drive housing. Withdraw the taper roller bearing from the differential housing using a universal puller with wide feet.
8 Remove the crown wheel to differential housing retaining bolts in a diagonal pattern and using a soft-faced hammer remove the crownwheel from the differential housing.

Reassembly:

Reassembly is the reverse procedure to dismantling but it should be pointed out that the pinion and crownwheel will have to be set so that the two gears are in correct mesh. For this information also see **Section 7:12.**

7:12 Crownwheel and pinion gear meshing

The pinion and crownwheel are carefully matched during manufacture and a serial number together with tolerances are inscribed on both components as shown in **FIG 7:22**. The number on the pinion is the deviation 'E' from the basic setting dimension 'D'. When fitting new crownwheel and pinion set the following procedure must be strictly adhered to:

1 Fit the crownwheel with the differential housing into the final drive casing and tighten down the bearing cap on the opposite side to a torque wrench setting of 18.1 lb ft.
2 Install the bearing cap on the crownwheel side and tighten the bolts evenly until the friction coefficient of the crownwheels seating amounts to approximately 17.4-24.3 inch lb. Also screw in the driving flange fastening bolts into the differential shaft gears and tighten lightly against the differential pinion shaft.
3 Using a feeler gauge measure the distance which now exists between the bearing cap and the housing and fit shims the same thickness as the feeler gauges.
4 Turn the friction coefficient gauge several times against the operating direction and then read off the friction coefficient in the operating direction which should amount to between 17.4-24.3 inch lb.

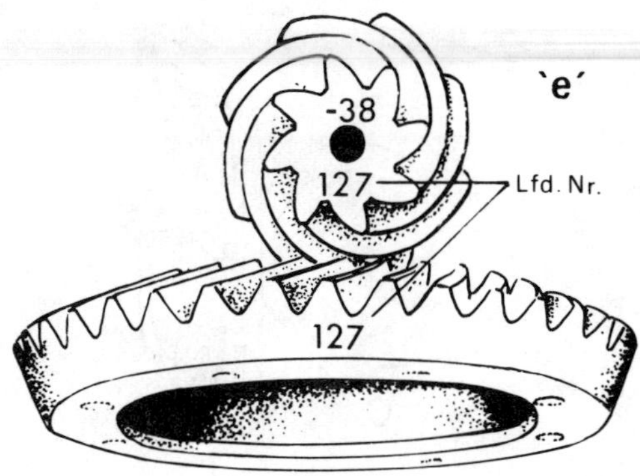

FIG 7:22 Crownwheel and pinion markings

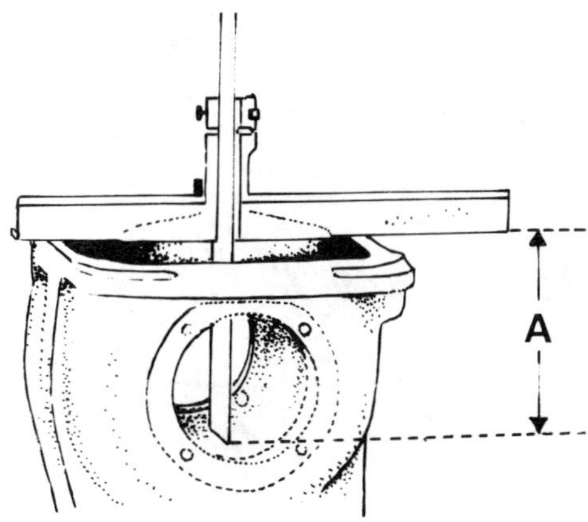

FIG 7:23 Final drive casing measurement

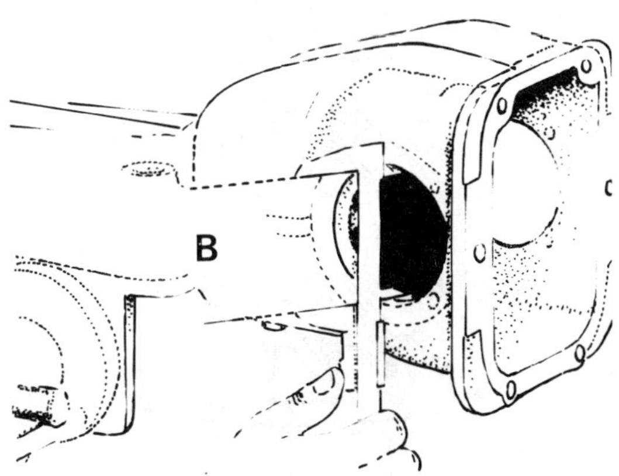

FIG 7:24 Final drive casing measurement

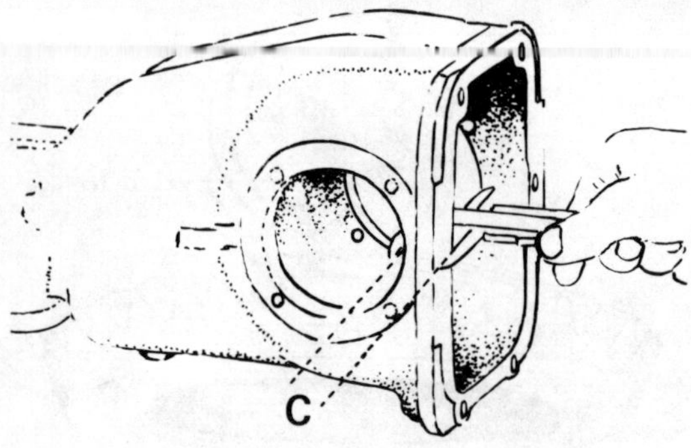

FIG 7:25 Final drive casing measurement

5 Remove the crownwheel and install the pinion without the distance bush with a shim 'X' between the pinion and the large taper roller bearing in the differential gearbox housing. Slide the three arm coupling onto the pinion splines and tighten the self-locking nut. Lightly tighten the three arm coupling retaining nut and using the friction gauge turn the drive pinion against the normal direction of rotation and then read off the friction coefficient in the direction of rotation. This should amount to approximately 10.42-14.76 inch lb.

6 Stand the final drive unit housing vertically and using a depth gauge measure dimension 'A' (see **FIG 7:23**). Also with the aid of vernier calipers measure dimension 'B', this being the bore diameter from the bearing cap (see **FIG 7:24**). Using a vernier gauge check dimension 'C' at the narrowest point in the bore or the bearing cap to contact surface of the final drive cover gasket (see **FIG 7:25**). With the values of 'A', 'B' and 'C' determine the shim thickness 'X' from the following table:

Type	*Reduction Ratio*	*No. of teeth*	*Basic Adjusting Dimension Gleason*[1]	*Backlash*
1600	4.375:1	35 8	52.20 mm 2.055"	.07–.12 mm .0028–.0047"
1600 T1	3.9:1	39 10	52.52 mm 2.068"	.07–.12 mm .0028–.0047"
1600-2	4.11:1	37 9	52.45 mm 2.065"	.07–.12 mm .0028–.0047"

[1] For input pinion heights above 32 mm (1.2598") the basic adjusting dimension is 52.52 mm (2.068").

7 Refit the pinion and spacer bush together with the appropriate shim 'X'. Tighten the flexible locknut and using a soft-faced hammer strike the end of the bearing trunnion sharply to seat the universal shaft centring. Apply the friction coefficient gauge and turn the pinion several times in the opposite direction to normal rotation and then read off the coefficient friction in the direction of rotation which should be in the order of 10-15 inch lb.

8 Fit the front bearing cap together with the slide spacer ring and three point coupling flange onto the pinion wheel teeth. Tighten the nut to a torque wrench setting of 108.5 lb ft.

9 Fit the crownwheel and measure the tooth backlash which should correspond to figures given in the table, see item 6 above. Referring to **FIG 7:26A** adjust the crownwheel position by altering around the shims from one bearing cap to another so that a correct tooth pattern as shown is obtained. To obtain this pattern use a small amount of engineers blue on the teeth and by adjustment obtain the pattern as shown in **FIG 7:26A1**, for no load conditions, A1 for the gears under load. Should difficulty be experienced in obtaining the correct tooth pattern the following notes should be of assistance.

(a) Refer to **FIG 7:26(1)**. High narrow contact marking (tip contact) on crownwheel.

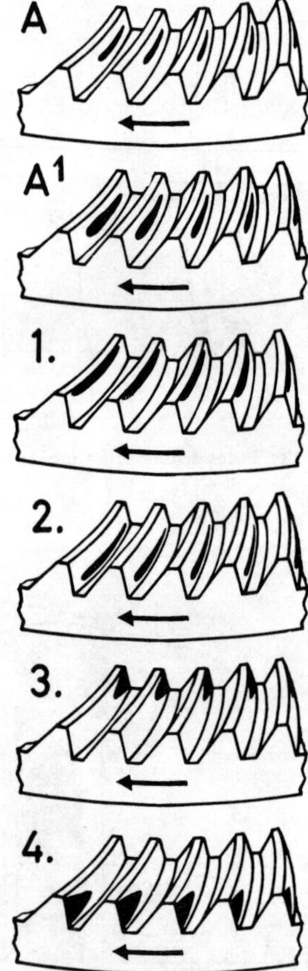

FIG 7:26 Crownwheel and pinion tooth mesh comparison

Correction:

Displace the pinion towards the crownwheel axis end, if necessary, correct backlash by moving the crownwheel away from the pinion.

(b) Refer to **FIG 7:26(2)**. Deeper, narrow contact marking (root contact) on crownwheel.

Correction:

Move the pinion away from the crownwheel axis and, if necessary, correct backlash by pushing the crownwheel towards the pinion.

(c) Refer to **FIG 7:26(3)**. Short contact marking on smallest tooth end (toe contact) of the crownwheel.

Correction:

Move the crownwheel away from the pinion and, if necessary move the pinion closer towards the crownwheel axis.

(d) Refer to **FIG 7:26(4)**. Short contact marking on large tooth end (heel contact) of the crownwheel.

Correction:

Move the crownwheel towards the pinion and, if necessary, move the pinion away from the crownwheel axis.

Differential gear set adjustment:

Explanation:

A is the measured distance from the face of the drive pinion to the contact surface on the differential housing cap gasket.

B is obtained from the measured bore diameter for accommodating the lateral bearing cap, divided by two.

C is measured from the narrowest point in the bore for accommodating the lateral bearing cap to the contact surface of the differential housing for cap gasket, to which B is added.

D basic adjusting dimension is obtained from the table. D is independent of type, reduction ratio and type of gearing system.

e indicates the deviation from D in hundredths of a mm and is, in each case, inscribed electrically on the face of the drive pinion.

e+ is to be added to D, e— to be subtracted from D.

D-desired is obtained from D and e.

D-actual are the measured values actually determined.

X or the shim thickness is obtained from D-desired plus or minus D-actual.

Example:

		mm	*in.*			*mm*	*in.*
1.	**B** (dia/2)	41.50	1.6338	2.	**A**	122.00	4.8031
	+C	28.00	1.1024		— **(B+C)**	69.50	2.7362
		69.50 =	2.7362		**D-actual**	52.50 =	2.0669

		mm	*in.*
3.	**D** (as per Table)	52.52	2.0677
	+e	.30	.0118
	D-desired	52.82	2.0795
	—**D-actual**	52.50	2.0669
	X =	—.32	—.0126

In this instance the shim thickness must be reduced by .32 mm (.126 inch).

If D-actual is greater than D-desired the shim thickness must be increased by .32 mm (.0126 inch).

7:13 Fault diagnosis

(a) Noisy final drive

1 Insufficient or incorrect lubricant
2 Worn bearings
3 Worn gears

(b) Excessive backlash

1 Worn gears, bearings or bearing housings
2 Worn halfshaft splines
3 Worn universal joints
4 Loose or broken wheel studs

(c) Oil leakage

1 Defective seals in hub
2 Defective pinion shaft seal
3 Defective seals on universal joint spiders

(d) Vibration

1 Propeller shaft or halfshafts out of balance
2 Worn universal joint bearings

(e) Rattles

1 Rubber bushes in damper links worn through
2 Dampers loose

(f) 'Settling'

1 Weak or broken spring

NOTES

CHAPTER 8

FRONT SUSPENSION AND HUBS

8:1 Description
8:2 Front axle carrier
8:3 Front axle carrier traction strut rubber bearing
8:4 Wheel hub and bearing servicing
8:5 Tie rod lever
8:6 Guide joint servicing
8:7 Transverse swinging arm rubber bearing
8:8 Anti-roll bar
8:9 Telescopic leg shock absorber assembly removal
8:10 Support bearing servicing
8:11 Coil spring
8:12 Telescopic leg shock absorber renewal
8:13 Fault diagnosis

8:1 Description

The front suspension system is shown in **FIG 8:1** and comprises MacPherson type struts with integral dampers and co-axial coil springs fitted into a transverse lower wishbone. An anti-roll bar is attached to each suspension unit, which, together with the independent front suspension, gives the car its very good road handling qualities.

8:2 Front axle carrier

1 Remove the wheel trim and slacken the wheel nuts. Jack up the front of the car until the wheels are clear of the ground and support on firmly based stands. Remove the road wheels.

2 Refer to **FIG 8:1** for part identification and loosen the self-locking nuts from the guide joint 25. Release the steering gear 27 from the front axle by removing the three retaining bolts 10, 11 and 12 as shown in **FIG 9:3.** Remove the bearing bracket for the steering guide lever by releasing three retaining bolts 1, 2 and 3 holding it to the front axle carrier as shown in **FIG 9:17.** It is recommended that the steering gear and also the steering guide lever bearing bracket be securely tied to a suitable component such as the gearbox.

3 Remove the front lefthand and righthand lower engine mounting retaining nuts and using a garage crane or overhead hoist, lift the engine upwards.

4 Using a garage hydraulic jack support the weight of the front axle carrier and release the fastening screws shown by arrows in **FIG 8:2** and carefully lower the front axle carrier and move the carrier forwards away from the underside of the vehicle.

5 Thoroughly clean down the axle carrier and then clamp firmly into a bench vice. Remove the cotter pins from the castellated nuts at the traction strut bearing of the front axle carrier and remove the castellated nuts. Also remove the cotter pins from the castellated nuts on the

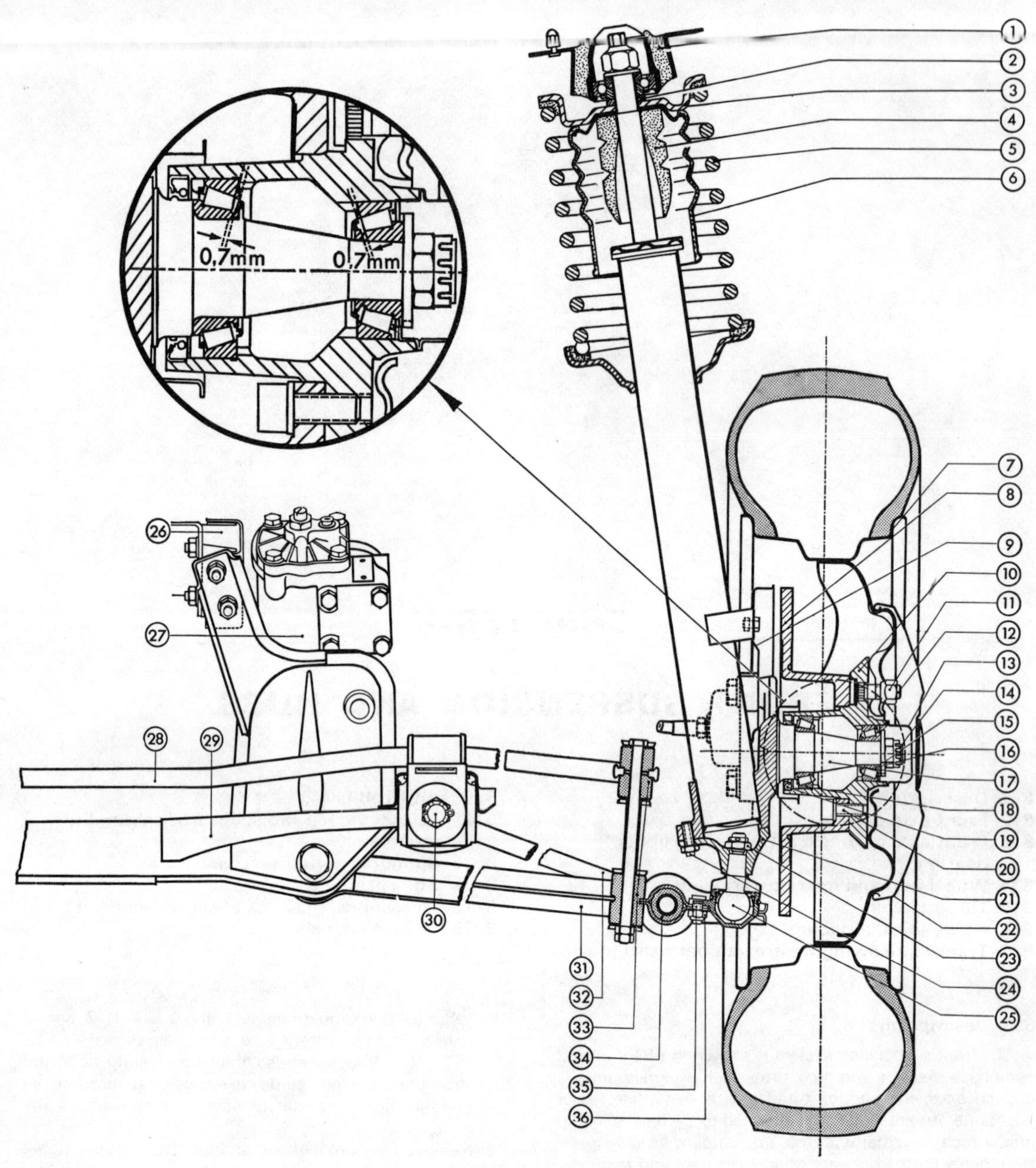

FIG 8:1 Front suspension unit and steering

Key to Fig 8:1 1 Telescopic leg support 2 Spacer 3 Upper spring cup 4 Hollow rubber spring 5 Coil spring 6 Telescopic leg shock absorber 7 Disc wheel 8 Brake disc 9 Protective plate 10 Wheel hub 11 Wheel nut 12 Splined wheel stud 13 Hub cap 14 Castellated nut 15 Thrust washer 16 Taper roller bearing, outer 17 Steering knuckle 18 Taper roller bearing, inner 19 Oil seal 20 Fillister head screw 21 Tie-rod lever 22 Wheel embellisher cap 23 Castellated nut M12 x 15 24 Securing screw M8 25 Guide joint 26 Rubber engine mounting 27 Steering gear 28 Stabilizer 29 Front axle carrier 30 Castellated nut M16 x 15.8.G.PHR 31 Wishbone 32 Traction stud 33 Rubber bearing 34 Rubber bearing 35 Splined bolt 36 Hex. nut M88.G.ZN

transverse swinging arm bearings at the front axle carrier and remove the transverse swinging arm bearing bolts at the front axle carrier. Gently ease out the traction struts from the rubber bearings. Take special note of the location of the spacer rings.

6 Remove the anti-roll bar by removing the locknut at the rubber bearings of the transverse swinging arms and release the fastening clips.

Reassembly:

Reassembly is the reverse procedure to dismantling but the following points should be noted:

1 When the anti-roll bar is being fitted the cranked centre section must face downwards.

2 When reassembling the transverse swinging arm bearings located at the front axle carrier the spacer rings that were previously removed must face the front axle carrier.

3 Tighten the castellated nuts located at the traction strut bearing of the front axle carrier to a torque wrench setting of 43.4 lb ft. This operation must be carried out with the vehicle under normal operating load, the specification of this being given in **Chapter 9, Section 9:7.** Fit new cotter pins.

4 Tighten the front axle carrier retaining bolts to a torque wrench setting of 34 lb ft.

5 Tighten the steering gear mounting bolts to a torque wrench setting of 34 lb ft.

6 Tighten the self-locking stop nuts from the guide joint to a torque wrench setting of 18 lb ft.

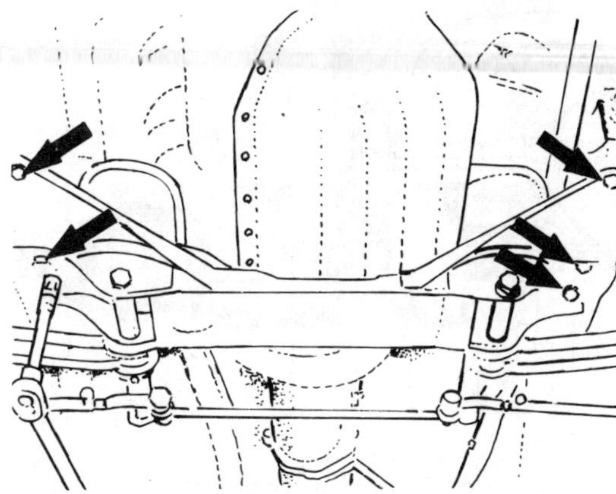

FIG 8:2 Front axle carrier

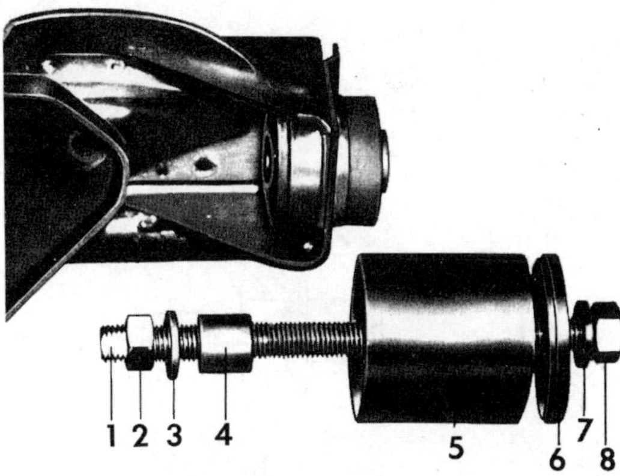

FIG 8:3 Traction strut rubber bearing and withdrawal tool

8:3 Front axle carrier traction strut rubber bearing

Removal:

1 Remove the self-locking stop nuts from the guide joints 25 (see **FIG 8:1**). Remove the cotter pins from the castellated nuts at the traction strut bearing of the front axle carrier and remove the castellated nuts. Carefully pull out traction struts from the rubber bearings and remove the anti-roll bar fitting as described in **Section 8:8.**

2 Refer to **FIG 8:3** and using BMW tool 6011 fit the threaded bolt 1 into the reception bore of the rubber bearings. Fit the sleeve 4 and washer 3 onto the threaded bolt and tighten the nut 2. Press the sleeve 5 over the rubber bearing against the front axle carrier and finally fit the discs 6 and 7 and nut 8. Tighten the nut and so pull out the rubber bearings.

Reassembly:

1 Coat the new rubber bearing with glycerine and press the rubber bearing 11 (see **FIG 8:4**) into the slip bush 7. Fit the threaded bolt 1 through the rubber bearing 11 into its location in the front axle carrier. Fit the thrust piece 8, the relief part of which should face the rubber bearing, and slide on the washer 9 and threaded bolt. Fit the nut 10 and place the bush 6 with the milled part at the rear top as shown in **FIG 8:4,** against the front axle carrier. Slide the bush 5 onto the threaded bolt and place the disc 4 with the milled part at the top against the bush 5. Finally place the washer 3 on the threaded bolt and fit the nut 2. Turn the nut 10 until the new bearing is correctly located.

2 Slacken the socket head screws of the slip bush 7 and remove the BMW tool 6011.

3 Refitting of the traction strut is the reverse procedure to dismantling as also is the fitting of the anti-roll bar. The car must be loaded to the specification as given in **Chapter 9, Section 9:7.**

8:4 Wheel hub and bearing servicing

Wheel bearing removal:

1 Remove the wheel trim and slacken the wheel nuts. Jack up the car and place on firmly based stands and remove the road wheel.

2 Remove the front brake disc caliper retaining bolts from the telescopic leg shock absorber.

3 Remove the wheel hub cap and clean away the grease from around the castellated nut. Remove the cotter pin and castellated nut from the hub.

4 Carefully lift away the disc and hub assembly and clamp the disc between soft faces in a vice. Using a universal two leg puller carefully remove the wheel hub.

5 Using a suitably sized bearing extraction tool ease out the taper roller bearings. It is important that hub

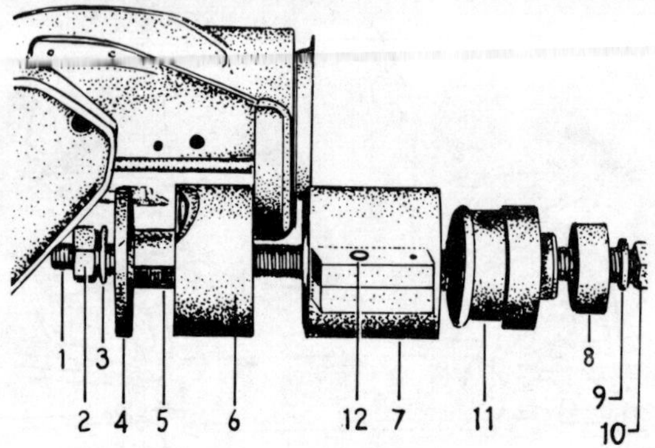

FIG 8:4 Rubber bearing on BMW tool 6011

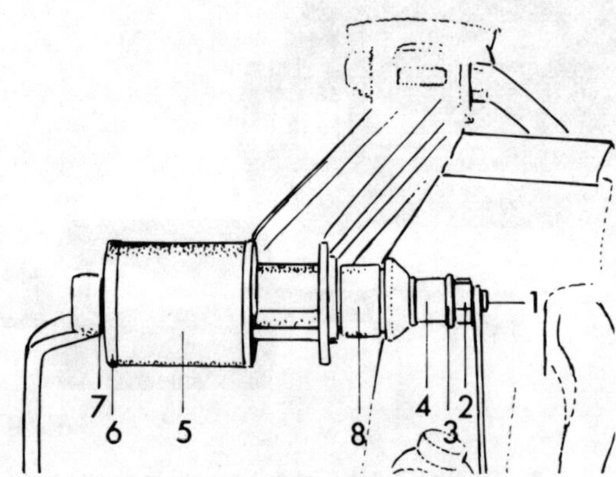

FIG 8:5 Swinging arm rubber bearing removing and replacement using tool 6011

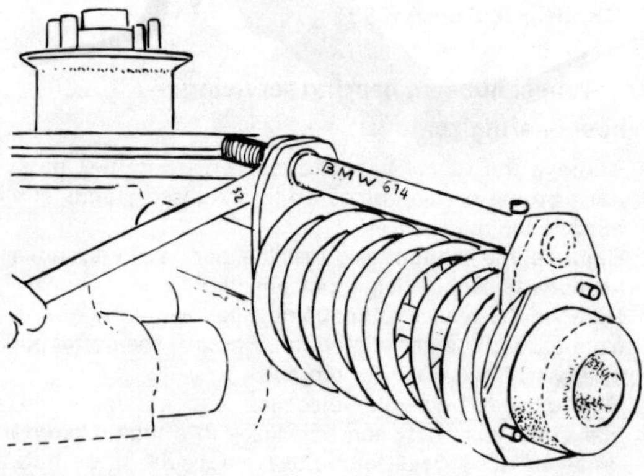

FIG 8:6 Coil spring compressed using BMW tool 614

bearings be replaced in pairs even if only one is defective. Thoroughly clean the wheel hub and disc assembly in preparation for inspection and reassembly.

Reassembly:

1 Fill a new oil seal with Graphite grease and carefully locate the rear taper roller bearing in the hub, followed by the oil seal and press into position using a suitably sized drift.
2 Fit the wheel hub and disc assembly to the front axle. Tighten the castellated nut to a torque wrench setting of 7.2 lb ft and turn the wheel hub a few times in the forward and reverse direction of rotation to ensure correct grease distribution.
3 Slacken the castellated nut by one third of a turn and place a screwdriver into the recess of the thrust washer 15 (see **FIG 8:1**). This thrustwasher must be easily movable both in the clockwise and anticlockwise direction.
4 Screw a universal dial indicator to the wheel hub using one of the threaded holes and align the dial gauge pointer to the front axle stub. Turn the wheel hub six turns in both directions and then firmly pull and push the hub assembly in the same axis as the steering knuckle assembly and read off the wheel bearing play from the dial gauge. Adjust the wheel bearing play to give a minimum reading of .00079 inch.

Wheel hub removal:

1 Remove the wheel as previously described and clamp the wheel hub and brake disc between soft faces in a vice.
2 Remove the brake disc to hub retaining screws and carefully separate the brake disc from the wheel hub. Should difficulty be experienced in this separation because of excessive rust, it is recommended that the wheel hub is mounted to the road wheel and placed on the floor with the disc facing upwards. Rotate the brake disc forward and backwards and at the same time pulling upwards as firmly as possible.
3 Thoroughly clean down the brake disc and using a micrometer at approximately 8 points throughout the circumference the permissible deviation in thickness must not exceed .00079 inch. Should it be necessary to reface the rubbing area of the disc, the thickness of the disc must not fall below .3347 inch otherwise overheating and distortion of the disc will occur.
4 If possible mount the disc in a lathe and check the lateral runout using a dial indicator gauge set. The runout must not exceed .00394 inch and if this figure is exceeded a new disc must be fitted.

Reassembly:

Reassembly is the reverse procedure to dismantling. The wheel hub to brake disc retaining screw must be tightened to a torque wrench setting of 43.4 lb ft.

8:5 Tie rod lever

Removal:

1 Remove the wheel hub assembly as detailed in **Section 8:4.**
2 Remove the self-locking nuts from the guide joint.
3 Remove the securing wire locking the three retaining

bolts of the tie rod lever to the steering knuckle assembly and remove the bolts. Carefully ease back the tie rod lever.

4 Remove the cotter pin from the castellated nut for the ball pivot and remove the castellated nut. Using BMW tool 6056 or a universal ball joint separator carefully press out the ball pivot.

5 Gently but firmly ease off the tie rod lever from the end of the telescopic leg shock absorber.

Reassembly:

Reassembly is the reverse procedure to dismantling but the following points should be noted:

1 The tie rod lever retaining bolts must be tightened to a torque wrench setting of 18 lb ft and finally locked using new soft iron wire.

2 The self-locking nuts for the guide joint must be tightened to a torque wrench setting of 18 lb ft.

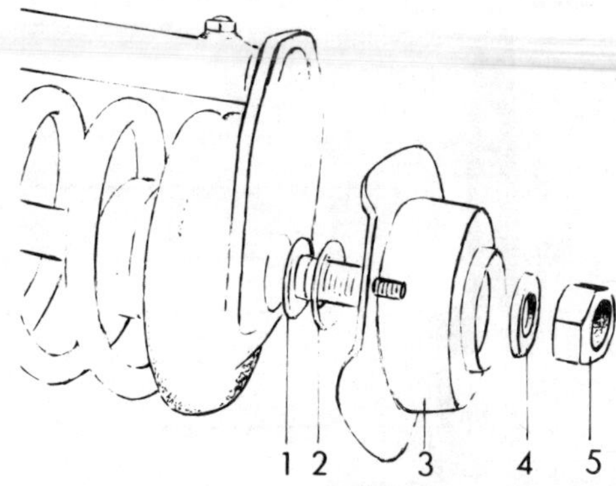

FIG 8:7 Shock absorber top assembly

8:6 Guide joint servicing

Removal:

1 Remove the wheel hub as described in **Section 8:4.**

2 Remove the tie rod lever as described in **Section 8:5.**

3 Clamp the tie rod lever between soft faces in a vice. Remove the cotter pin from the castellated nut and remove the nut.

4 Using a suitably sized drift and a nut placed on the end of the screw thread press out the guide joint from the tie rod lever.

Reassembly:

Reassembly is the reverse procedure to dismantling but the following points should be noted:

1 The specially shaped knurled pins must be pressed into the new guide joint using a suitably sized drift.

2 The tie rod lever castellated nut must be tightened to a torque wrench setting of 50.6 lb ft, and a new cotter pin fitted.

3 The wheel bearing play must be adjusted as described in **Section 8:4.**

4 If a new tie rod lever has been fitted the front wheel toe-in setting for the straight-ahead position and also the angle of toe-out on turns must be checked and adjusted as necessary. For this operation accurate steering geometry checking equipment is required and this work should be entrusted to the local Service Station.

8:7 Transverse swinging arm rubber bearing

Removal:

1 Remove the wheel trim, slacken the wheel nuts and jack up the car and place on firmly based stands. Remove the road wheel.

2 Remove the cotter pin from the castellated nut of the strut bearing at the front axle carrier and remove the nut.

3 Remove the cotter pin from the castellated nut of the swinging arm at the front axle carrier and remove the nut.

4 Remove the self-locking nuts from the guide joints. Carefully withdraw the long bolt for centre of the swinging arm bearing from the front axle carrier. Take special note of the location of the spacer ring.

5 Withdraw the traction strut together with the transverse swinging arm towards the rear.

6 Clamp the transverse swinging arm between soft faces in a vice and using a sharp knife blade or hacksaw blade cut off as much rubber as possible from the rubber bearing at one side of the swinging arm. If the excess rubber is not removed the sleeve will be pulled together with the bearing and the swinging arm becomes unserviceable.

7 Refer to **FIG 8:5,** place the bush 4 of BMW tool 6011 at the side of the swinging arm at which the rubber bearing had been trimmed and fit the threaded bolt 1 together with the washer 3 and nut 2 through the rubber bearing 8. Place the bush 5 against the swinging arm and fit the disc 6 together with disc 7 onto the threaded bolt 1 and screw on the nut. Tighten the nut so pulling out the rubber bearings.

Reassembly:

Reassembly is the reverse procedure to dismantling but the following points should be noted:

1 Before refitting a new rubber bearing the outside must be coated with glycerine otherwise damage could result to the bearing.

2 Refit the special spacer ring so that it faces the front axle carrier.

3 Tighten the self-locking nuts at the drive joint to a torque wrench setting of 18 lb ft.

4 Tighten the castellated nut at the swinging arm and front axle carrier location with the vehicle loaded as specified in **Chapter 9, Section 9:7.** Tighten to a torque wrench setting of 108.5 lb ft.

5 Tighten the castellated nut of the strut bearing at the front axle carrier to a torque wrench setting of 43.4 lb ft, with the vehicle loaded as specified in **Chapter 9, Section 9:7.**

8:8 Anti-roll bar

Removal:

1 Remove the locknut of the rubber bearings located at the transverse swinging arms position.

2 Carefully detach the fastening clip for the anti-roll bar located at either end of the anti-roll bar.

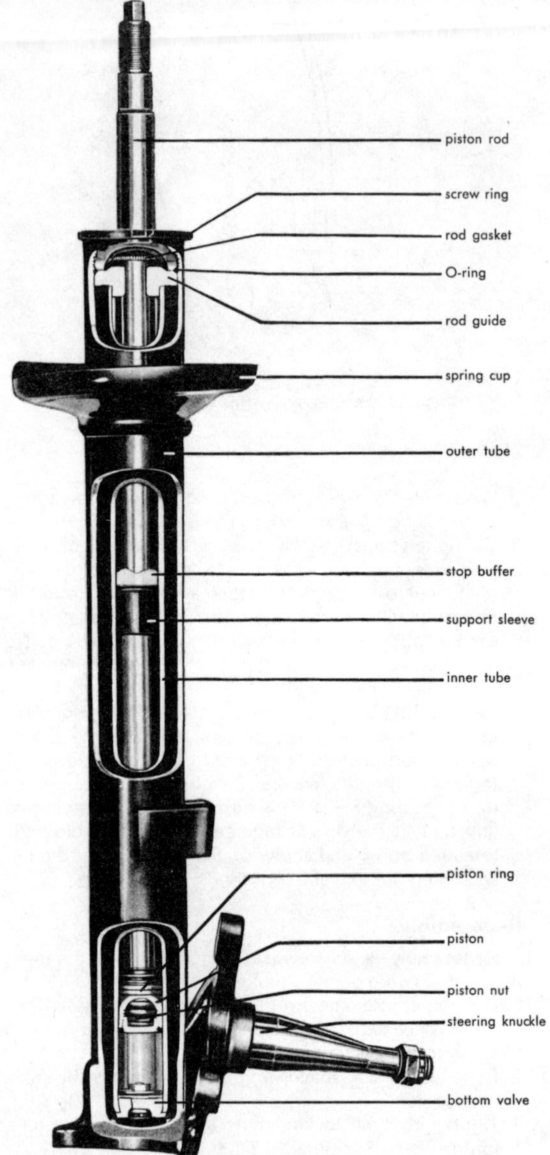

FIG 8:8 **Section view telescopic leg shock absorber**

Reassembly:

Reassembly is the reverse procedure to dismantling. Ensure that the anti-roll bar is correctly refitted with the cranked centre section facing downwards.

8:9 Telescopic leg shock absorber servicing

Removal:

1 Remove the wheel trim, slacken the wheel nuts and jack up the car and place on firmly based stands. Remove the road wheel.

2 Carefully remove the disc brake caliper and tie up the caliper away from the telescopic leg shock absorber.

3 Refer to **FIG 8:1** and remove the self-locking nuts from the guide joints. Remove the cotter pin from the castellated nut of the ball pivot and remove the castellated nut. Using BMW tool 6056 or a universal ball joint separator, carefully press out the ball pivot.

4 From the engine compartment slacken the three retaining nuts for the telescopic leg support.

5 Carefully withdraw the telescopic leg shock absorbers from the underside of the car.

Reassembly:

Reassembly is the reverse procedure to dismantling but the following points should be noted:

1 When reassembling the telescopic leg support the three holes drilled in the body panel are specially offset so the support bearing must be rotated until correct location is obtained. Tighten the nuts to a torque wrench setting of 18 lb ft.

2 Tighten the self-locking nuts at the guide joint to a torque wrench setting of 18 lb ft.

3 Tighten the brake caliper mounting bolts to a torque wrench setting of 68.7 lb ft.

8:10 Support bearing servicing

Removal:

1 Remove the telescopic leg shock absorber as detailed in **Section 8:9**, items 1 to 5.

2 Clamp the telescopic leg shock absorber firmly in a vice (see **FIG 8:6**) and using the special BMW tool 614 compress the spring. It is exceedingly dangerous to use any other means of compressing the spring otherwise should the spring slip from an improvization whilst compressed a considerable amount of damage or bodily harm can be unnecessarily caused.

3 Using a screwdriver carefully prise away the cap located at the top of the shock absorber. Remove the self-locking stop nut revealed by removal of the top cap and lift away the spring leg support bearing. This is shown in **FIG 8:7**.

Reassembly:

Reassembly is the reverse procedure to dismantling but the following points should be noted:

1 It is recommended that the complete spring leg support bearing be renewed if necessary and not just parts of it. Reassemble in the following order. Washer 1 (see **FIG 8:7**), sealing ring 2, support bearing 3, washer 4 and self-locking nut 5. Before finally tightening the self-locking nut ensure that the sealing ring 2 is correctly located in position.

2 Tighten the self-locking nut 5 (see **FIG 8:7**), to a torque wrench setting of 57.8 lb ft.

8:11 Coil spring

Removal:

1 Remove the telescopic leg shock absorber as detailed in **Section 8:9**, items 1 to 5.

2 Remove the support bearing as detailed in **Section 8:10**.

3 Carefully unscrew BMW tool 614 until the spring cup, rubber spring and the coil spring may be lifted out.

4 It should be noted that up to Chassis No. 917583 the spring length in the unloaded condition is 13.583 inch. The diameter of the wire being .4685 inch. From Chassis No. 917584 the spring length in the unloaded condition is 12.106 inch with a wire diameter of .4921 inch. In both specifications the spring rating is identical and as follows:

Red—640 to 660 lb . . soft rating
White—662 to 682 lb . . medium rating
Green—684 to 706 lb . . hard rating

It is very important that identical springs be fitted to both front suspension assembly units.

Reassembly:

Reassembly is the reverse procedure to dismantling but it is important to ensure that both the spring ends are correctly located into the spring cups before compressing the spring.

8:12 Telescopic leg shock absorber renewal

The telescopic leg shock absorber assembly combined with the steering knuckle is shown in **FIG 8:8.**

Removal:

1 Remove the telescopic leg shock absorber assembly as detailed in **Section 8:9,** items 1 to 5.
2 Remove the support bearing as detailed in **Section 8:10.**
3 Carefully unscrew the BMW tool 614 until the coil spring and rubber spring may be lifted out.
4 Remove the hub grease cap and release the cotter pin from the castellated nut. Remove the nut. Carefully pull off the hub and thrust washer.
5 Release the tie rod lever retaining bolts securing wire and remove the bolts. Carefully separate the tie rod lever and guide joints from the telescopic leg, the assembly being shown in **FIG 8:9.** Loosen the brake backplate from the telescopic leg shock absorber by removing the retaining bolts.
6 It should be noted that various lengths of telescopic leg shock absorbers have been fitted to the BMW 1600 models and this has entailed modifications to the coil springs. Refer to Technical Data for full information and chassis number change points.

Reassembly:

Reassembly is the reverse procedure to dismantling but the following points should be noted:

1 Tighten the tie rod lever retaining bolts to a torque wrench setting of 18 lb ft and lock using a new soft iron wire.
2 When reassembling the hub assembly adjust the wheel bearing play as detailed in **Section 8:4.**

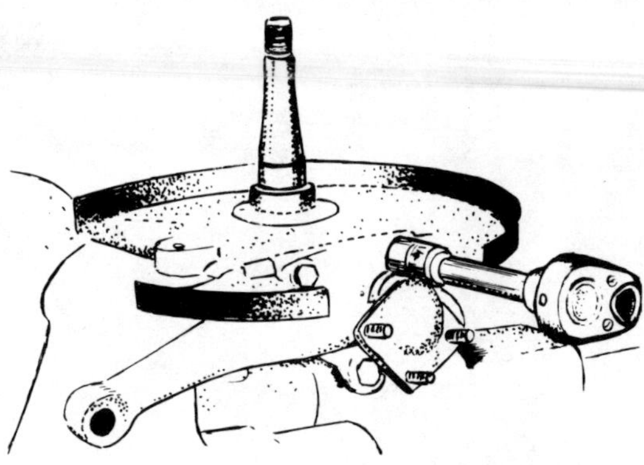

FIG 8:9 Tie rod lever as fitted to telescopic leg shock absorber

3 Ensure that the coil spring ends seat correctly into the spring cups before compressing the spring using BMW tool 614.

8:13 Fault diagnosis

(a) Wheel wobble

1 Worn hub bearings
2 Broken or weak front coil springs
3 Uneven tyre wear
4 Worn suspension strut
5 Loose wheel fixings

(b) 'Bottoming' of suspension

1 Check 2 in (a)
2 Telescopic leg shock absorber weak

(c) Heavy steering

1 Neglected swivel pin lubrication
2 Wrong suspension geometry

(d) Excessive tyre wear

1 Check 4 in (a), and 2 in (b) and 2 in (c)

(e) Rattles

1 Check 2 in (a)
2 Pivot lubrication neglected, rubber bushes worn
3 Damper mountings loose or worn
4 Radius arm mountings loose or worn
5 Anti-roll bar mountings loose, bearings worn

(f) Excessive 'rolling'

1 Check 2 in (a) and 2 in (b)
2 Anti-roll bar broken, mountings loose, bearings worn

NOTES

CHAPTER 9

THE STEERING GEAR

9:1 Description
9:2 Removal and refitting steering box
9:3 Dismantling, adjustment and reassembly of steering box
9:4 Adjusting the steering mechanism
9:5 Renewal of steering spindle bearing
9:6 Removing and refitting bearing block for steering guide lever
9:7 Tracking
9:8 Maintenance
9:9 Fault diagnosis

9:1 Description

The ZF Gemmer worm and roller steering gear with an overall gear ratio of 17.58-1 is fitted into a three-piece track rod system. A small splined universal joint is fitted between the spindle and the steering worm to accommodate for any adjustment necessary.

If, during maintenance, the front wheels are lifted clear of the ground do not move them forcefully from lock to lock otherwise serious damage to the steering system may result.

9:2 Removal and refitting steering box

1 Slacken the air filter attachment screw at the wheel arch inner panel and remove the air filter. Mark the position of the upper joints flange at the steering spindle using a scriber to ensure correct adjustment upon reassembly.

2 Refer to **FIG 9:1** and slacken the retaining screws 1 and 2 for the joint flanges. Loosen the self-locking nuts from the universal joint disc. Release the steering spindle earthing strap 3 and carefully slide the upper joint flange 4 upwards to the stop on the steering spindle 5. Finally remove the joint disc.

3 Jack up the front of the car until the road wheels are free to rotate and support on firmly based stands. Remove the cotter pin from the castellated nut located at the middle of the tie rod at the pitman arm. Refer to **FIG 9:2** and using a universal ball joint remover or BMW Tool No. 6056 remove the middle tie rod from the pitman arm.

4 Slacken the fastening screws 10 to 12 (see **FIG 9:3**) for the steering gear from the front axle carrier. Carefully lift outwards the steering gear from the guide sleeves and take off from the underside of the car.

Reassembly:

Reassembly is the reverse procedure to dismantling but the following points should be noted:

1 When tightening the steering gear retaining screws as shown in **FIG 9:3**, tighten the screws to a torque wrench setting of 34 lb ft.

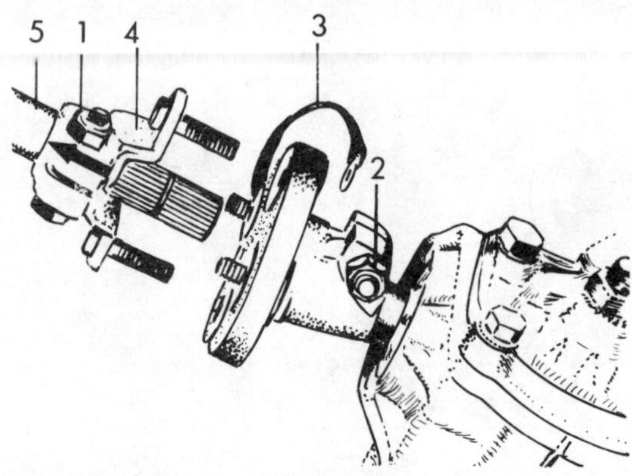

FIG 9:1 Steering shaft universal joint

FIG 9:2 Separation of middle tie rod from pitman arm

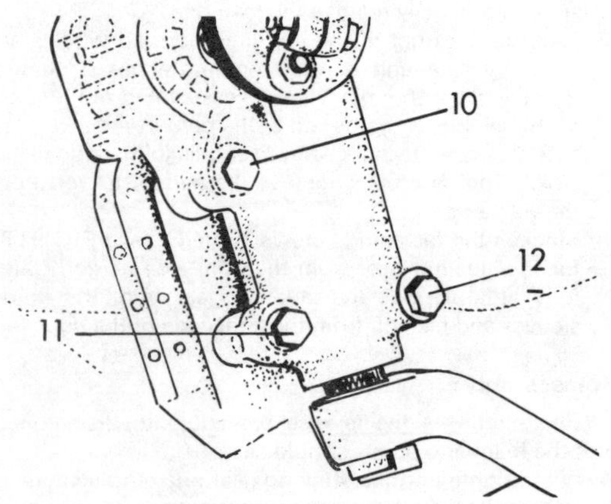

FIG 9:3 Steering gearbox mounting

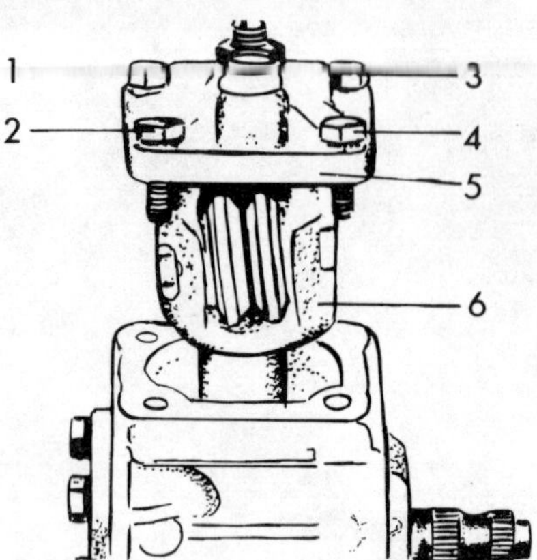

FIG 9:4 Steering case cover removal

2 Tighten the castellated nut at the pitman arm and middle tie rod to a torque wrench setting of 25.3 lb ft and fit a new cotter pin.
3 When reassembling the universal joint disc, ensure that the front wheels and steering wheel are in the straight-ahead position.
4 Tighten the universal joint disc self-locking nuts to a torque wrench setting of 10.8 lb ft.
5 Tighten the universal joint flange fastening screws 1 and 2 as shown in **FIG 9:1** to a torque wrench setting of 18 lb ft.
6 Upon reassembling the steering spindle bearing it should be fitted with an initial load of .079 to .098 inch. Ensure a firm pressure is placed onto the steering wheel in order to achieve this correct fitting position.

9:3 Dismantling, adjustment and reassembly of steering box

1 Remove the steering gearbox as detailed in **Section 9:2.**
2 Carefully pull off the joint flange, lift out the oil drain plug and allow the oil to drain into a suitably sized container.
3 Clamp the steering gearbox into a vice and open the drop arm retaining nut locking plates. Remove the fastening nut from the pitman arm and using a universal puller remove the pitman arm.
4 Refer to **FIG 9:4** and remove the retaining screws 1 to 4 of the cover. Carefully lift away the case cover 5 and the steering shaft 6.
5 Slacken the adjustment locknut shown at the top of the cover in **FIG 9:4** and unscrew the adjustment screw from the housing cover.
6 Unscrew the fastening bolts 1 to 4 of the cover (see **FIG 9:5**), and it should be noted that the fastening screw 4 is of the socket head type for which an Allen key is required.
7 Refer to **FIG 9:6** and remove the cover 10, shim washer 11, ballrace 12, ball cage 13, worm 14 and the ball cage 15 from the steering gear case 16.

Adjustment and reassembly:

1 Refer to **FIG 9:7** and fit the worm assembly to the

FIG 9:5 Steering case side cover

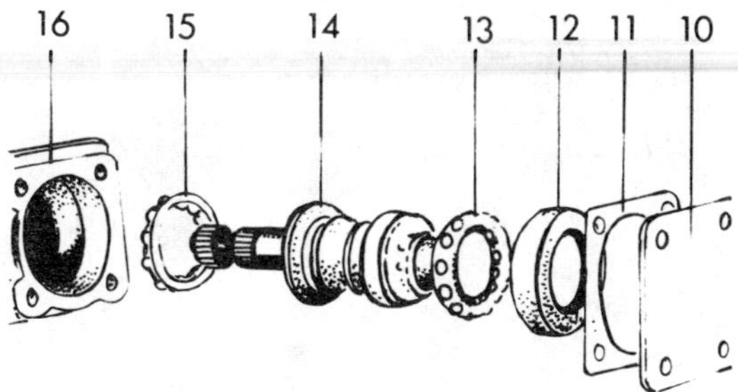

FIG 9:6 Steering worm assembly

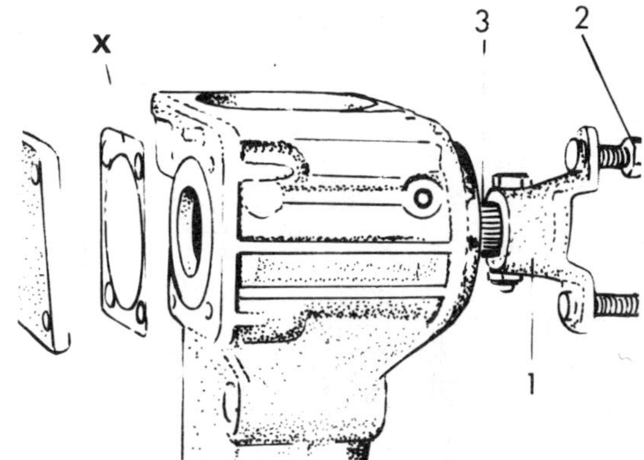

FIG 9:7 Steering case end cover shim

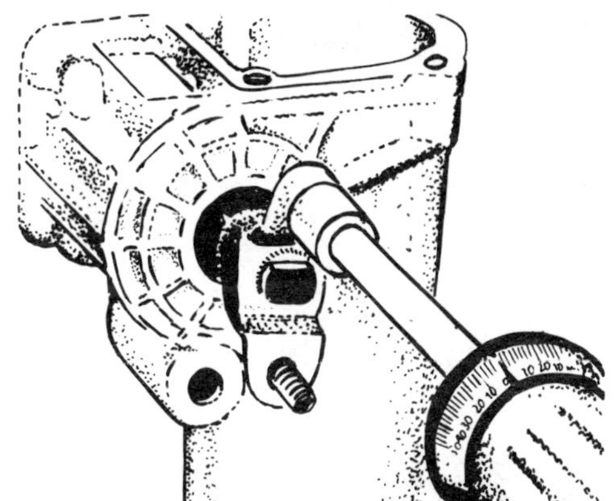
FIG 9:8 Determination of friction coefficient for steering worm

steering gear case with one shim **X** to be located as shown. Whilst turning the worm continuously, slowly tighten the fastening screw using a torque wrench set to read between 13.0 to 14.5 lb ft.

2 Using a special friction coefficient gauge as shown in **FIG 9:8** determine .the friction coefficient which should be between .072 to .181 lb ft. Should the friction coefficient be too low reduce the thickness of the shim washer, or, conversely should the friction coefficient be too high the shim washer thickness should be increased.

3 Reassemble the cover to the steering gear case with the machined edge **A** of the cover towards the bottom side as shown in **FIG 9:5.**

4 The head of the adjustment screw 5 (see **FIG 9:9**), is held into the steering roller shaft by a snap ring. Maximum permissible play between the adjustment screw 5 and the steering roller shaft is .0021 inch and may be adjusted accordingly by guide washers. These are available in various thicknesses and may be ordered under spare part Nos. 2670144-2670149.

5 Reassemble the locknut and adjustment screw to the housing cover and assemble the steering shaft and case cover to the steering case ensuring that the mark **A** (see **FIG 9:10**) scribed on the steering shaft **W** is pointing towards the middle of the housing seam. Also ensure that the marking **B** (see **FIG 9:11**) coincides with the mark **C** on the steering gear face.

6 Reassemble the pitman arm to the steering shaft ensuring that the mark on the steering shaft end is in line with the arrow on the pitman arm. Fit a new locking plate and tighten the nut and bed over the three locking plate tabs.

7 Fill the steering gearbox with .5 Imp. pint of Hypoid gear oil SAE.90. Refit the oil plug, the joint flange and reassemble to the car as detailed in **Section 9:2.**

9:4 Adjusting the steering mechanism:

1 Turn the steering wheel so that the front wheels are in the straight-ahead position taking care not to put excessive strain on the steering gear.

2 Refer to **FIG 9:11** and finally align the worm shaft marking with the marking on the steering gear case.

3 Jack up the front of the car until the road wheels are clear of the ground and support on firmly based stands. Remove the cotterpin from the castellated nut located at the middle of the tie rod at the pitman arm and remove the middle tie rod using a universal ball joint separator or BMW tool No. 6056.

4 Remove the steering wheel cover cap and turn the steering wheel approximately one turn to the left.

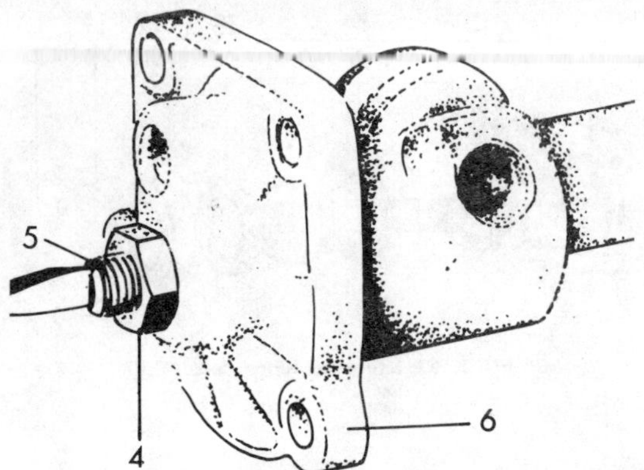

FIG 9:9 Steering case adjustment screw

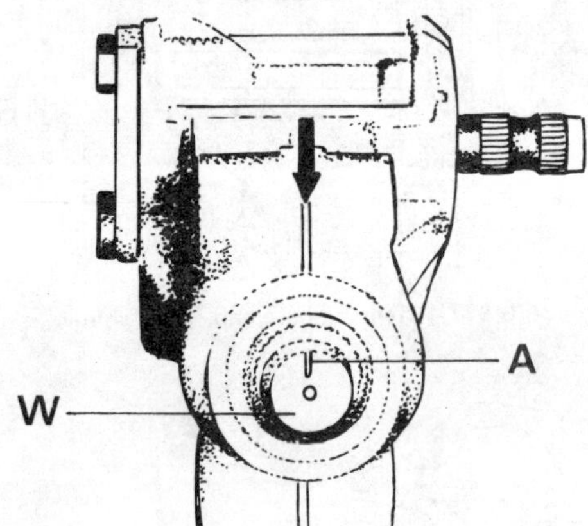

FIG 9:10 Steering shaft to steering case alignment

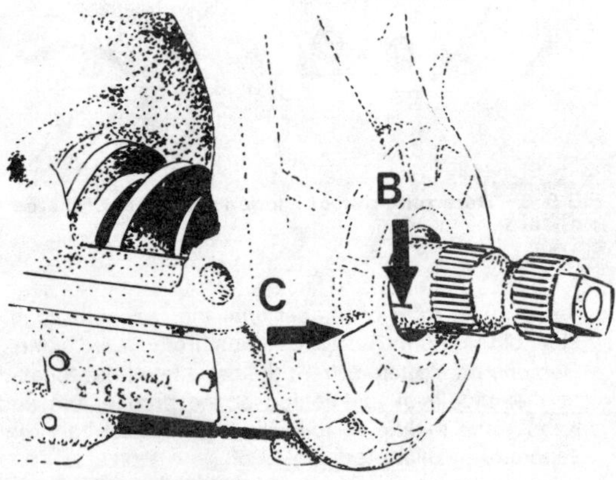

FIG 9:11 Steering gear to steering case alignment

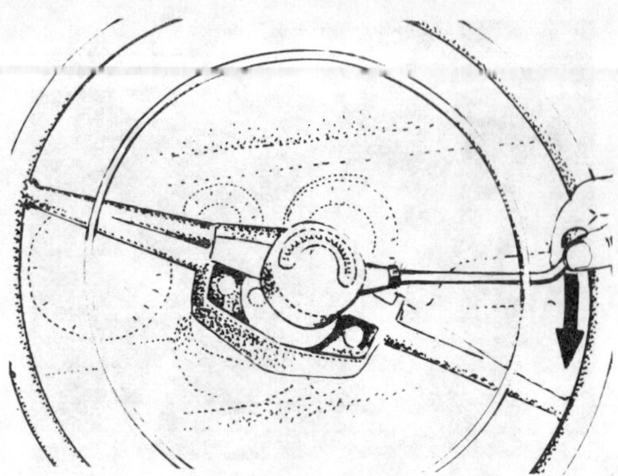

FIG 9:12 Friction coefficient gauge attached to steering shaft

5 Using a friction coefficient gauge on the fastening nut of the steering wheel as shown in **FIG 9:12**, adjust the friction coefficient to between .72 to 1.16 lb ft.

6 Refer to **FIG 9:13** and slacken the locknut 1 and carefully turn the adjustment screw using a screwdriver until constant repetition of the friction coefficient test gives the required reading previously given.

7 When the test is complete, tighten the locknut 1 and reassemble in the reverse procedure to dismantling, tightening the castellated nut using a torque wrench setting of 25.3 lb ft.

9:5 Renewal of steering spindle bearing:

1 Disconnect the earth terminal from the battery and referring to **FIG 9:14** loosen the fastening screw 1 of the joint flange.

2 Lift off the steering wheel cover cap 2 (see **FIG 9:15**), remove the steering wheel retaining nut 3, washer 4 and carefully remove the steering wheel from the steering spindle.

3 Pull off the return cam and remove the undercovering fastening screws 1 to 5 as shown in **FIG 5:10** and carefully lift away the covering. Remove the fastening screws 6 to 11 for covering the centre panel **M.** Carefully pull the connectors from behind the heater fan switch and ease the covering downwards and turning towards the left as shown by the arrow.

4 Remove the fastening screws from the slip ring holder and carefully pull out the plug connection from the slip ring. Remove the underside switch covering. Carefully disconnect the plug connection from the starter control and loosen the fastening nuts for the top covering. Remove the top covering by lifting upwards.

5 Remove the fastening screws for the light and flasher switch and lift away. Carefully disconnect the plug connections from the steering/ignition lock. Make a careful note of their locations.

6 Remove the fastening screws for the steering column clamp bracket and remove the bracket together with its spacer. Remove the fastening screw for the clip at the base of the outer steering column and carefully

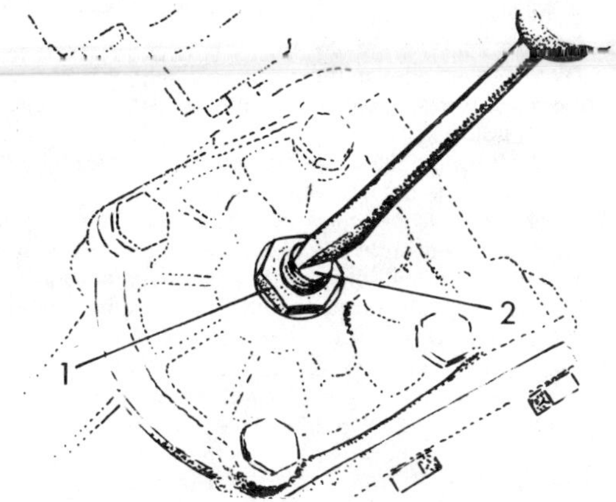

FIG 9:13 Steering shaft friction coefficient adjustment

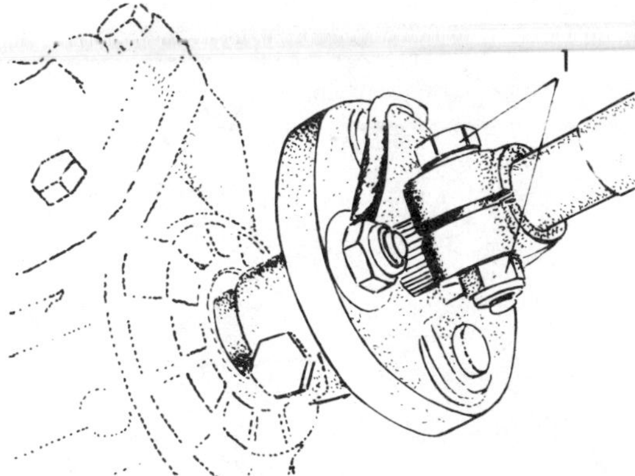

FIG 9:14 Steering shaft universal joint earth cable location

ease upwards the steering tube together with the steering shaft away from the bearing bracket.

7 Refer to **FIG 9:16** and carefully pull off the collar 32. Using pointed nose pliers lift out the snap ring together with the washer, coil spring and seating ring. Using a screwdriver gently ease out the steering shaft bearing from the outer tube.

Reassembly:

Reassembly is the reverse procedure to dismantling but the following points should be noted:

1 Drive the steering shaft bearing into the tube using a suitably sized drift until it is a snug fit.

2 When reassembling the collar assembly the ring must have its shank inserted into the steering spindle bearing. Repack the recess in the collar with grease and reassemble to steering spindle.

3 Plug connections for steering/ignition lock.

Plug connection	*Cable colour code*
30	red
50	black
15	green
15	black/green
R	yellow
P	grey

4 The steering wheel retaining nut should be tightened to a torque wrench setting of 28.9 lb ft.

9:6 Removing and refitting bearing block for steering guide lever

1 Remove the cotter pin from the castellated nut at the middle tie rod and remove the castellated nut.

2 Remove the tie rod from the steering guide rod lever using a universal ball joint separator or BMW tool No. 6056.

3 Refer to **FIG 9:17** and remove the fastening screws 1 to 3 for the bearing bracket from the front axle carrier.

Reassembly:

Reassembly is the reverse procedure to dismantling but the following points should be noted:

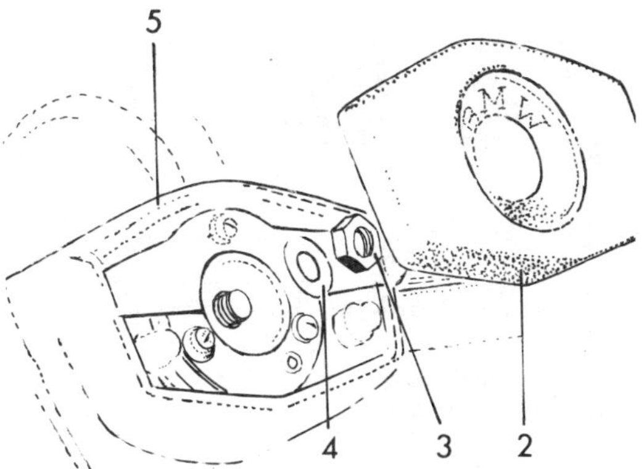

FIG 9:15 Steering wheel cover cap

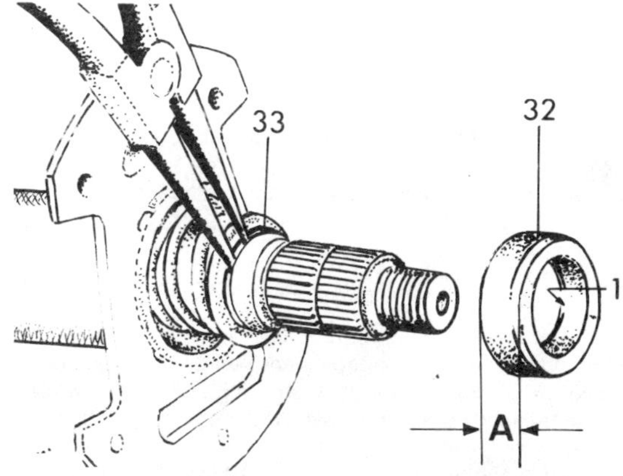

FIG 9:16 Steering spindle bearing assembly

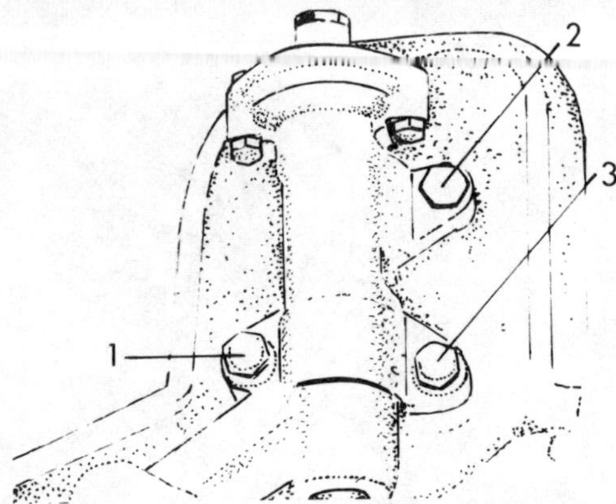

FIG 9:17 Steering guide lever mounting

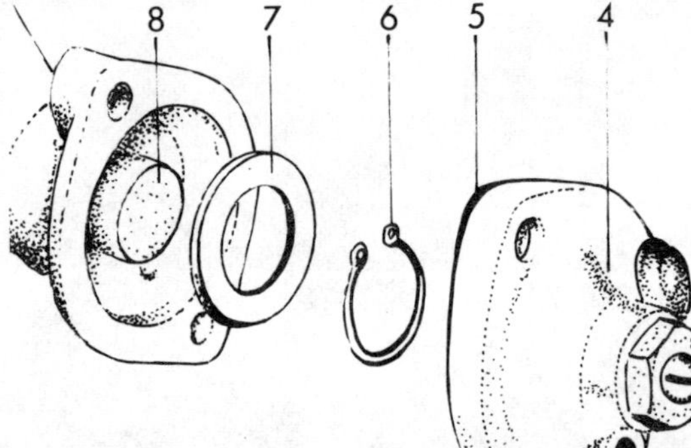

FIG 9:18 Bearing bracket end cover assembly

1 The fastening screws 1 to 3 (see **FIG 9:17**) must be tightened to a torque wrench setting of 18.1 lb ft.
2 Tighten the castellated nut of the middle tie rod to a torque wrench setting of 25.3 lb ft.

Bearing bracket dismantling and reassembly:

1 Carefully clamp the bearing bracket at both fastening plates into a vice and loosen the fastening screws for the cover 4 as shown in **FIG 9:18.** Remove the cover 4 and gasket 5.
2 Lift out the snap ring 6 using a pair of circlip pliers and also remove the washer 7. Carefully pull out the steering guide lever 8.
3 Reassembly is the reverse procedure to dismantling and the steering guide lever is adjusted by slackening the lock nut located at the top of the cover and rotating the adjusting screw until it is free from vertical play. Lock the adjusting screw into the desired position.

9:7 Tracking

Before checking the front wheel toe-in ensure that the steering connections, kingpins and wheel bearings are in good order and that the tyres are inflated to the correct recommended pressures. Ensure that the vehicle is standing on level ground and that the car is loaded with 2 x 140 lb on the rear seat and 1 x 140 lb on the front seat and 65 lb in the luggage compartment on the lefthand side. Also ensure that the fuel tank is full. Then proceed as follows:

1 Turn the wheels to the straight-ahead position and chalk a vertical line in the centre of each tyre tread at wheel hub height.
2 Mark off on a straight wood lath held horizontally the exact distance between two lines.
3 Carefully pull the car forward without moving the steering wheel until the chalk marks are at the same height behind the wheel as they were at the front.
4 Compare the chalk marks with their original distance as marked on the lath. If the marks are now wider apart the front wheels are toeing-in. The correct setting with the car loaded is a toe-in of between 1 and 2 millimetres (.0394 to .0787 inch).
5 If alignment is incorrect loosen the clamps of the rod sleeve adjusters and turn in or out both sleeves an equal amount so as to vary the rod length of the two outside track rods. Tighten the sleeve clamps ensuring a gap is left at the clamp ends and that the gaps in the sleeve adjuster and in the clamps are on the same side and flush.

9:8 Maintenance

No grease nipples are provided as the steering linkages are sealed for life. The steering gear has a capacity of .5 Imp. pint and is filled with Hypoid SAE.90 gear oil at a plug location in the gear casing. It is recommended that the oil level be checked every 3750 miles and topped up as necessary.

9:9 Fault diagnosis

(a) Wheel wobble

1 Unbalanced wheels and tyres
2 Slack steering connections
3 Incorrect steering geometry
4 Excessive play in steering gear
5 Broken or weak front springs
6 Worn hub bearings

(b) Wander

1 Check 2, 3 and 4 in (a)
2 Front suspension and rear axle mounting points out of line
3 Uneven tyre wear
4 Uneven tyre pressure
5 Weak dampers or springs

(c) Heavy steering

1 Check 3 in (a)
2 Very low tyre pressures
3 Neglected lubrication
4 Wheels out of track
5 Steering gear maladjusted
6 Steering column bent or misaligned
7 Steering column bushes tight

(d) Lost motion

1 End play in steering column
2 Loose steering wheel, worn splines
3 Worn steering box idler
4 Worn ball joints
5 Worn suspension system and swivel axle

CHAPTER 10

THE BRAKING SYSTEM

10:1 Description
10:2 Maintenance
10:3 Friction lining renewal (single caliper)
10:4 Friction lining renewal (dual caliper)
10:5 Front brake caliper overhaul (single caliper)
10:6 Front brake caliper overhaul (dual caliper)
10:7 Front brake discservicing
10:8 Rear brakes
10:9 Bleeding the brakes
10:10 Brake master cylinder removal
10:11 Brake master cylinder removal (tandem)
10:12 Brake master cylinder overhaul
10:13 Wheel cylinders
10:14 Removing flexible hose
10:15 Handbrake cable
10:16 Brake servo-unit removal—1600TI
10:17 Brake servo-unit—removal—twin circuit system
10:18 Brake servo-unit fitting 1600-2
10:19 Brake servo-unit operation and maintenance
10:20 Fault diagnosis

10:1 Description

Disc brakes are fitted to the front wheels and drum brakes to rear. All four are hydraulically operated by the brake pedal, whilst the handbrake operates the rear brakes only through a mechanical linkage which normally requires no separate adjustment.

The later BMW models covered by this manual have four piston calipers fitted whilst the earlier models have two piston calipers fitted. The front brakes are of the rotating disc and rigidly mounted caliper type, each caliper comprising two friction pad assemblies between which the disc rotates.

The friction pads are applied by pistons operated under hydraulic pressure from the master cylinder. They are automatically retracted when pedal pressure is released. Wear is taken up automatically and no adjustment is provided. The pistons in the caliper unit operate simultaneously to exert equal pressure onto the friction pads. This type of assembly is shown in **FIG 10:1.**

The later calipers fitted with four pistons incorporate a twin circuit system whereby pressure exerted by the brake fluid is directed by the way of duplicate brake lines to two pairs of wheel brake cylinders in each front brake disc caliper together with the wheel brake cylinders in each of the drum brakes at the rear. Should the circuit which couples only one pair of front wheel cylinders fail, braking effort is retained at all four wheels. If the other circuit supplying all four wheels should fail the second pair of brake cylinders in the front calipers will continue to operate.

The rear brakes are of the internal expanding type with one leading and one trailing shoe to each brake unit. A double ended cylinder expands both the shoes into contact with the drum under hydraulic pressure from the master cylinder. When the pedal pressure is released, the shoes are retracted by springs. This type of assembly is shown in **FIG 10:29.**

The braking system fitted to the BMW 1600TI and 1600-2 USA has a servo-unit fitted as standard but on 1600-2 models may be fitted in kit form. The brake pedal is directly coupled to the hydraulic master cylinder where pressure on the fluid is generated. This is transmitted to the brake units by a system of metal and flexible pipes.

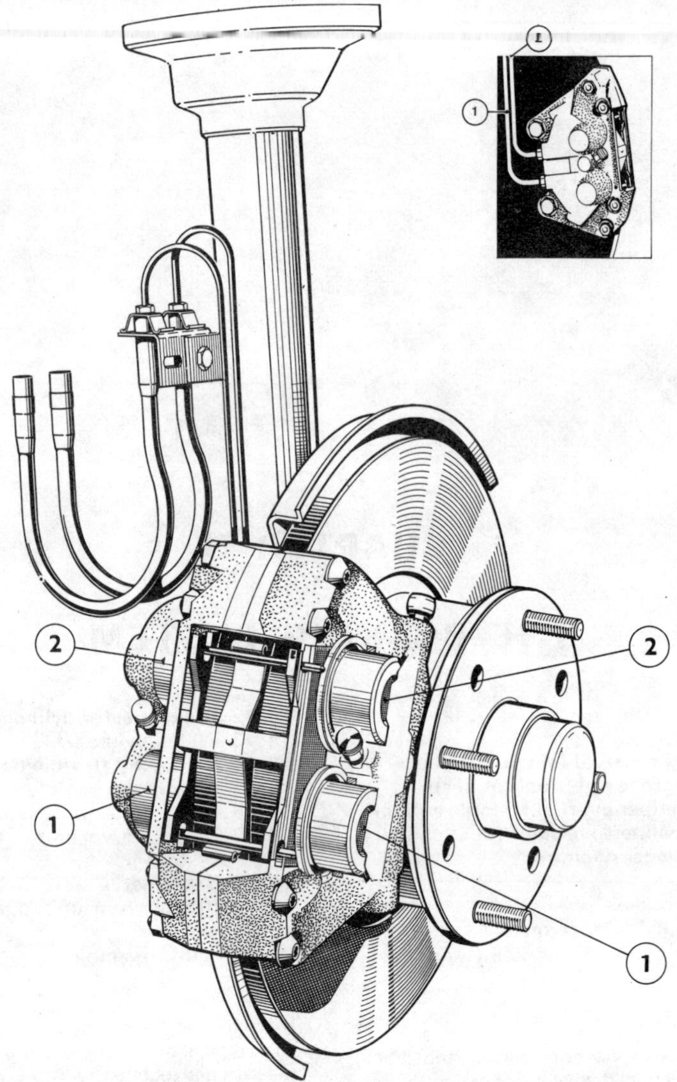

FIG 10 : 1 Front disc and caliper assembly

10 : 2 Maintenance

Periodically check the level of fluid in the master cylinder supply tank and top up the tank to the required level. If frequent topping up is necessary there must be a leak in the system which should have immediate attention. Wipe dirt from around the cap before unscrewing it. Always use a recommended grade of hydraulic fluid. Adjust the rear brake shoes when pedal travel becomes excessive. Full details of this operation are given in **Section 10 : 8.**

Preventative maintenance:

Regularly examine the friction pads, rear brake linings and all pipes, unions and hoses. If one front friction pad is more worn than the other change them over.

Change all the brake fluid every 12 months as brake fluid absorbs moisture through the supply tank vent hole. The boiling point of the fluid falls slowly from the original specification of 240°C to 160°-180°C. If the fluid is not renewed, bubbles of steam may form when the brakes are applied hard for long periods of time so causing brake failure.

Every three years check all flexible hoses and fluid seals in the complete system and renew if necessary. The bores of all cylinders should be highly polished and without signs of pitting or corrosion.

Never use anything but the recommended grade hydraulic fluid. Do not leave it in unsealed containers as it will absorb moisture which can be dangerous. It is best to discard fluid drained from the system or after bleeding.

Observe absolute cleanliness when working on all parts of the hydraulic system.

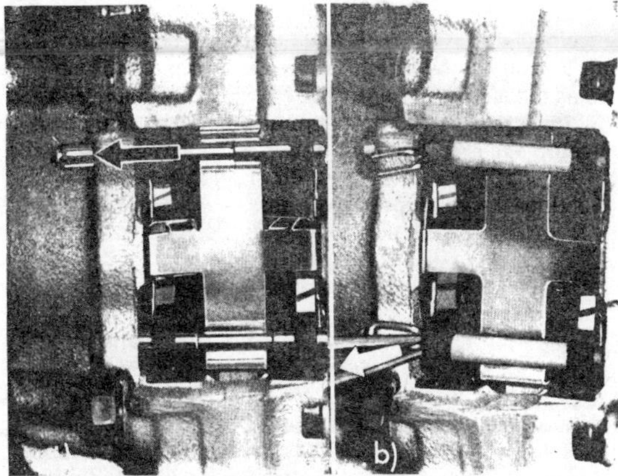

FIG 10:2 Disc pad retaining pins early and late type

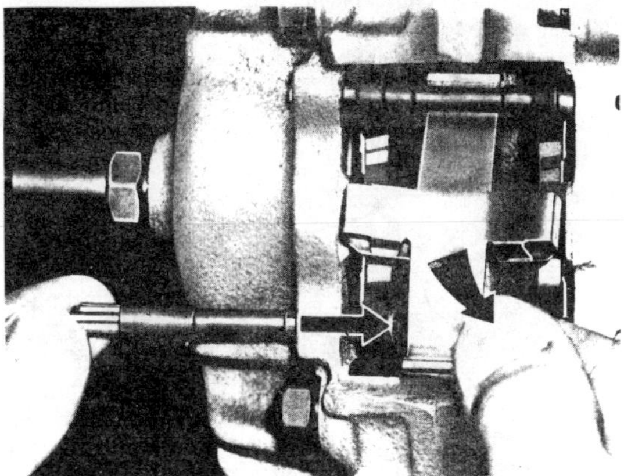
FIG 10:3 Cross spring removal

10:3 Friction lining renewal (single caliper)

Removal:

1 Before the caliper assembly is worked upon be sure that it has cooled down to normal room temperature.
2 Remove the wheel trim and slacken the wheel nuts. Lift up the front of the car and support on firmly based stands. Remove the wheel nuts and lift away the road wheel.
3 Using a drift and hammer, carefully drive out the retaining pins from the caliper or on the earlier type first remove the securing lugs from the fastening pins using a pair of pointed pliers (see **FIG 10:2**). It is important that the securing lugs be renewed and the original ones not refitted.
4 Carefully lift away the cross spring and using a suitably shaped hook carefully pull out the brake pads (see **FIG 10:3**).
5 It is important that new brake pads are fitted if the original linings are worn down to a thickness of .07 inch or less. Only use brake pads coded Necto 244.

Reassembly:

1 Ensure that the level in the brake master cylinder supply tank is below the recommended level and using a pair of piston press-back pliers return the pistons in the wheel cylinder (see **FIG 10:4**).
2 Ensure that on calipers with pistons fitted without protection caps that the 20 deg. of the piston setting is correct by using the special piston gauge as detailed in **Section 10:5**—reassembly item 2. This is important, as incorrect adjustment of the piston causes fluttering or squeaking of the brake assembly.
3 Reassembly is the reverse procedure to dismantling.

10:4 Friction lining renewal (dual caliper)

Removal:

1 Before the caliper assembly is worked upon be sure that it has cooled down to normal room temperature.
2 Remove the wheel trim and slacken the wheel nuts. Lift up the front of the car and support on firmly based stands. Remove the wheel nuts and lift away the road wheel.
3 Carefully drive out the retaining pins from the caliper using a suitably sized drift and hammer. It is important that the original pins are discarded and new ones fitted. The pins can be seen in **FIG 10:5.**
4 Carefully lift away the cross-spring and using a suitably shaped hook carefully pull out the brake linings.

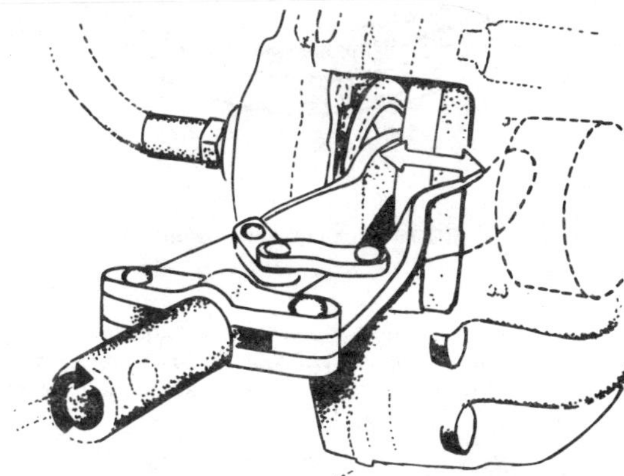
FIG 10:4 Piston retraction using spring-back pliers

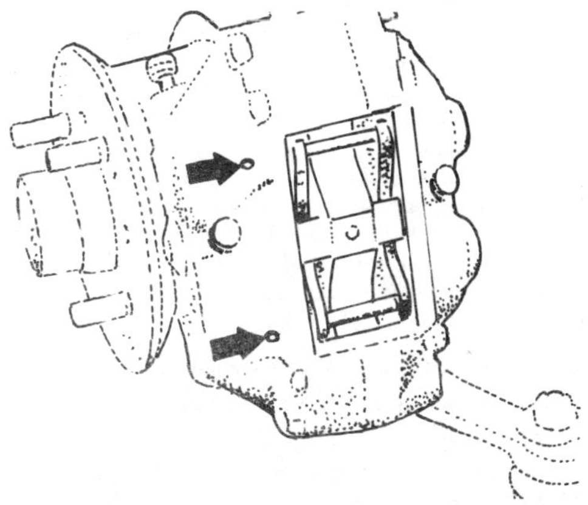
FIG 10:5 Disc pad retaining pins

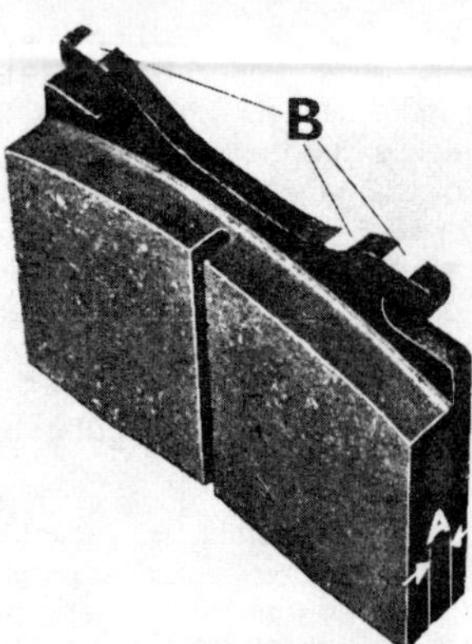

FIG 10:6 Pad identification

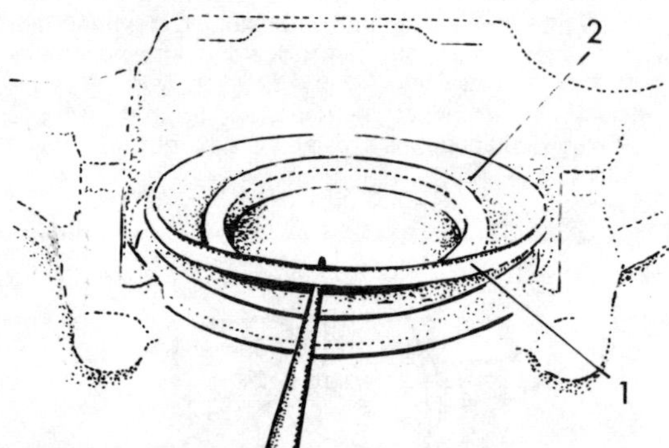

FIG 10:7 Clamp ring removal

5 It is important that new brake pad linings are fitted if the original linings are worn down to a thickness of .079 inch or less. Only use brake pads coded Necto 244.

Reassembly:

1 Ensure that the level in the brake master cylinder supply tank is below the recommended level and using a pair of piston press-back pliers return the pistons in the wheel cylinder.
2 As a matter of principle all four brake pads should be renewed as a set. Ensure that the pads are to correct specification as detailed by colour coding marked B (see **FIG 10:6**). Carefully insert the pads into the caliper and correctly locate the cross-shaped spring. Fit new retaining pins and ensure that the open end is correctly splayed outwards so that there is no chance of the pin working out of the caliper.
3 Reassembly is the reverse procedure to dismantling.

10:5 Front brake caliper overhaul (single caliper)

Removal and dismantling caliper:

1 Before the caliper assembly is removed ensure that it has cooled down to normal room temperature.
2 Remove the wheel trim and slacken the wheel nuts. Lift up the front of the car and support on firmly based stands. Remove the wheel nuts and lift away the road wheel.
3 Detach the hydraulic brake hose from the brake line as detailed in **Section 10:14.** Plug the ends to ensure that no dirt enters the hydraulic system and also to stop excessive loss of fluid.
4 Remove the two caliper mounting bolts and carefully lift away the caliper assembly.
5 Remove the friction linings as detailed in **Section 10:3.**
6 Thoroughly clean the exterior of the caliper, preferably using a compressed air line and a soft non-fluffy rag.
7 Carefully clamp the caliper between soft faces in a vice and using a pair of engineers pliers lift away the protection cap if fitted. This must be discarded and a new one fitted on reassembly.
8 Release the clamp rings 1 (see **FIG 10:7**), and rubber caps 2. Take care not to damage or mark the piston. Remove the bleed valve and cover the flexible pipe union thread with a plastic plug.
9 Using a pair of brake piston retaining pliers 4 and a block of wood 5 (see **FIGS 10:4** and **10:8**), retain the piston on the bleed valve side of the caliper body. Apply a compressed air jet through the bore of the bleeder valve 6 and push out the piston using as little pressure as possible.

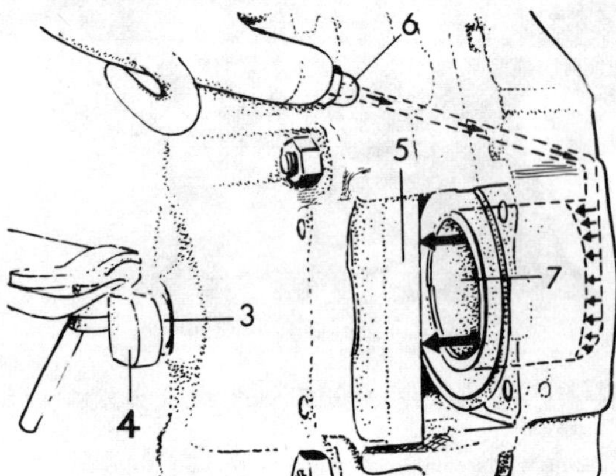

FIG 10:8 Piston retention

FIG 10:9 Caliper sealing rings location

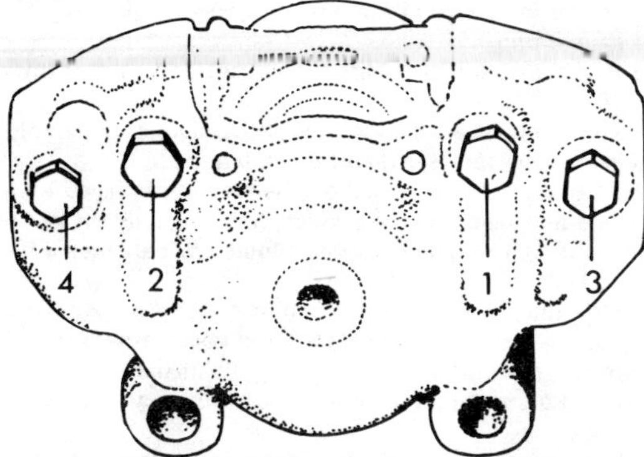

FIG 10:10 Caliper body clamping bolt tightening order

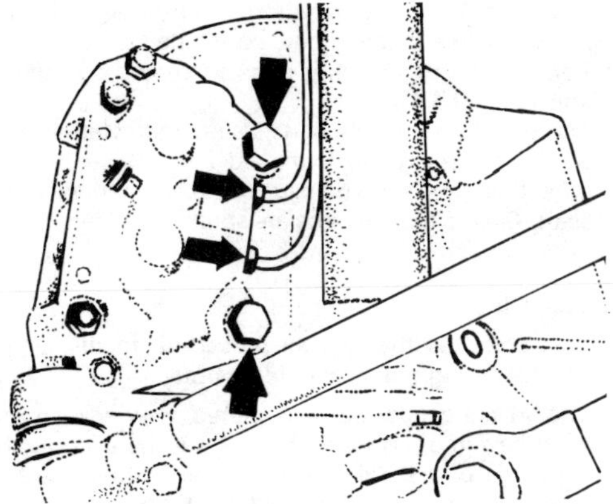
FIG 10:11 Caliper mounting bolts

10 Carefully remove the bore sealing ring using a wooden or plastic needle to ensure no damage to the face of the bore.

11 To remove the opposite piston, first replace the first piston without the bore seal and clamp using the retaining pliers. Insert the bleeder valve and remove the second piston using a compressed air jet to the flexible pipe unions.

12 If either of the body sealing rings 'D' (see **FIG 10:9**) are leaking the body must be split by removing the four clamping bolts in the order shown in **FIG 10:10**.

13 Thoroughly clean all the parts using methylated spirits or the correct grade hydraulic brake fluid. Never use any other fluid otherwise damage could result to the rubber seals. Ensure that all parts are spotlessly clean.

Reassembly:

Reassembly is the reverse procedure to dismantling but the following points should be noted:

1 Should the caliper body be parted, new sealing rings must be fitted. Also new bolts are to be used as they are made of special ductile steel. Tighten the bolts in the sequence shown in **FIG 10:10** referring to the below table for correct torque wrench settings. Set the torque wrench to 50 per cent of the final setting and tighten. Reset the torque wrench to a final setting and tighten.

Threads:	8G (lb ft)	10K (lb ft)
M 8	—	24.5
M 10	34.0	47.0
10 x 1.0	39.8	56.4
12	56.4	81.7
12 x 1.5	68.7	97.6
14	86.8	126.6
14 x 1.5	101.3	144.7

2 When reassembling the pistons ensure that they are correctly set with the mark on the piston inclined 20 deg. against the direction of incoming brake disc when driving forward.

3 Lubricate well the two bore rubber sealing rings with correct grade hydraulic fluid to stop tilting when the the piston is replaced.

4 Always fit a new protection cap if one was originally fitted to ensure that no road dust can find its way into the piston assembly. Should no protection cap have been originally fitted it is possible to fit a protection cap only if the pistons have a shoulder of .0315 inch.

Refitting caliper:

To refit the caliper is the reverse procedure to dismantling but the following points should be noted:

1 The caliper must only be refitted when it is at the normal room temperature.

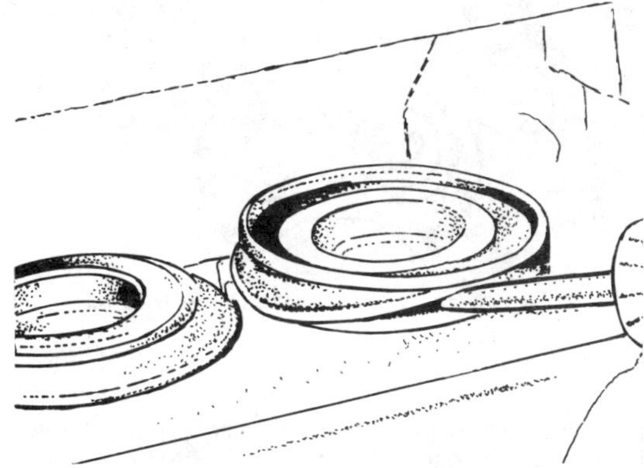
FIG 10:12 Seal and dust cover removal

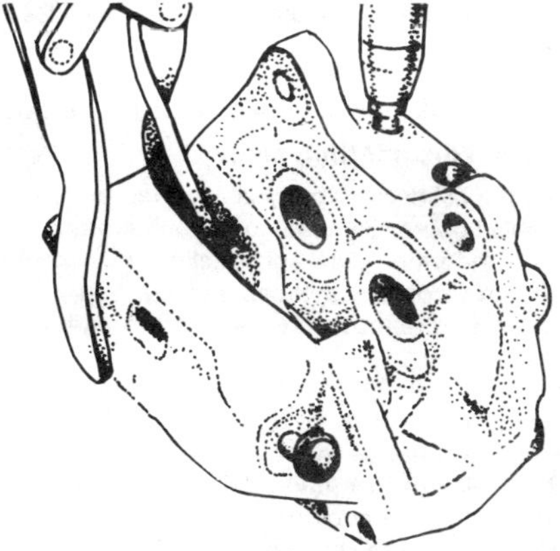
FIG 10:13

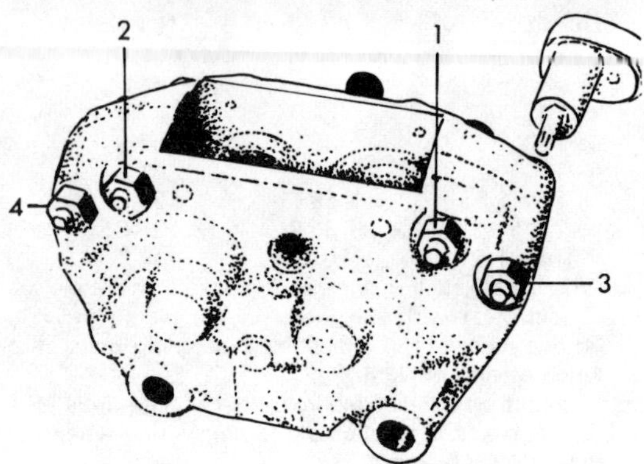

FIG 10:14 Caliper body clamping bolts

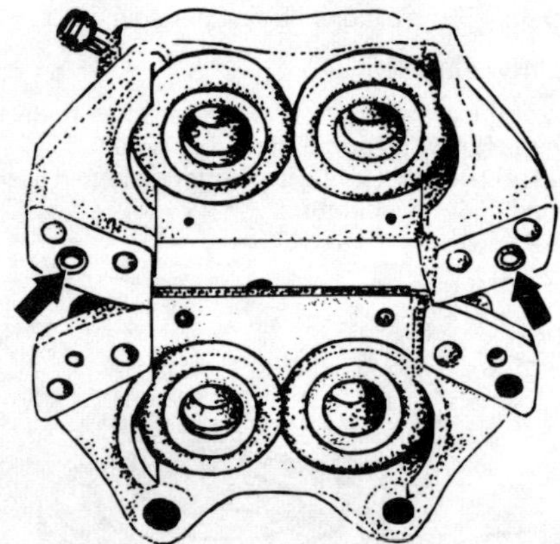

FIG 10:15 Caliper sealing rings location

2 Tighten the two caliper retaining screws to a torque wrench setting of 68.7 lb ft.

3 Tighten the flexible brake hose union to a torque wrench setting of 9.4 to 11.6 lb ft.

4 Bleed the hydraulic system as detailed in **Section 10:9.**

10:6 Front brake caliper overhaul (dual caliper)

Removal and dismantling caliper:

1 Before the caliper assembly is removed ensure that it has cooled down to normal room temperature.

2 Remove the wheel trim and slacken the wheel nuts. Lift up the front of the car and support on firmly based stands. Remove the wheel nuts and lift away the road wheel.

3 Refer to **FIG 10:21** and seal off the reservoir against escape of brake fluid by suitably plugging the two outlet pipes. Release the two brake pipes at the back of the brake caliper unit, the two locations being shown by the dark arrows in **FIG 10:11.**

4 Release the caliper by removing the two retaining bolts, the location of which are indicated by the light arrows in **FIG 10:11** and finally carefully lift away the caliper unit.

5 Remove the friction linings as detailed in **Section 10:4.**

6 Thoroghly clean the exterior of the caliper, preferably using a compressed air jet and soft non-fluffy rag.

7 Carefully clamp the caliper between soft faces in a vice and using a screwdriver, very carefully lift away the clamp ring and rubber protective cap (see **FIG 10:12**).

8 Referring to **FIG 10:13** secure one piston with the special piston retraction tool and insert a hard wood or felt pad in the stirrup recess. Push the piston out using a compressed air jet directed through the bleed hole.

9 Very carefully remove the sealing ring using a pointed plastic rod or a discarded knitting needle.

10 To split the caliper into two halves, remove the taper bolts 1 to 4 in the order shown in **FIG 10:14.** These must be discarded and new bolts fitted.

11 Remove the two sealing rings as shown by the dark arrows in **FIG 10:15.**

12 Thoroughly clean all parts using methylated spirits or the correct grade hydraulic fluid. Never use any other fluid otherwise damage could result to the rubber seals. Ensure that all parts are spotlessly clean.

Reassembly:

Reassembly is the reverse procedure to dismantling but the following points should be noted:

1 Should the caliper body be parted, new sealing rings must be fitted, also new bolts are to be used as they are made of a special ductile steel. Tighten the bolts in the sequence shown in **FIG 10:10** to the correct torque wrench setting as detailed in Technical Data. Set the torque wrench to 50 per cent of the final setting and tighten. Reset the torque wrench to final setting and tighten.

2 When reassembling the pistons ensure that they are correctly located in the bores and that they are well lubricated with the correct grade hydraulic fluid.

3 Lubricate well the two bore rubber sealing rings with the correct grade hydraulic fluid to stop tilting when the piston is replaced.

4 Always fit a new protection cap to ensure that no road dust will find its way into the piston assembly.

Refitting caliper:

To refit the caliper is the reverse procedure to dismantling but the following points should be noted:

1 The caliper must only be refitted when it is at a normal room temperature.

2 Tighten the two caliper retaining screws to the correct torque wrench setting.

3 Special attention should be given to bleeding the caliper assembly the details are given in **Section 10:9,** they should be strictly adhered to and the two top pistons should be bled at the top on the outside of the caliper and the lower pistons should always be bled at the bottom, otherwise great difficulty will be experienced in eliminating all the air from the hydraulic system.

10:7 Front brake disc servicing

Removal:

1 Before the caliper assembly is removed ensure that it has cooled down to room temperature.

2 Remove the wheel trim and slacken the wheel nuts. Lift up the front of the car and support on firmly based stands. Remove the wheel nuts and lift away the road wheel.

3 Remove the caliper from the telescopic leg shock absorber assembly by releasing the two retaining bolts. Remove the hub cap from the wheel hub and extract the cotter pin from the castellated nut. Remove the castellated nut and washer. Carefully pull the wheel hubs and brake disc from the steering knuckles and clamp the wheel hub and brake disc assembly between soft faces fitted between the jaws of a bench vice. Remove the Allen screws holding the brake disc to the hub assembly and part the two. If the brake disc is rusted to the wheel hub it is suggested that the wheel hub is screwed slightly in towards the rim and then turn the brake disc backwards and forwards whilst pulling.

Inspection:

1 Thoroughly inspect the brake disc for signs of overheating, hairline cracks or distortion. The maximum permissible runout measured at the circumference of the disc is .00394 inch.

2 Should the contact faces be badly scored the disc may be refaced by turning on a centre lathe and skimming the areas affected provided that the thickness of the disc does not fall below the limits given in Technical Data.

Refitting:

Refitting is the reverse procedure to dismantling but the following points should be noted:

1 Tighten the Allen head screws holding the brake disc to the hub assembly to a torque wrench setting of 43.4 lb ft.

2 Refit the brake disc and hub assembly to the stub axle as detailed in **Chapter 8, Section 8:4.**

10:8 Rear brakes

Dismantling:

1 Remove the wheel trim and slacken the wheel nuts. Lift up the rear end of the car and support on firmly based stands. Remove the wheel nuts and lift away the road wheel.

2 Remove the brake drum and carefully ease two brake shoes from the anchor points at the bottom of the backplate assembly.

3 Carefully pull out the brake shoes from their locations in the wheel cylinder. Ease the handbrake Bowden cable from the brake lever and separate the brake shoes by detaching the return springs from the shoe webs having first made a note of the spring location. Do not press the brake pedal while the shoes are away from the backplate. It is considered a good idea to put wire or rubber bands around the wheel cylinder pistons to prevent accidental ejection and if the car is to be left without the brake shoes fitted for a while a notice should be hung on the steering wheel to warn against the pressing of the pedal, otherwise the wheel cylinders will have to be checked and parts refitted.

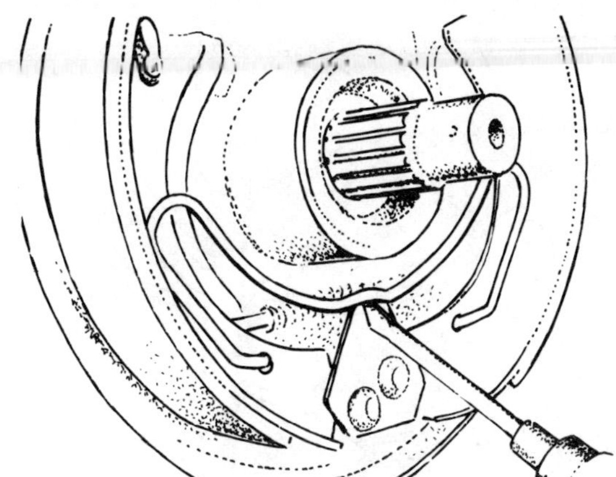

FIG 10:16 Rear brake shoe spring removal

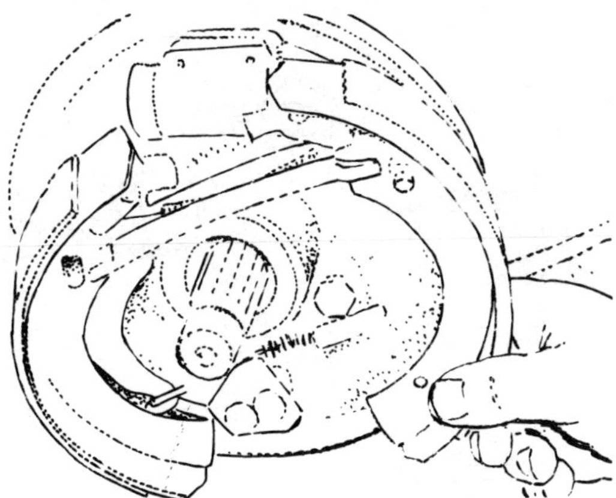

FIG 10:17 Brake shoe removal

Relining rear brake shoes:

If the linings are worn down to the rivets, renewal is necessary. It is not recommended that owners should reline brake shoes themselves. It is important that linings should be perfectly bedded down on the shoes and then ground to perfect concentricity with the brake drums. For this reason, it is best to obtain sets of replacement shoes already lined. The correct lining material is given in Technical Data. Do not fit odd shoes and do not mix materials or unbalanced braking will occur.

Do not allow grease or paint to contact the friction lining. If the original linings are contaminated with oil or grease do not attempt to clean them with solvents as nothing useful can be done.

Refitting brake shoes:

This is the reverse procedure to dismantling. Ensure that the pull-off springs are correctly fitted to the holes in the webs and that the shoes register correctly in the slotted ends of the pistons and adjusters. Before trying to

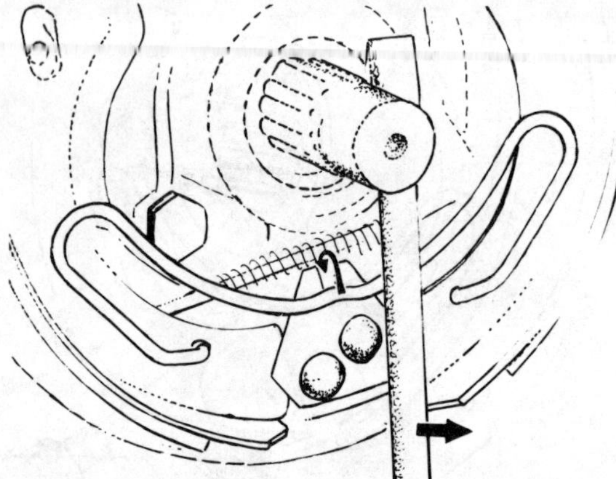

FIG 10:18 Rear brake shoe spring refitting

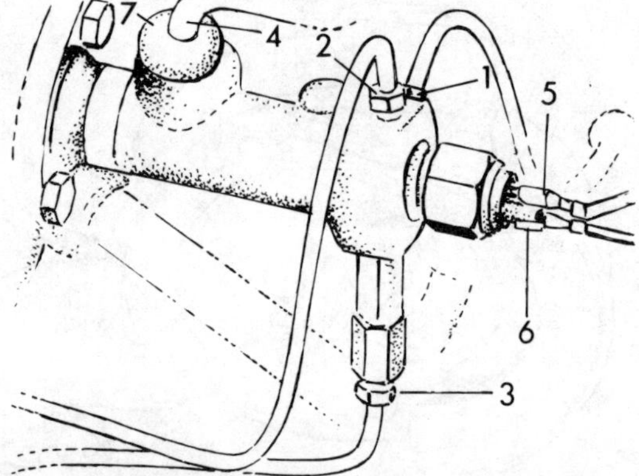

FIG 10:19 Supply line connection

fit the drum, slacken off the brake adjuster completely. Also fully release the handbrake. Readjust the shoes when assembly is completed. This will also set the handbrake correctly.

Brake shoe adjustment:

1 Ensure that the handbrake is in the fully off position.
2 Turn the eccentric adjustment screw, lefthand brake unit anticlockwise, righthand brake unit clockwise, whilst turning the road wheel until the wheel locks. Slacken the adjustment screw about one eighth of a turn until the wheel is just free to rotate. This should also adjust the handbrake.

Rear wheel brake shoe removal and replacement 1600-2/1600TI

The procedure for removing the brake shoes is slightly different to that for the basic 1600 model and this should be carried out as follows:

1 Slacken the brake shoe adjustment by rotating the lefthand cam clockwise and the righthand cam anticlockwise.
2 Remove the wheel trim and extract the cotter locking the castellated nut and slacken the nut retaining the drum to the splined shaft.
3 Lift up the rear end of the car and support on firmly based stands. Completely remove the castellated nut and lift away the road wheel together with the brake drum and drive flange.
4 Refer to **FIG 10;16** and release the brake shoe spring using a screwdriver as shown in the diagram.
5 Carefully compress the brake shoes at the bottom of brake unit and withdraw the shoes from their locations on the wheel cylinder. Carefully release the pushrod and handbrake cable as shown in **FIG 10:17.**
6 Reassembly is the reverse procedure to dismantling. Care should be taken to correctly insert the brake shoe spring, once assembled to the brake shoes as shown in **FIG 10:18.** The castellated nut should be tightened to a torque wrench setting of 217+36 lb ft.
7 Finally adjust the brake shoe clearance by rotating the lefthand cam in an anticlockwise direction and the righthand cam in a clockwise direction whilst the road wheel is being rotated. Once the wheel locks the cam should be very carefully slackened off until the road wheel just runs freely.

10:9 Bleeding the brakes

This is not routine maintenance and is only necessary if air has entered the hydraulic system because parts have been dismantled and because the fluid level in the master cylinder supply reservoir has dropped so low that air has been drawn in through the hole in the cylinder bore mentioned in **Section 10:12.**

1 Fill the master cylinder supply reservoir with the correct grade of hydraulic fluid. During bleeding operations fluid will be used and constant topping up of the supply reservoir will be needed. If this is not done it is possible for air to enter the master cylinder, which will nullify the operation and necessitate a further start.
2 Attach a length of rubber or plastic tube to the bleeder screw in a rear wheel cylinder, or to the screw on the caliper in the case of front brakes. Immerse the free end of the tube in a small volume of the correct grade hydraulic fluid in a clean glass jar.
3 Open the bleed screw one turn and with the assistance of a second operator press down slowly on the brake pedal. After a full stroke let the pedal return without

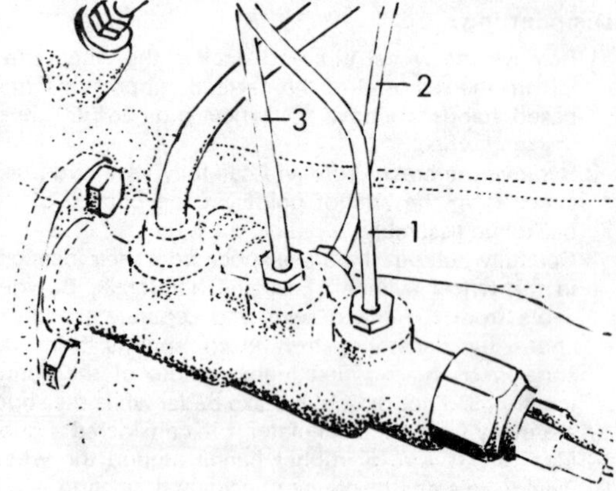

FIG 10:20 Master cylinder connections

assistance, pause for a moment and repeat the down stroke. At first there will be air bubbles issuing from the bleed tube, but when fluid alone is ejected, hold the pedal firmly down on the floorboards and tighten the bleeder screw. Repeat this on both rear brakes and then do both the front. Where a four piston caliper is fitted as used with the twin circuit brake system it is necessary that the two top pistons should be bled at the top on the outside of the caliper and the lower pistons should be bled from the bottom otherwise difficulty will be experienced in eliminating all the air from the hydraulic system.

4 On completion, top up the fluid in the supply reservoir to the correct level. Discard all dirty fluid. If the fluid is perfectly clean, let it stand for twenty four hours to become clear of air bubbles before using again.

10:10 Brake master cylinder removal—1600

Removal:

1 Remove the two battery terminals, slacken the battery mounting clamp and carefully lift away and put in a safe place ready for refitting.
2 Using a small suction pump or syphon tube carefully draw off the brake fluid from the hydraulic fluid reservoir so that upon removal there is no chance of hydraulic fluid coming into contact with the paintwork.
3 Refer to **FIG 10:19** and disconnect the hydraulic fluid supply line 4 from the sealing plug 7. It is recommended that the sealing plug is sealed to prevent any dirt ingress.
4 Disconnect the hydraulic brake line pipes at the master cylinder shown in locations 1, 2 and 3 in **FIG 10:19.**
5 Carefully ease off the stoplight switch electrical connections 5 and 6.
6 Using a pair of engineers pliers carefully remove the brake pedal pivot bolt locking plate and lift away the bolt.
7 Remove the master cylinder to bulkhead retaining screws and carefully lift away the master cylinder forwards ensuring that no hydraulic fluid comes into contact with any paintwork.
8 Carefully wash the exterior of the master cylinder using methylated spirits or other non-caustic solvent and carefully dry using a compressed air jet.

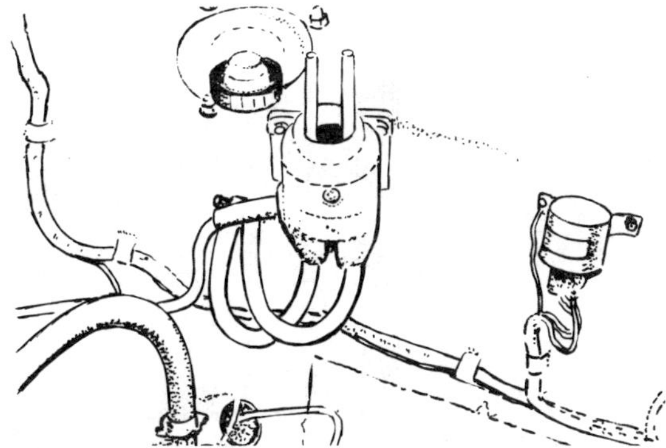

FIG 10:21 Master cylinder fluid reservoir feed pipe plugged

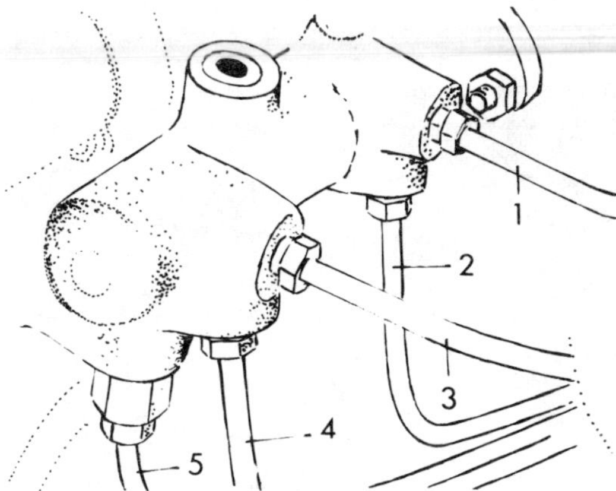

FIG 10:22 Master hydraulic pipe connections

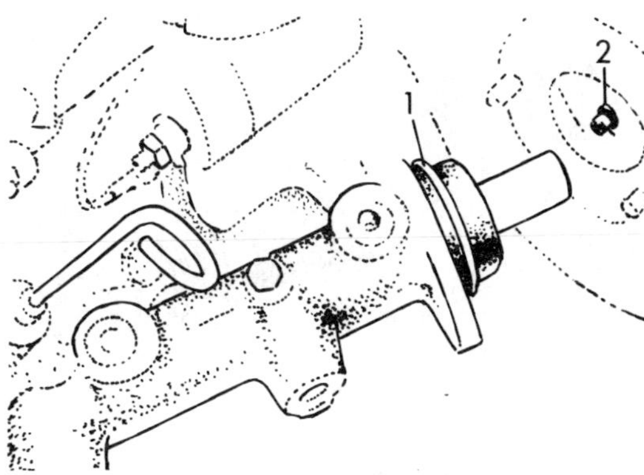

FIG 10:23 Master cylinder seating ring and pushrod shim

Refitting

Refitting the master cylinder is the reverse procedure to dismantling but the following points should be noted:

1 The correct play between the piston rod and piston should be .0197 inch.
2 Once the master cylinder has been refitted the system must be bled as detailed in **Section 10:9.**

10:11 Brake master cylinder removal (tandem)

Removal:

1 Refer to **FIG 10:21** and plug the hoses with two tapered pieces of wood approximately .24 inch in diameter. Carefully withdraw the hoses from the tandem master cylinder and fold upwards as shown in the diagram.
2 Carefully release the brake lines in the following order referring to **FIG 10:22** for the correct sequence.
Second brake circuit:
1 Lefthand front.
2 Righthand front.
First brake circuit:
3 Lefthand front.
4 Righthand front.
5 Rear wheel brake.

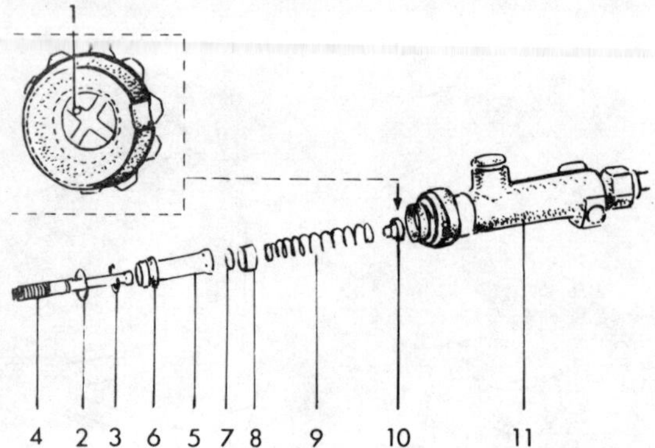

FIG 10:24 Master cylinder components

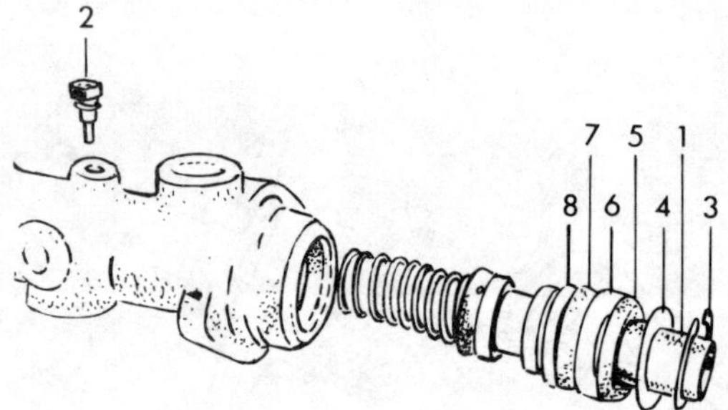

FIG 10:25 Master cylinder front piston assembly

3 Release the two master cylinder to servo retaining bolt nuts and carefully withdraw the master cylinder.
4 Clean the master cylinder with methylated spirits or other non-caustic solvent and dry using a compressed air jet.

Refitting:

1 Inspect the rubber sealing ring on the face of the master cylinder to ensure that it is not damaged and fit a new ring as necessary. This is shown in **FIG 10:23.**
2 If a new tandem master cylinder is fitted check the clearance between the master cylinder piston and the pushrod with Plastigage and if necessary adjust to .002 inch by means of shims 2 (see **FIG 10:23**), placed behind the mushroom-shaped head.
3 Reassembly of the various brake lines is the reverse procedure to dismantling. The braking system should be bled as detailed in **Section 10:9.**

10:12 Brake master cylinder overhaul

Single circuit brake system master cylinder:

1 Refer to **FIG 10:24** and remove the snap ring 2 using a pair of circlip pliers.
2 Lift away the disc 3, piston rod 4, piston 5 together with the secondary sleeve 6, spacer disc 7, primary sleeve 8, pressure spring 9 and special bottom valve 1 from the master cylinder body 11.
3 Thoroughly clean all parts removed in correct grade hydraulic brake fluid and dry using compressed air. Inspect all parts for scoring, signs of seizure, rust spots or other kinds of superficial damage. If any part is suspect it must be renewed. Always renew the rubber parts when overhauling the master cylinder. Should polishing of the master cylinder be necessary use special lapping cloth wrapped around a piece of wooden rod. Turn the rod at approximately 1000 rev/min for a few seconds and then inspect. It should be noted that the compensation bore must be completely open and there must be no signs of bared edges.
4 To ensure that no damage to the sealing rubbers is caused upon reassembly it is recommended that the special grease be used that is normally supplied with the master cylinder overhaul kit.
5 Refitting the various parts is the reverse procedure to dismantling. Care must be taken that the special bottom valve shown in the inset to **FIG 10:24** is thoroughly clean otherwise if the throttle bore becomes blocked it will cause overheating of the disc brake and caliper. The correct clearance between the piston rod and the piston upon reassembly should be .0197 inch.

Tandem master cylinder:

1 Refer to **FIG 10:25** and exert a slight pressure on the piston 1 which will enable the stop bolt 2 to be unscrewed.
2 Remove the circlip 3 and extract the piston 1.
3 Carefully pull off the stop washer 4, secondary sleeve 5, spacer ring 6, secondary sleeve 7 and stop ring 8.

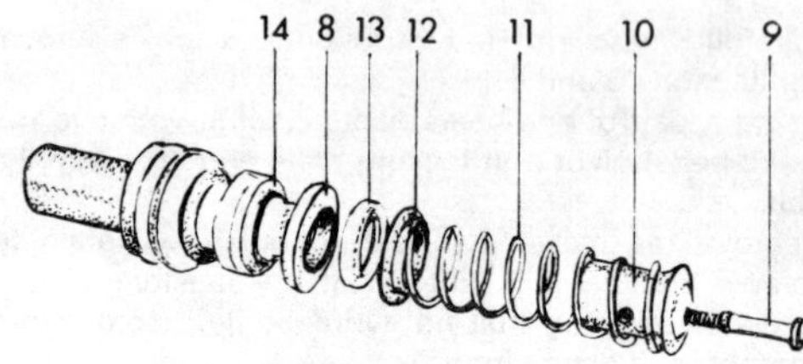

FIG 10:26 Master cylinder rear piston assembly

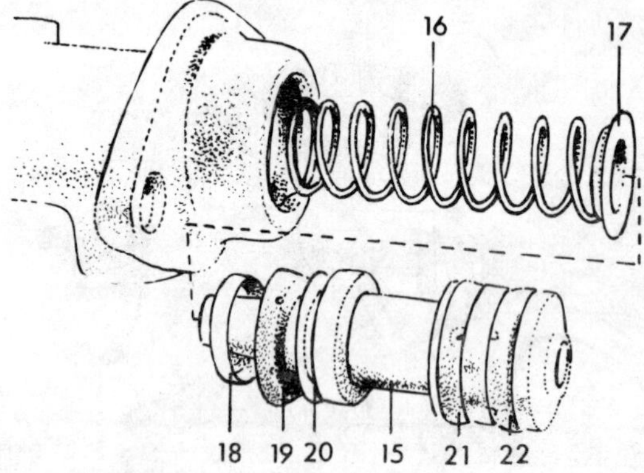

FIG 10:27 Rear piston sealing rubbers

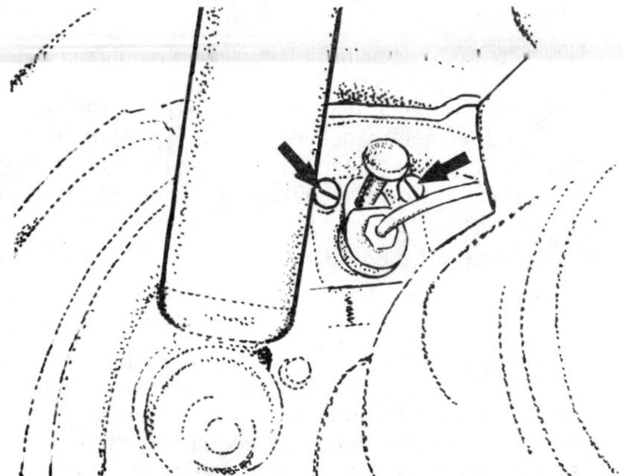

FIG 10:28 Wheel cylinder retaining screws

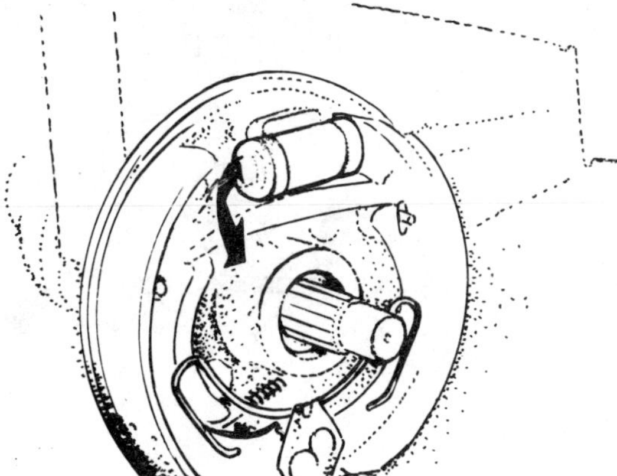

FIG 10:29 Wheel cylinder removal

4 To dismantle the primary sleeve 8 from the assembly, unscrew the special bolt 9 as shown in **FIG 10:26.** Remove the spring cap 10, spring 11, spring cup 12, pressure cup 13 and packing washer 14.

5 Using a compressed air jet, carefully push out the piston assembly 15 from the tandem master cylinder body. Refer to **FIG 10:27** and carefully withdraw spring 16, spring cup 17, pressure cup 18, primary sleeve 19 and packing washer 20. Also remove the secondary sleeve 21 and primary sleeve 22 from the piston.

6 Thoroughly clean all parts removed in the correct grade of hydraulic fluid and dry using compressed air. Inspect all parts for scoring, signs of seizure, rust spots or other signs of superficial damage. If any part is suspect it must be renewed. Always renew the rubber parts when overhauling the master cylinder. Should polishing of the master cylinder be necessary use special lapping cloth wrapped round a piece of wooden rod. Turn the rod at approximately 1000 rev/min for a few seconds and then inspect. It should be noted that all the drillings must be completely open and there must be no signs of sharp edges.

7 Reassembly of the parts is the reverse procedure to dismantling and it is recommended that **FIGS 10:25 10:26** and **10:27** be carefully inspected to ensure that the correct sequence is obtained. It is recommended that the piston shank be smeared with silicone grease and also that the copper sealing ring under the stop bolt head 2 is renewed to ensure no hydraulic fluid leaks occur.

10:13 Wheel cylinders

Removal, 1600:

1 Remove the wheel trim and slacken the wheel nuts. Lift the rear of the car and support on firmly based stands. Remove the wheel nuts and lift away the road wheel.

2 Remove the brake drum and detach the brake hoses at the bottom. These should be suitably plugged to ensure that total loss of the hydraulic fluid does not occur due to syphoning action.

3 Move the brake shoes fully outwards by means of the adjustment screws. Remove the wheel cylinder retaining screws and press together both wheel cylinder pistons. Move the wheel cylinder to the right as far as it will travel, tilt forwards and carefully pull it out.

Removal 1600-2/1600TI:

1 Remove the road wheel, brake dum and drive flange as previously described in **Section 10:8.**

2 Release the brake hydraulic line, bleed screw and two bolts located as shown by the dark arrows in **FIG 10:28** from the back of the wheel cylinder.

3 Refer to **FIG 10:29** and carefully push the wheel cylinder to the right and pull out forwards as shown by the dark arrow.

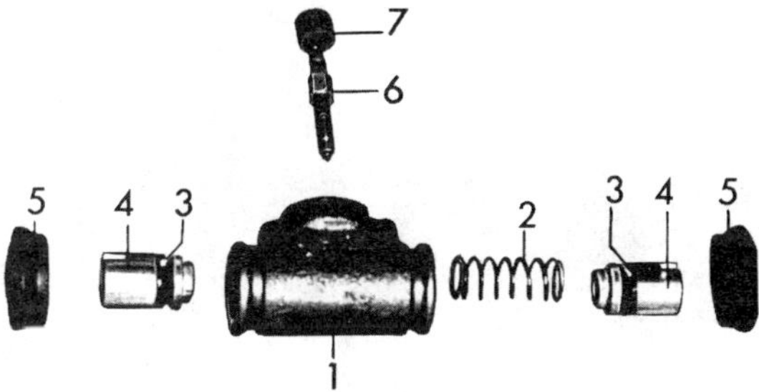

FIG 10:30 Wheel cylinder component parts

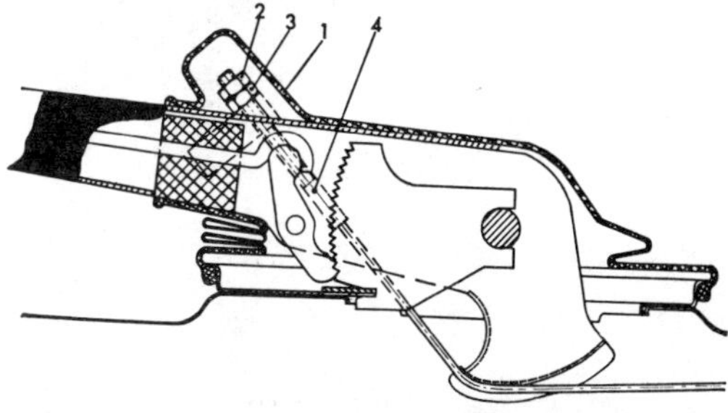

FIG 10:31 Handbrake lever assembly

Overhaul:

1 Refer to **FIG 10:30** and remove the protection cap 5, piston assemblies 4, spring 2, and bleeder valve 6 with dust cap 7.

2 Clean all the internal parts with correct grade hydraulic fluid. If any other solvents, such as petrol have been used to clean the metal parts every trace must be dried off before reassembly.

3 Renew the rubber seals at every overhaul, or if there is any sign of leakage. Inspect the piston and cylinder bore and renew parts which are worn or pitted with corrosion.

4 Fit the new seals using fingers only. Assemble all internal parts after wetting with correct grade hydraulic fluid. Refit the cylinder to the backplate in the reverse order of dismantling. Upon completion the brake shoes must be adjusted as detailed in **Section 10:8**, after the system has been bled according to the instructions in **Section 10:9**.

10:14 Removing a flexible hose

Never try to release a flexible hose by turning the ends with a spanner. The correct procedure is as follows:

Unscrew the metal pipe line union nut from its connection and remove the locknut which secures the hose to the bracket. The hose can now be turned without twisting the flexible part by using a spanner on the hexagon at the other end.

10:15 Handbrake cable

Removal:

1 Remove the wheel trims and slacken the wheel nuts of the two rear wheels. Lift the rear of the car and support on firmly based stands. Remove the wheel nuts and lift away the road wheel.

2 Remove the brake drum and referring to **FIG 10:31** slide off the rubber cap 1 from the handbrake lever. Remove the locknut 2 and adjustment nut 3 from the handbrake cable 4.

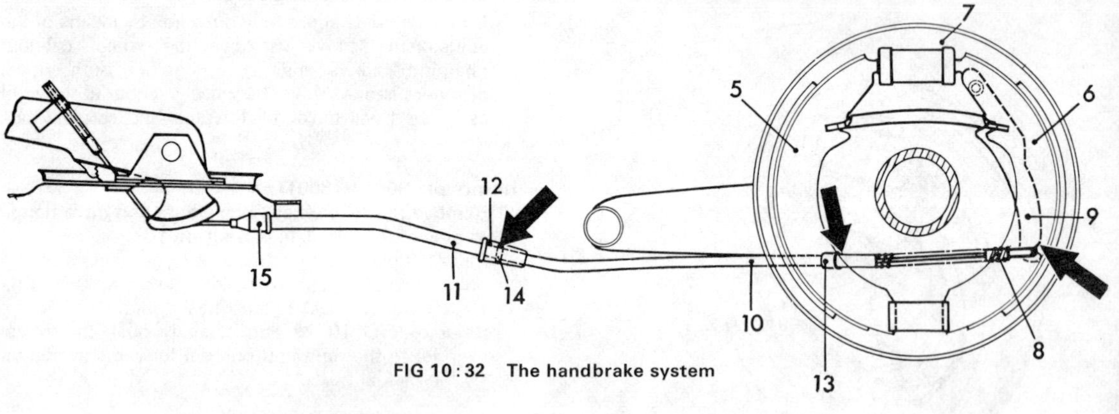

FIG 10:32 The handbrake system

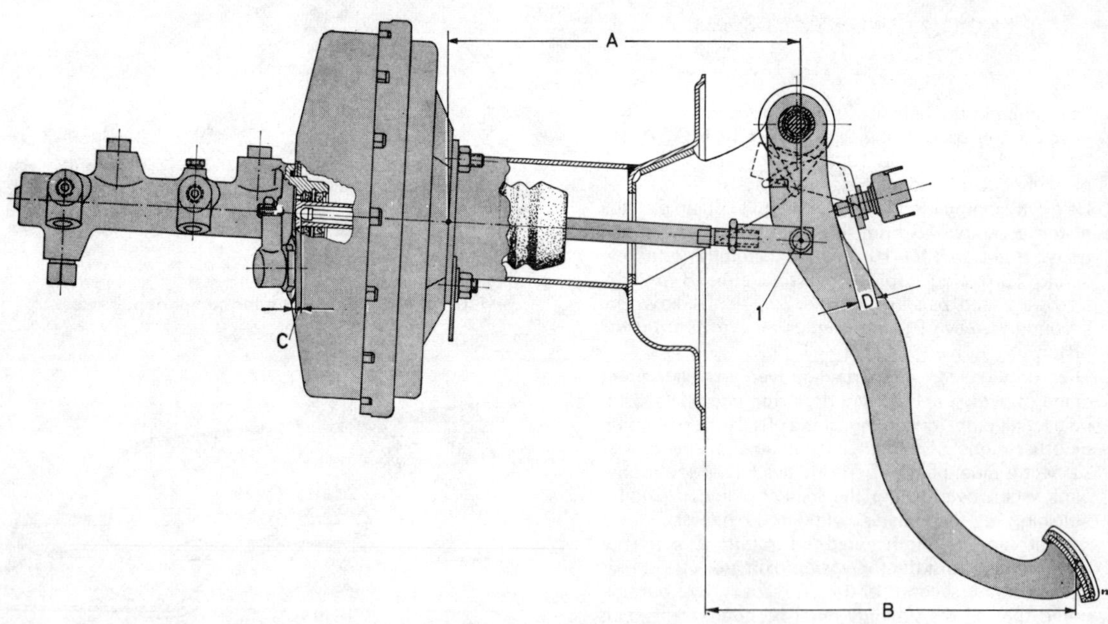

FIG 10:33 Brake servo unit and pedal assembly

3 Remove the brake shoes 5 and 6 (see **FIG 10:32**), from the brake carrier 7. Release the handbrake cable 8 from the brake lever 9. Slacken the fastening clip at the longitudinal swinging suspension arm and carefully pull out the handbrake cable 10 from the pipe 11 together with the rubber grommet 12.

Refitting:

Refitting is the reverse procedure to dismantling but the following points should be noted:

1 The collar of the handbrake cable 13 (see **FIG 10:32**), must lay correctly within the brake carrier 7 and collar 14 must align correctly with the pipe end 11. Ensure that the two rubber grommets 12 and 15 are correctly fitted.

2 To adjust the handbrake cable after refitting, first adjust the brake shoes as detailed in **Section 10:8.** Adjust the handbrake cable at the handbrake lever making sure that the brakes are equally tight on the fifth tooth of the toothed ratchet.

10:16 Brake servo-unit removal—1600TI

Removal:

1 Remove the union bolt from the end of the servo-unit. Release the brake line connection to the master cylinder and plug the pipe to ensure that no fluid is lost due to syphoning action.

2 Disconnect the vacuum hose and release the bolts from the rear bracket.

3 Unscrew the front bracket support nut and carefully lift the servo-unit away towards the rear.

Refitting:

Refitting is the reverse procedure to dismantling but the following points should be noted:

1 Tighten the servo mounting bracket retaining nut to a torque wrench setting of 11.6 + 2.9 lb ft.

2 Tighten the rear bracket mounting bolts to a torque wrench setting of 13.8+3.65 lb ft.

3 Tighten the union nut to a torque wrench setting of 9.5 to 11.6 lb ft.

4 Bleed the hydraulic system as detailed in **Section 10:9.**

10:17 Brake servo-unit removal, twin circuit system

Removal:

1 Remove the pushrod to brake pedal pivot pin.

2 Disconnect the vacuum hose and all pipe connections from the tandem master cylinder in the order shown in **FIG 10:22.** Plug the hydraulic fluid reservoir pipes to ensure that fluid does not syphon out.

3 Release the brake servo unit to mounting retaining nuts and carefully lift the unit away towards the front.

Refitting:

Refitting is the reverse procedure to removal but the following adjustments must be made:

1 Refer to **FIG 10:33** and adjust the piston rod so that distance **A**=8.091 inch.

2 Adjust brake pedal position by ensuring that dimension **B**=8.661 inch.

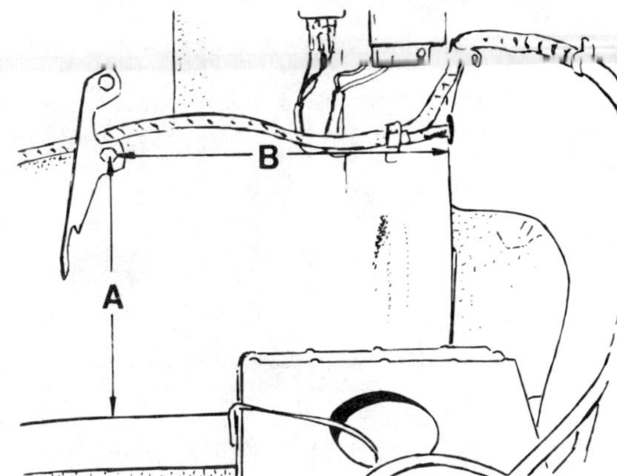

FIG 10:34 Rear bracket hole location

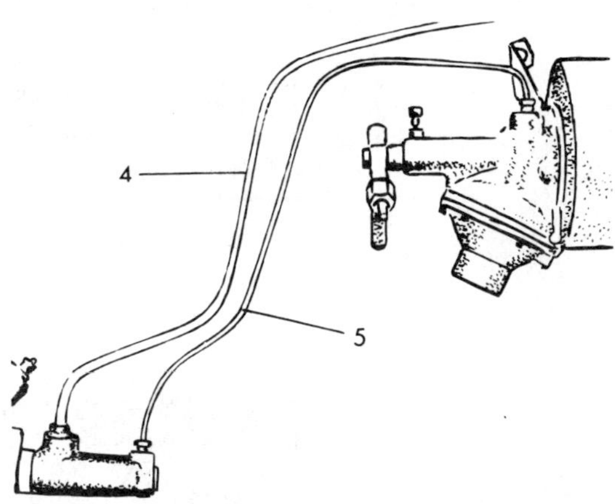

FIG 10:35 Master cylinder pipe connections

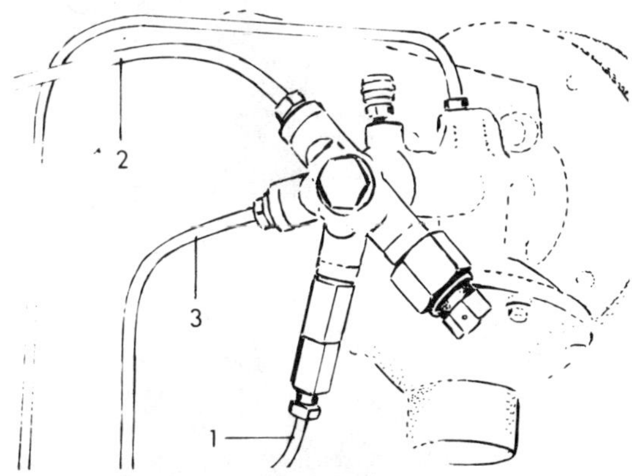

FIG 10:36 Annular union brake line connections

3 Ensure that the clearance between the pushrod and piston **C**=.002 inch.

4 Adjust the stoplight switch so that **D**=.275+.040 inch.

5 Bleed the hydraulic system as detailed in **Section 10:9.**

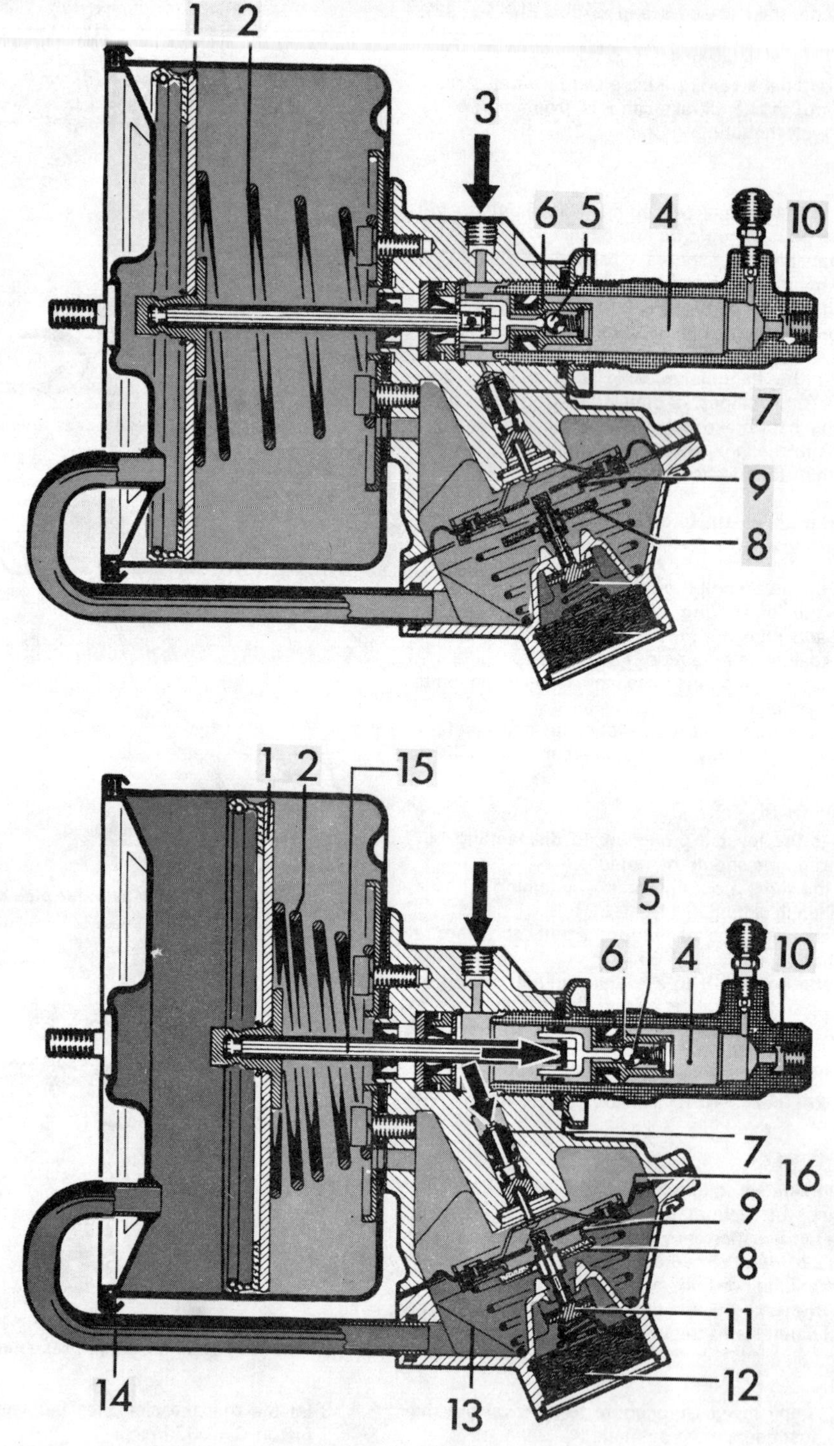

FIG 10 : 37 Brake servo unit type T50

10:18 Brake servo-unit fitting—1600-2

A brake servo-unit kit is available for subsequent fitting to BMW 1600-2 models. Full fitting instructions are supplied with the kit but the following summary will act as an additional guide.

1 Refer to **FIG 10:34** and mark the lower location hole using dimension **A**=3+.179 inch and dimension **B**= 12.2+.118 inch. Using the rear bracket as a guide, mark the upper hole location and drill the two holes. Mount the rear bracket and tighten the retaining bolts to a torque wrench setting of 11.6+2.9 lb ft.

2 Mount the front bracket to the brake servo-unit but do not tighten the retaining bolts fully. Attach the brake servo-unit to the rear mounting bracket.

3 Using the front mounting bracket as a guide, mark and drill a hole .331 inch diameter in the wheel arch panel. Tighten the mounting bracket retaining bolt to a torque wrench setting of 11.6+2.9 lb ft.

4 Refer to **Section 10:11** and remove the master cylinder. Fit the new master cylinder and connect the steel line 4 (see **FIG 10:35**) to the compensation reservoir. Fit the brake line 5 and tighten the union nuts to a torque wrench setting of 9.5 to 11.6 lb ft.

5 Bend the brake lines carefully and connect to annular union in the order shown in **FIG 10:36** where;

1 Rear wheel brake.
2 Disc brake lefthand.
3 Disc brake righthand.

Tighten the union nuts to a torque wrench setting of 9.5 to 11.6 lb ft.

6 Secure the non-return valve to the vacuum pipe. It may be necessary to cut a new thread in the induction manifold to the same size as the thread on the non-return valve.

7 Connect the vacuum hose and finally bleed the hydraulic system as described in **Section 10:9.** Road test the vehicle to ensure correct operation and then thoroughly inspect all connections for hydraulic fluid leaks.

10:19 Brake servo-unit operation and maintenance

1600TI application:

Description:

The piston 1 (see **FIG 10:37**) is retained under the pressure of spring 2 located on the lefthand side of the vacuum cylinder. In this position the brake fluid may pass through the bore 3, helper master cylinder space 4 and the open ball check valve 5 in the helper master cylinder piston 6, and so through to the wheel cylinders. The control piston 7 is in its top end position whilst the control valve 8 is unseated from the valve seat 9 which is connected to the diaphragm.

When the brake pedal is depressed the accummulating pressure in the pedal master cylinder is transmitted via the ball check valve 5, helper master cylinder space 4 and connection passage 10 to the wheel cylinder. At the same time the control piston 7 and the diaphragm 16 are depressed downwards whereby the valve seat 9 tightens the control valve 8. The exterior ball valve 11 which is connected to the control valve is opened when moved further downwards. Outside air is drawn in through the filter 12 and guided into the lower chamber 13 of the valve case thereafter through the guide tube 14 into the lefthand chamber of the vacuum cylinder in the rear of the piston 1, where the vacuum is reduced. The pressure difference between both sides of the piston 1 causes the piston to move to the right together with the helper master cylinder pison 6 which is connected to the pressure rod 15. This movement will overcome the action of the spring 2 and so pressure now accumulating in the helper master cylinder is transmitted to the wheel cylinder. Upon further operation of the brake pedal the increase in pressure in the master cylinder which will also be acting on the control piston 7 keeps the outside air valve 11 open. The force obtained from the pressure difference moves the piston 1 so overcoming the return spring 2. At the same time the pressure rod 15 moves the helper master cylinder 6 connected to the right end position. The brake servo-unit will be operating giving maximum assistance. When the brake pedal is released, the hydraulic control pressure will be reduced and so the outside air valve 11 is shut causing the control valve 8 to open. The pressure will be equalized and the servo-unit will be ready for further operation.

Operational check:

1 With the engine switched off, operate the brake pedal 8 to 10 times and thereafter hold the brake pedal in the fully depressed position.

2 Start the engine and it should be noted that as soon as the brake unit supports the braking efficiency the brake pedal should move further towards the floor although the pressure that is being exerted by the foot should remain constant.

3 If the above check indicates that the system is not working correctly it is recommended that as the brake servo-unit is a non-repairable component and cannot be supplied on a unit for unit exchange basis, a new servo-unit be fitted.

Servicing:

It is important that for correct operation the air filter 12 (see **FIG 10:37**) is kept thoroughly clean. Remove the circlip and lift away the little filter element which may be cleaned and refitted.

1600-2 and twin circuit application

Description:

When the brake pedal is depressed the piston 1 (see **FIG 10:38**) in the master cylinder is moved forward. Pressure that is applied to the hydraulic fluid is transmitted throughout all the pipelines so that the brake shoes are applied to the brake discs 4 and the brake drums 5 by the pistons 2. When the brake pedal is released, the return springs will move the brake shoes back to their rest positions. The disc brakes are automatically returned by pressure release through the special bottom valve 7 in the connection with the pre-loaded sealing rings 8. The pre-pressure valve 6 is designed to maintain a pressure reserve of approximately 11.6 lb/sq inch for the drum brakes.

Full compensation in the master cylinder is effected by the compensating bore 9, which is situated in front of the primary sleeve 10 and providing a connection between the compensating reservoir 12 and the pressure

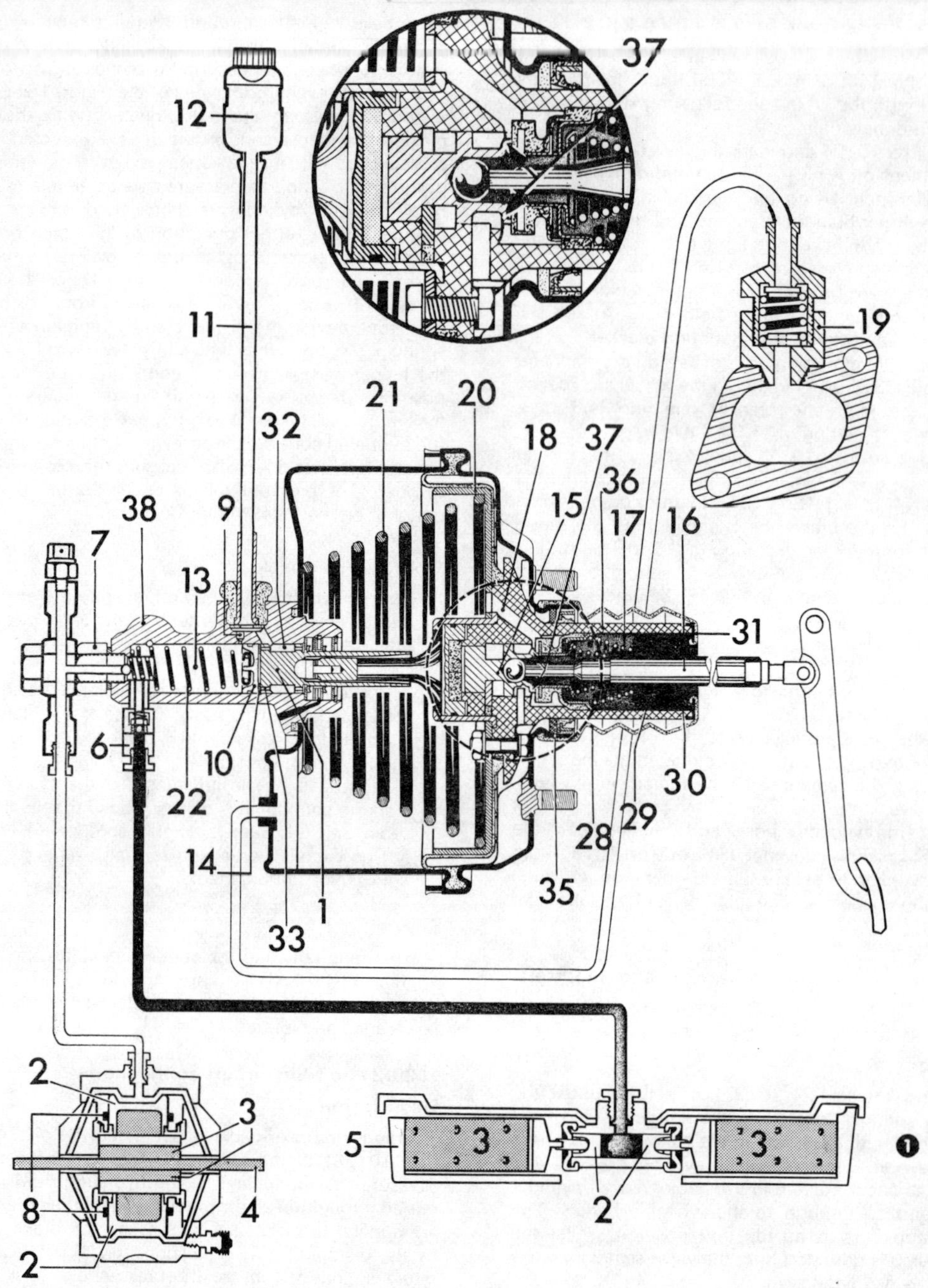

FIG 10:38 The brake servo unit type T51 and hydraulic system

chamber of the cylinder 13. To avoid the possible ingress of air into the hydraulic system because of the pressure drop when the brake pedal is released, a fluid space 32 is arranged in the rear of the primary sleeve 10 at the circumference of the piston 1 so allowing the brake fluid to flow into the brake line via the special filling bore 33 and filling valve 14.

Servicing:

The brake servo-unit is a non-repairable component and cannot be supplied on a unit for unit exchange basis. Only the vacuum check valve, the protective cap 28, the filter 29 and silencer 30 may be exchanged. If the protective cap 28 is renewed it is essential that the filter 29 and silencer 30 are renewed at the same time. To perform this operation proceed as follows:

1 Carefully pull off the protective cap 28 from the neck of the vacuum cylinder 35 and disconnect from the silencer holder.
2 Lift the silencer holder 31 away from the control casing 36 using a screwdriver.
3 Remove the silencer 30 and filter 29 from the control casing 36.
4 Upon reassembly fit the plastic foam strip 29 over the piston rod 16 and then insert the felt silencer 30 into the control casing 36. After fitting the silencer holder 31 fit the protective cap 28 and connect to silencer holder and ensure that it is well over the neck of the vacuum cylinder.
5 For hydraulic brake servo-units equipped with a vacuum check valve, press the vacuum check valve against the bottom of the vacuum cylinder on removing. Then turn to the left using a spanner to disengage from the bayonet catch. Upon reassembly of a new vacuum check valve together with its sealing ring, coat both parts with a multi-purpose grease.
6 If a new brake servo-unit has been fitted it is important that the piston rod is correctly adjusted details of which are given in **Section 10:17.**

10:20 Fault diagnosis

(a) Spongy pedal

1 Leak in the system
2 Worn master cylinder
3 Leaking wheel cylinders
4 Air in the fluid system
5 Gaps between rear shoes and underside of linings

(b) Excessive pedal movement

1 Check 1 and 4 in (a)
2 Excessive lining wear

(c) Brakes grab or pull to one side

1 Distorted discs or drums
2 Wet or oily pads or linings
3 Rear brakes backplate loose
4 Disc loose on hub
5 Worn suspension or steering connections
6 Mixed linings of different grades
7 Uneven tyre pressures
8 Broken shoe return springs
9 Seized handbrake cable
10 Seized piston in wheel cylinder
11 Loose caliper fixings

NOTES

CHAPTER 11

THE ELECTRICAL SYSTEM

11 :1 Description
11 :2 The battery
11 :3 The generator
11 :4 The starter
11 :5 The regulator
11 :6 The headlamps
11 :7 Windscreen wiper motor
11 :8 Fuel tank sender unit
11 :9 Electrically heated rear screen
11 :10 Lighting circuits
11 :11 The alternator
11 :12 Electronic tuning system
11 :13 Fault diagnosis

11 :1 Description

BMW 1600 models covered by this manual were fitted with a six volt system but from chassis number 1533868 they were changed to a twelve volt system and fitted with an alternator. In either case the negative terminal of the battery was earthed. To enable many of the electrical diagnosis procedures to be completed accurate moving coil meters are necessary. Cheap and unreliable instruments will make accurate adjustments virtually impossible.

There are wiring diagrams in Technical Data at the end of this manual to enable those with electrical experience to trace and rectify wiring faults.

For the UK market the headlamps are of the double filament, separate bulb and reflector type, with adjustments for beam settings.

The electrical system is protected by four eight amp fuses and two 25 amp fuses all located in one fuse box. The battery is situated on the lefthand side of the engine compartment.

Detailed instructions are given for servicing the electrical equipment but it must be emphasized that in many cases it is not worthwhile to try to repair equipment which is seriously defective, mechanically or electrically. Such items should be replaced by new units which can be easily obtained.

11 :2 The battery

This is of the lead/acid type and has to meet heavy demands for current particularly in the winter. To maintain the performance of the battery at its maximum, it is essential to carry out the following operations.

The top of the battery and the surrounding parts must be kept dry and clean. Clean off the corrosion from the metal parts of the battery mounting with diluted ammonia and paint them with anti-sulphuric paint. If the terminal posts are corroded, remove the cables and clean with diluted ammonia. Smear the posts with petroleum jelly before making the connections and fit the terminal clamps securely. High electrical resistance due to corrosion at the terminal posts is often responsible for lack of sufficient current to operate the starter motor.

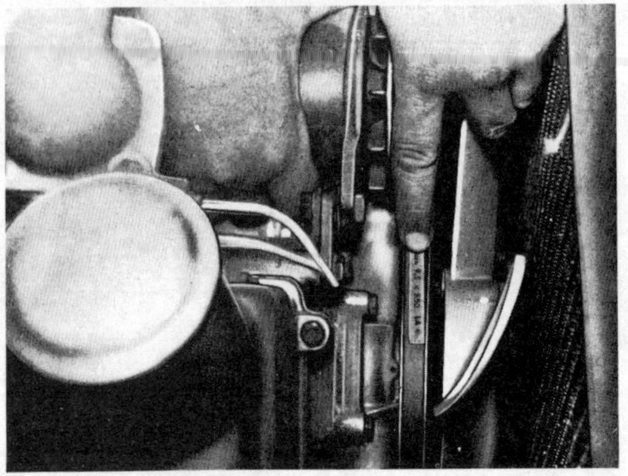

FIG 11:1 Fan belt adjustment

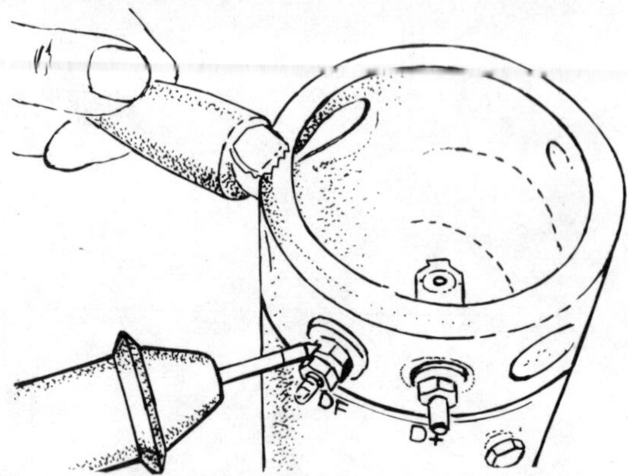

FIG 11:4 Field coil test 1

FIG 11:2 Brush removal

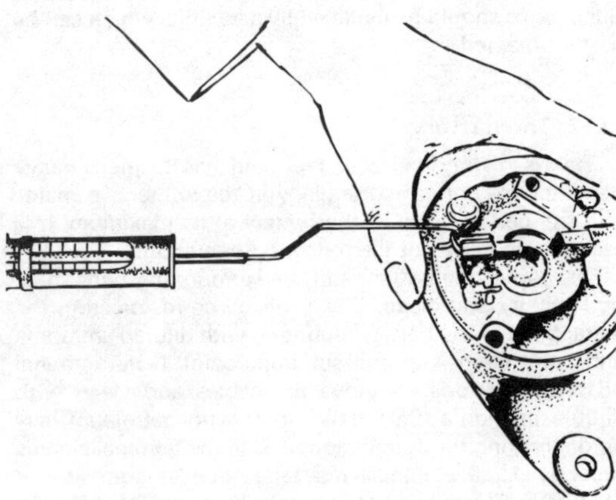

FIG 11:3 Brush spring tension test

During battery operation distilled water must be periodically added so that the separators do not emerge from the electrolyte. Never add neat acid. If it is necessary to make new electrolyte due to loss by spillage, add sulphuric acid to distilled water. It is highly dangerous to add water to acid. The final level of the electrolyte should be approximately .25 inch above the top of the plates.

To test the condition of the cells use an hydrometer to check the specific gravity of the electrolyte and this reading is proportional to the state of charge as shown below:

For climates below 27°C or 80°F:

Cell fully charged	Specific gravity 1.270 to 1.210
Cell half charged	Specific gravity 1.190 to 1.210
Cell discharged	Specific gravity 1.110 to 1.130

For climates above 27°C or 80°F:

Cell fully charged	Specific gravity 1.210 to 1.230
Cell half charged	Specific gravity 1.130 to 1.150
Cell discharged	Specific gravity 1.050 to 1.070

These figures are given assuming an electrolyte temperature of 16°C or 60°F. If the temperature of the electrolyte exceeds this add .002 to the readings for each 3°C or 5°F rise. Subtract .002 if it drops below 16°C or 60°F.

All cells should read approximately the same. If one differs radically from the rest it may be due to an internal fault or to spillage or leakage of the electrolyte.

If the battery is in a low state of charge take the car for a long daylight run or put it on charge at 4 amps until it gases freely. When putting a battery on charge, take out all the vent plugs and refrain from using a naked light when it is gasing.

If the battery is to stand unused for long periods give a freshening up charge every month. It will be ruined if left unused.

12:3 The generator

Removal and refitting (6 volt system):

1 Disconnect the negative cable from the battery and wipe away any corrosion on the terminals and clamps so that no accidental damage occurs to the paintwork.

2 Disconnect the three cables from the generator making

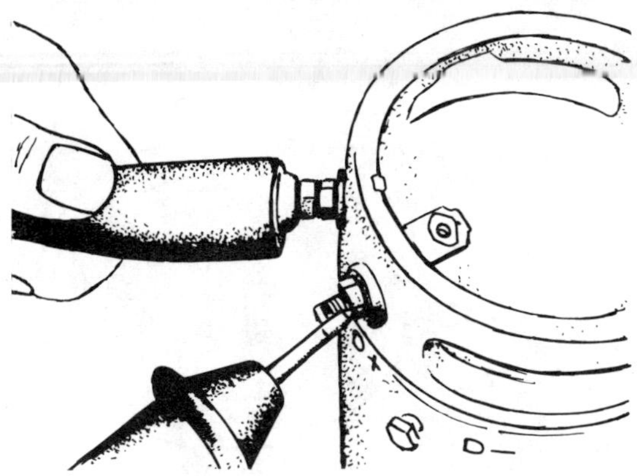

FIG 11:5 Field coil test 2

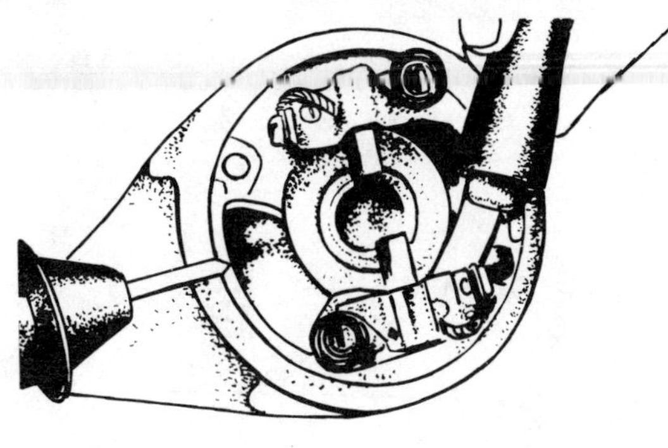

FIG 11:6 Brush insulation test 1

a note that D (black cable), DF (black/red cable), M (brown cable), are the correct connections.

3 Slacken the generator mounting bolts and push the generator downwards so slackening the fan belt tension. Lift the fan belt away from the generator pulley and finally remove the three mounting bolts. Carefully lift away the generator.

4 Refitting is the reverse procedure to dismantling. The fan belt when fitted must be correctly tensioned and it should be possible to press in the fan belt between .19 to .39 inch on the run between the water pump and generator pulleys (see **FIG 11:1**).

Dismantling the generator:

To dismantle the generator once it has been removed from the engine proceed as follows:

1 Lock the pulley by holding the fan belt in the V-groove and remove the pulley retaining nut.

2 Using a universal two-legged puller or by holding the generator in the hand and striking the shaft stub lightly with a soft-faced hammer remove the pulley. Lift away the spring washer from the shaft.

3 Remove the carbon brushes protective cover by removing the retaining bolt. Using an electricians screwdriver ease back the carbon brush retaining springs and slide the carbon brushes from their holders (see **FIG 11:2**).

4 Release the two through-bolts and withdraw from body. Lift off commutator end head. Tap off the driving end head which will bring with it the armature. Unless the bearing is faulty in the driving end head it need not be removed. To remove the armature from the end head use a suitable hand press.

Servicing brushes:

Refit each brush to its holder and ensure that the brush moves easily. If the movement is sluggish remove the brush and polish the sides with a fine file. Be sure to mark it before removal so that it will be replaced in its original working position.

Test the brush springs with a spring tension scale as shown in **FIG 11:3**. New springs have a tension of 2 lbs.

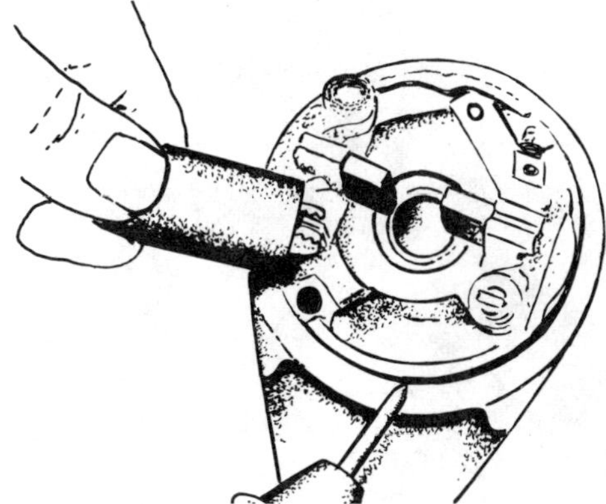

FIG 11:7 Brush insulation test 2

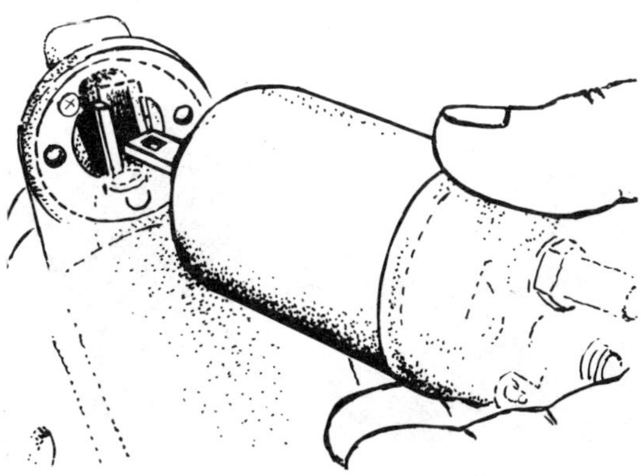

FIG 11:8 Solenoid removal

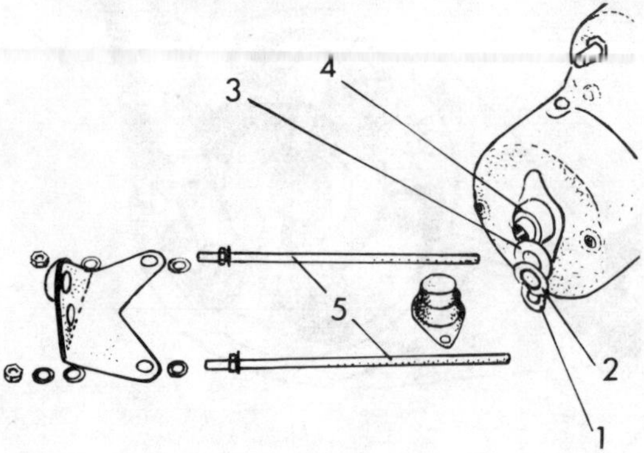

FIG 11:9 Starter motor rear end components

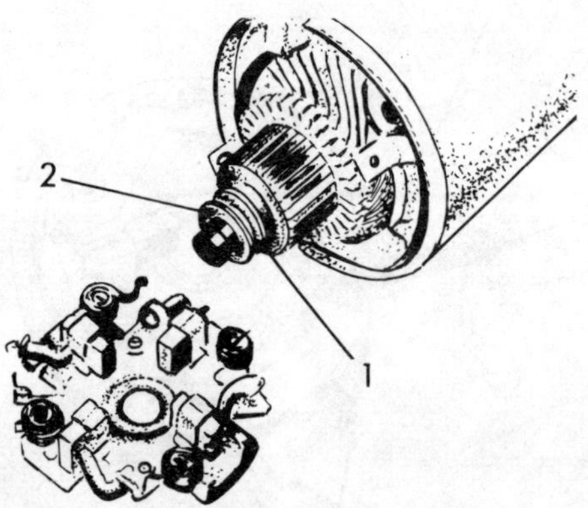

FIG 11:10 The brush gear

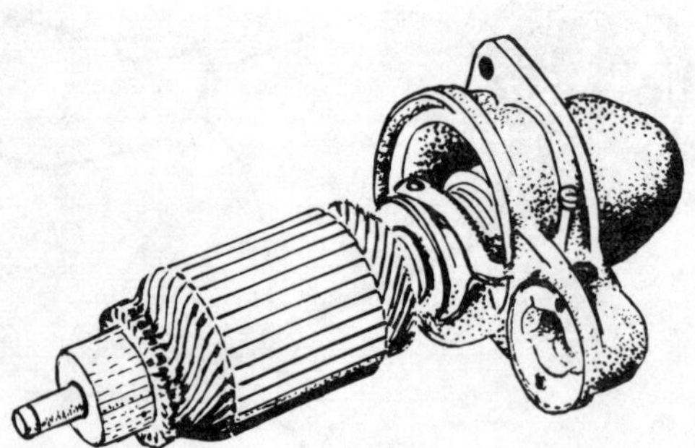

FIG 11:11 Armature and pinion assembly

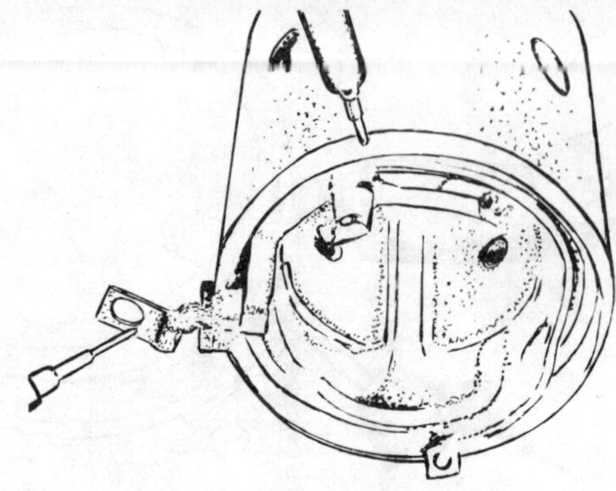

FIG 11:12 Field coil insulation test

Bed in new BMW brushes by wrapping sandpaper round the commutator pressing down on the brush and rotating the commutator under it, or draw the paper to and fro. Be sure to remove all traces of dust before finally reassembling.

Servicing the commutator:

A commutator in good condition should be smooth and free from pitting or burnt segments. Use a non-fluffy rag to clean the commutator and if necessary polish with fine glasspaper whilst the armature is rotating. Do not use emerycloth. If the commutator is badly worn it may be skimmed on a lathe. Use a high speed, ensure that the lathe tool is sharp and take a light cut. Remove only enough metal to clean up the surface and finally polish with fine glasspaper. To undercut the insulation between the segments, grind a hacksaw blade on the sides until it is the thickness of the insulation and carefully work between each pair of segments, until the insulation has been cut to a depth of .04 inch throughout its length and width.

Generally inspect the armature as it may show the cause of a failure. Breaks in the armature windings cause burnt commutator segments. Shortcircuited windings are discoloured by overheating, with badly burnt commutator segments.

The armature:

Besides reconditioning the commutator there is very little else that can be done to the armature itself. Never try to straighten a bent shaft and never machine the armature core. Any further testing requires equipment which a normal car owner would not possess, therefore if the armature is suspect the only check that he can do is to substitute an armature of known reliability.

Field coils test:

Using a test lamp connected to a battery and two wander leads connect one wander lead to terminal DF and the other terminal to earth. The test light must not light up. If the lamp does light this means that there is a shortcircuit between the field coils and earth (see **FIG 11:4**).

FIG 11:13 The pinion assembly

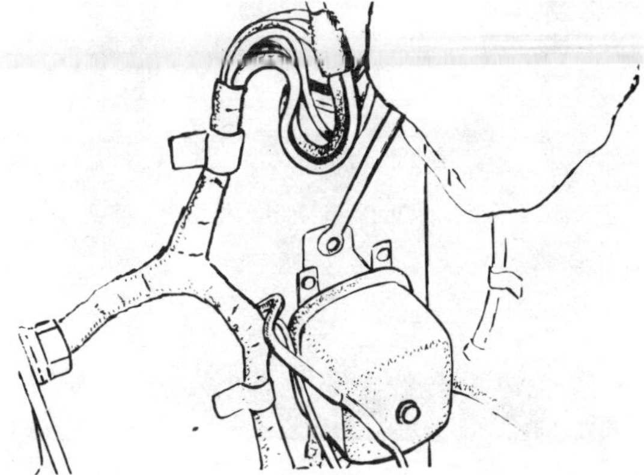

FIG 11:14 Regulator mounting bracket

To ensure that current is able to pass through the field coils put one lead on terminal DF and the other lead to terminal D+ or the coil end. This time the test lamp must light up. Should the test lamp not light up this indicates a break in the field coil circuit (see **FIG 11:5**).

Carbon brush holder insulation test:

Using a test lamp and six volt battery together with two wander leads, place one lead on the positive brush holder and the other lead to earth (see **FIG 11:6**). The test lamp must not light up. Should the test lamp light up, this indicates a failure in insulation between the carbon brush holder and the generator end plate. Remove the wander lead from the positive brush holder and connect it to the negative brush holder and repeat the test (see **FIG 11:7**). This time the test lamp must light up. Should the test lamp not light up this indicates that a good electrical connection is not being maintained between the brush holder and the generator end plate.

Reassembling and refitting the generator:

To reassemble the generator is the reverse procedure to dismantling. To assemble the commutator end head to the yoke, partially withdraw the brushes and trap them in this position by letting the springs bear on the sides of the brushes. Lubricate the two bearings using engine oil and fit the commutator end head to the armature shaft and when it is approximately half an inch from the yoke face, lift the springs with a thin screwdriver and this will allow the brushes to drop into place on the commutator. Ensure the springs now bear correctly on the tops of the brushes and push the end covers fully home. Ensure that they are correctly located to the main generator body and insert the two through-bolts, ensuring that the two end plates are still correctly located and tighten the bolts securely.

Generator output test:

Test 1—off load voltage:

1 Remove the connection 51 from the voltage regulator and connect the positive lead of an accurate moving coil voltmeter which is able to measure up to 15 volts.

FIG 11:15 Front grille retaining screw locations

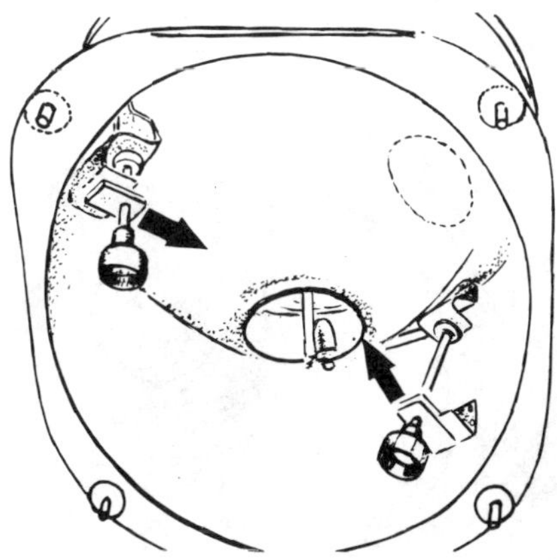

FIG 11:16 Headlamp reflector removal

FIG 11:17 Headlamp retaining bracket

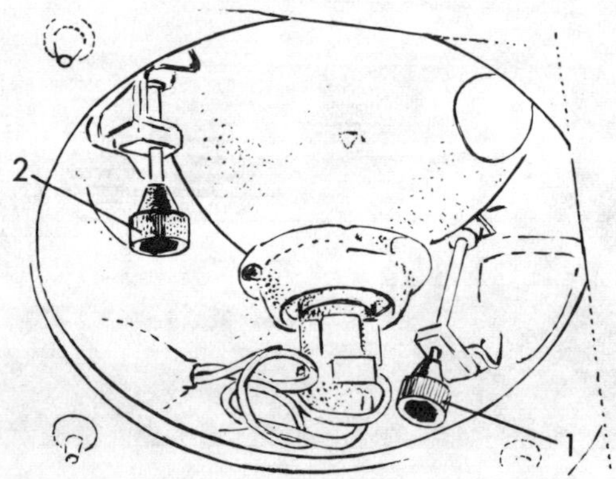

FIG 11:18 Beam setting adjustment screws

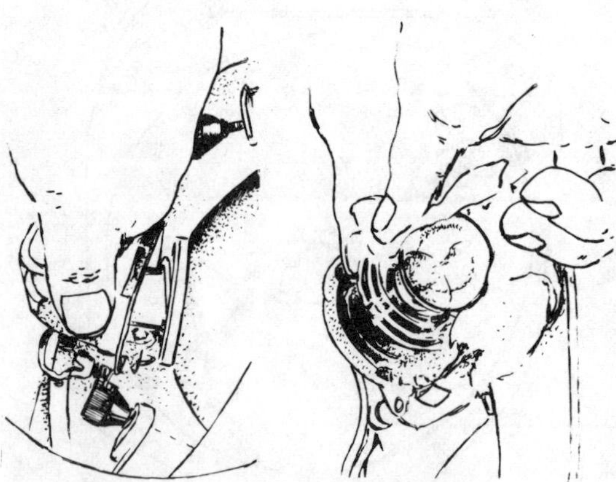

FIG 11:19 Headlamp bulb removal

Connect the negative lead of the voltmeter to the generator mounting bracket.

2 Start the engine and allow to run at a fast idle speed. The voltmeter should indicate a value of between 6.9 and 7.5 volts.

Test 2—Check under load:

With the generator working under load by the insertion of a suitably sized resistance into the circuit together with an ammeter the maximum current should be approximately 50 amps.

11:4 The starter

Test for starter which does not operate:

Check the condition of the battery and particularly the connection to the terminals and earth. If the battery is fully charged, switch on the headlights and operate the starter motor control. If the lights go dim but the starter does not turn, it shows that current is reaching the starter motor. If the lamps do not dim, check the starter switch. At the same time check all the connections and cables from the battery to the switch and starter motor. If the starter still does not operate, remove it from the engine.

Removal:

1 Remove the negative terminal from the battery, also the plug connection and main supply cable to the starter motor switch.
2 Remove the starter motor from the engine by removing the two retaining bolts.

Starter motor solenoid:

The solenoid should be removed once the starter motor has been removed from the engine. Unscrew the cable to the field coil of the solenoid and unscrew the solenoid from its mounting. Lift upwards so disconnecting the engagement arm and draw the solenoid backwards (see **FIG 11:8**). Reassembly is the reverse procedure to dismantling.

Renewing carbon brushes:

1 Refer to **FIG 11:9** and remove the support bracket and dust cap.
2 Detach the lockwasher 1, shim 2 and seal 3. Unscrew the polehousing bolts 5. Gently ease away the end cover.
3 To renew the brushes unsolder them one at a time. Secure each new brush in place taking care not to let the solder run along the flexible lead. The brushes are preformed so that they do not need bedding in to the curvature of the commutator.
4 On reassembly ensure that the axial play of the armature does not exceed .0039 to .0059 inch and should be shimmed as necessary, **FIG 11:10** shows the location of shims 1 and 2. At the same time ensure that the commutator bearing 4 (see **FIG 11:9**) is in a servicable condition.

The armature:

1 To remove the armature first remove the solenoid as previously described in this section.
2 Lift out the positive brushes and detach the brush holder plate.

3 Part the pole housing from the drive bearing and unscrew the pivot bolt on the engagement arm. Extract the armature with the engagement arm (see **FIG 11:11**).

4 Examine the armature shaft for straightness. Accidental engagement whilst the engine is running may bend the armature shaft. Do not try to straighten a bent shaft or machine the armature core to obtain clearance.

The starter may run at very high speeds if it is engaged while the engine is running and this may cause the copper wire to lift from the commutator. This could be a reason for failure. Besides reconditioning the commutator there is very little else that can be done to the armature itself. Any further testing requires equipment which a normal car owner would not possess, therefore if the armature is suspect the only check that he can do is to substitute an armature of known reliability.

Field coils test:

Using a test lamp connected to a battery and two wander leads connect one wander lead to the terminal and the other to earth (see **FIG 11:12**). The test light must not light up. If the lamp does light this means that there is a shortcircuit between the field coils and earth.

To test for continuity of the windings within the field coils use a test lamp and battery connecting the leads so that the coil windings are in series. If the bulb does not light there is a break in the field coil windings.

The pinion drive:

Remove the armature as previously described and referring to **FIG 11:13** push back the thrust ring and lift out the small circlip. Carefully ease forward the starter pinion assembly. Check for worn, cracked or broken springs. If the screwed sleeve is worn, or damaged it is necessary to renew both the sleeve and the pinion assembly. After cleaning, assemble the drive, smearing a slight trace of silicone grease on the thread and engagement ring. This will ensure smooth operation.

11:5 The regulator

Removal:

1 Disconnect the negative cable from the battery terminal and also the connections at the top of the regulator. Note that the red cable goes to the B+ terminal and the blue cable goes to terminal 61.

2 Remove the retaining bolts from the regulator to body bracket and ease away from the bulkhead (see **FIG 11:14**).

3 Release the cables at the bottom of the regulator noting that the brown cable is earthed and the black/red cable is connected to terminal DF.

4 Refitting is the reverse procedure to dismantling.

Regulator test:

To quickly check the operation of the regulator whilst it is mounted in the car an accurate moving coil ammeter should be connected in line with the charging relay and the battery. Disconnect terminal 51 and connect the negative ammeter lead. Connect the positive ammeter lead to the red cable at terminal 51. With the engine running the ammeter must indicate a charge. Conversely

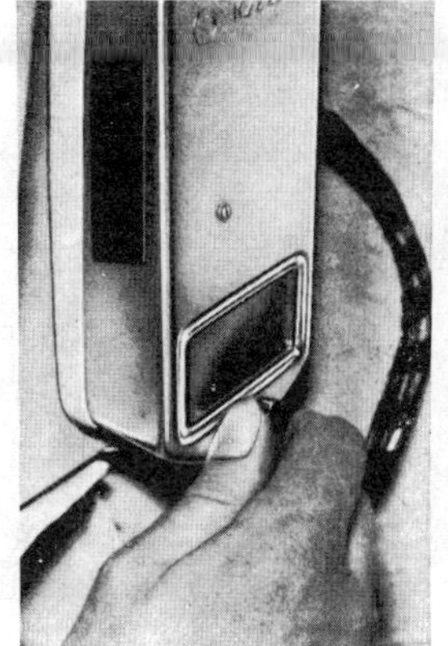
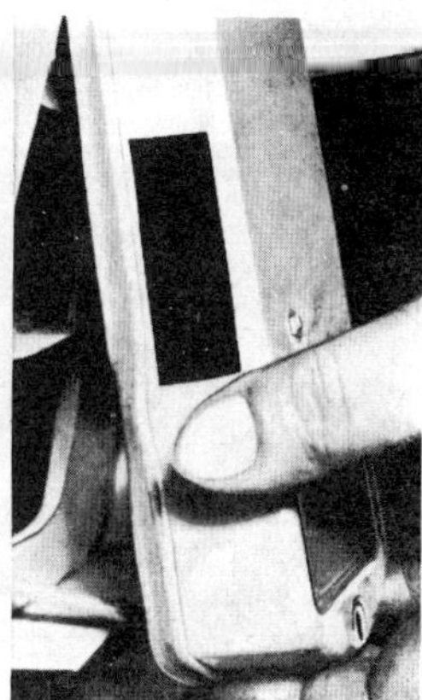

FIG 11:20 Rear light cluster removal

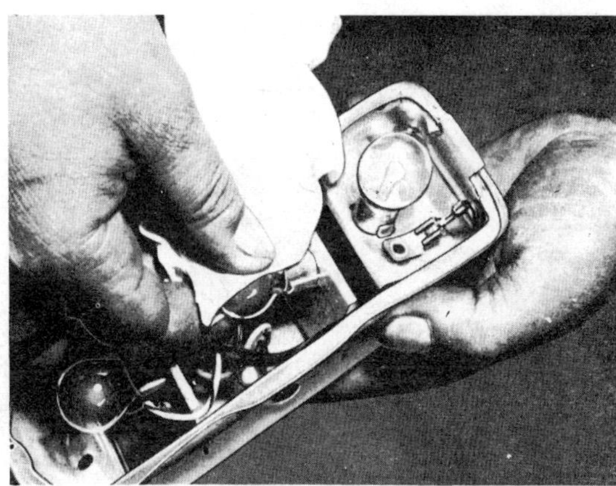

FIG 11:21 Cluster bulb removal

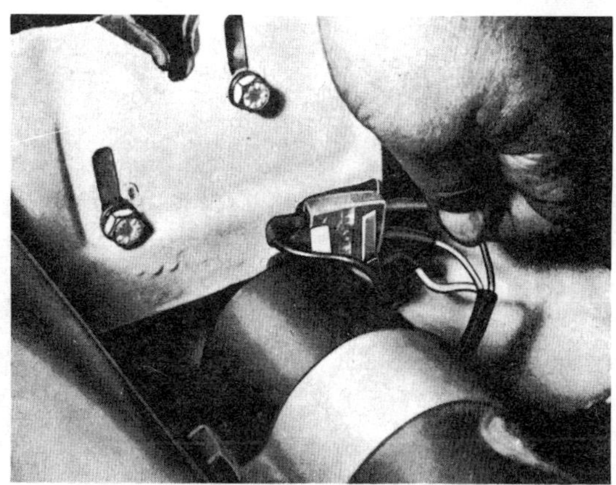

FIG 11:22 Screen wiper cable removal

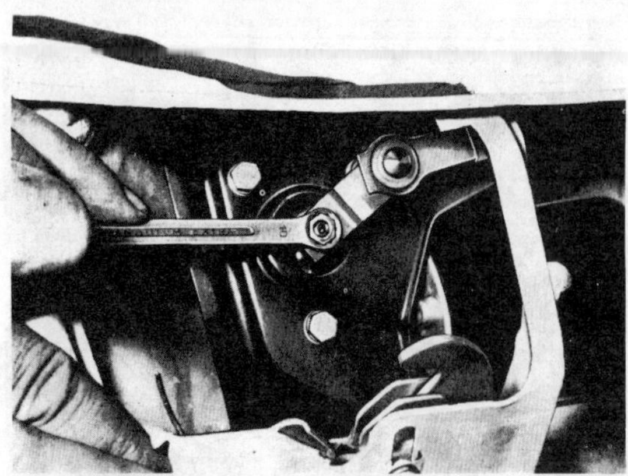

FIG 11:23 Screen wiper linkage connection

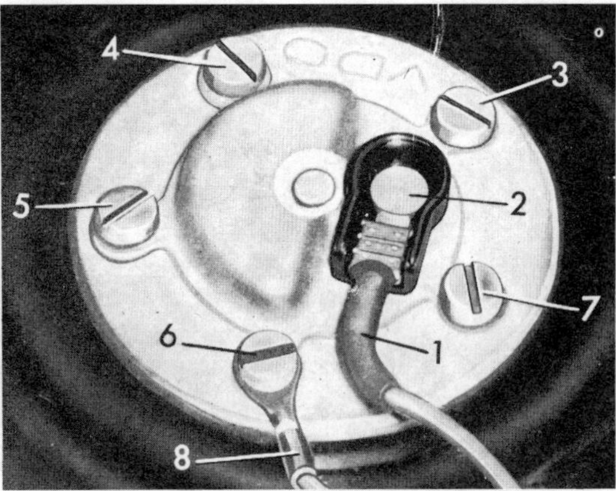

FIG 11:24 Tank sender unit type 1

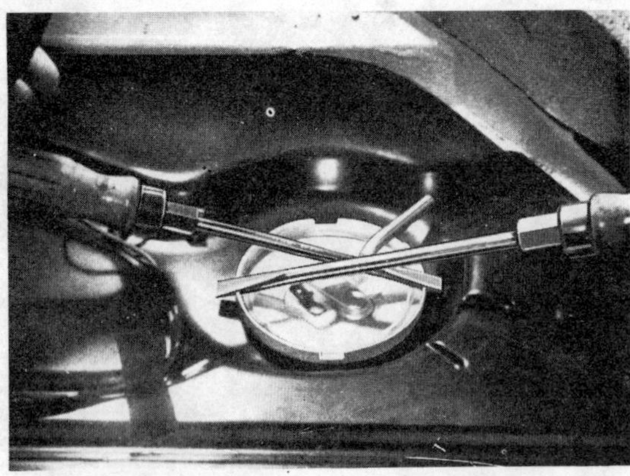

FIG 11:25 Tank sender unit removal type 2

when the engine is stationary the ammeter needle must not fall below zero.

Should this quick test prove negative then it is recommended that the regulator be renewed.

11:6 The headlamps

Lens replacement:

1 Remove the radiator grille by releasing the retaining screws as shown by the arrows in **FIG 11:15**.
2 Using a small wide blade screwdriver gently ease the lens forwards away from its circular mounting.
3 Upon refitting smear the lens to housing contact area with glycerine to ensure a weatherproof joint.

Reflector:

To remove the reflector proceed as follows:

1 Remove the radiator grille, the mounting points being shown in **FIG 11:15**.
2 Remove the terminal cover cap and bulb.
3 Carefully unscrew the headlamp housing and remove.
4 If the Hella reflector is fitted, push out the two setting screws together with the guides. Gently push the reflector together with its rubber mounting out of the housing (see **FIG 11:16**).
5 If the Bosch reflector is fitted unscrew the bearing bracket from the housing. Push out the threaded plate from the rubber mounting and lift the reflector together with the rubber mounting out of the housing (see **FIG 11:17**).
6 In both cases the reflector setting should be carried out with the vehicle in its normal position suitably loaded with 2 x 143 lb weights on the back seat and 143 lbs on the front seat and 67 lbs in the boot compartment and the fuel tank full of petrol. Refer to **FIG 11:18** whereby screw 1 is for the lateral adjustment and screw 2 is for the vertical adjustment.

Headlamp bulb renewal:

1 Remove the headlamp cover cap using a screwdriver.
2 Turn the bulb holders slightly to the left and lift away from the back of the headlight reflector.
3 Using a clean cloth or piece of paper so that the fingers do not touch the glass, turn the bulb towards the left and remove as shown in **FIG 11:19**.
4 Reassembly is the reverse procedure to dismantling. Take care that the three cover cap retaining lugs fully engage.

Rear light bulb renewal:

1 Release the milled nut on the bulb holder and pull the bulb holder off at the bottom and push upwards from the mounting as shown in **FIG 11:20**.
2 Use a piece of clean cloth or piece of paper between the fingers and the glass of the bulb and release the bulb from the holder by turning to the left and lifting away as shown in **FIG 11:21**.
3 Refitting is the reverse procedure to dismantling.

11:7 Windscreen wiper motor

To remove the windscreen wiper motor proceed as follows:

1 Open the engine bonnet and protect the wing panels with covers.

2 Separate the cable connections at the windscreen wiper motor as shown in **FIG 11 : 22**, making a note that the sequence of the cables from top to bottom are, black (top), green (middle), yellow (bottom).
3 Refer to **FIG 11 : 23** and remove the fastening nuts for the crank guide.
4 Remove the windscreen wiper motor attaching bolts and carefully manipulate the wiper motor from the attachment bracket into the free space towards the heater, thereafter moving it downwards.
5 Refitting is the reverse procedure to dismantling. Ensure that the windscreen wiper is in the parked position before attempting to refit the drive crank.

FIG 11 : 26 Alternator cable disconnection

11 : 8 Fuel tank sender unit

Type 1—removal and refitting:

1 Refer to **FIG 11 : 24** and remove the rear floor panel.
2 Detach the positive lead 1 from the socket 2.
3 Release the clamp screws 3 to 7 together with the earth lead 8. Carefully lift out the immersed tube indicator and cover the hole with a clean metal plate to ensure that no dirt finds its way into the fuel tank.
4 Refitting is the reverse procedure to dismantling.

Type 2—removal and refitting:

1 Remove the rear floor panel.
2 Detach the fuel hose and cables making a note that the cable coloured blue/yellow is the positive lead, whilst the brown cable is the earthing lead.
3 Using two crossed screwdrivers as shown in **FIG 11 : 25**, carefully unscrew the sender unit in an anti-clockwise direction.
4 Cover the hole with a metal plate to stop any dirt finding its way into the fuel tank.
5 Refitting is the reverse procedure to dismantling. Always fit a new seal to ensure that there is no possibility of a fuel or vapour leak into the boot compartment.

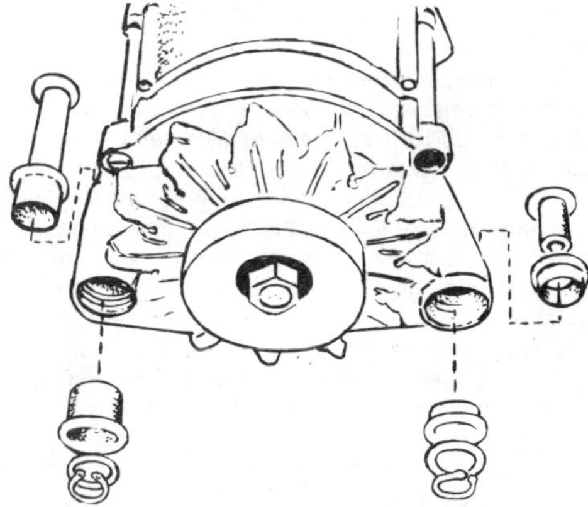

FIG 11 : 27 Alternator mounting bushes

Testing:

The most effective way of testing the fuel gauge sender unit is by substituting with one of known reliability.

11 : 9 Electrically heated rear screen

Full removal and fitting details are given in **Chapter 12, Section 12 : 7**. The circuit is shown in **FIG 13 : 4**.

11 : 10 Lighting circuits

Lamps give insufficient light:

Test the state of charge of the battery and recharge it if necessary from an independent supply. Check the setting of the lamps. If the bulbs have darkened through age fit new ones.

Bulbs burn out frequently

If this is accompanied by a need for frequent topping up of the battery and high hydrometer readings, check the charging rate with an ammeter when the car is running. Any reading in excess of the normal charging indicates that adjustment of the regulator is required.

FIG 11 : 28 Fan belt tension with alternator fitted

Lamps light when switched on but gradually fade:

Check the battery as it is incapable of supplying current for any length of time.

Lamp brilliance varies with speed of car:

Check the condition of the battery. Examine the battery connections. Make sure they are tight and fit new cables should faulty cables be found.

11:11 The alternator

Description (12 volt system):

Due to the development of the generator over a period of time substantial reductions in size and weight for output ratings have been made. Unfortunately now their design has reached a stage whereby any further development to improve the normal low speed output and maximum rating would necessitate a large and far more complicated and heavier machine. Alternators can be designed to meet both requirements and yet at the same time be reduced in size and weight by comparison. Although the alternator is a somewhat different form of generator, it should be understood that from the point of the other items of the electrical equipment of the car nothing is changed.

An alternator as its name suggests produces alternating currents and this is converted to direct current before being connected to the car electrical system. It is in this respect that the alternator and the d.c. generator are similar. The current generated in the armature winding of the normal generator is also alternating in nature and has to be changed to direct current before it can be connected to the other electrical circuits. It is by this method of conversion, sometimes known as rectification is accomplished which differs.

To test or overhaul an alternator requires specialist knowledge and equipment so that it is recommended if the alternator performance is suspect the vehicle be taken along to the local automobile electricians who will have the necessary equipment to give a full diagnostic check.

Alternator removal:

1 Disconnect the negative lead from the battery terminal. Carefully ease off the flat pin plug from the back of the alternator (see **FIG 11:26**).

2 Unscrew the cable from the back of the alternator making a note that the brown cable is connected to earth and the red cable to B+ terminal.

3 Unscrew the retaining bolt at the tension plate and also at the mounting and carefully lift out the alternator.

4 Refer to **FIG 11:27** and check the mounting bushes for wear and fit new as necessary.

5 Upon refitting adjust the tension of the V-belt and by between .2 and .4 inch as shown in **FIG 11:28**.

11:12 Electronic tuning system

On late model cars, after 1970, provision is made for the connection of an external electronic engine tuning equipment. This consists of two multi-pin sockets, one located above the water pump and the other at the rear of the engine compartment.

11:13 Fault diagnosis

(a) Battery discharged

1 Terminals loose or dirty
2 Lighting circuit shorted
3 Generator not charging
4 Regulator or cut-out units not working properly
5 Battery internally defective

(b) Insufficient charging current

1 Loose or corroded battery terminals
2 Generator driving belt slipping

(c) Battery will not hold a charge

1 Low electrolyte level
2 Battery plates sulphated
3 Electrolyte leakage from cracked casing or top sealing compound
4 Plate separators ineffective

(d) Battery overcharged

1 Voltage regulator needs adjusting

(e) Generator output low or nil

1 Belt broken or slipping
2 Regulator unit out of adjustment
3 Worn bearings, loose polepieces
4 Commutator worn, burned or shorted
5 Armature shaft bent or worn
6 Insulation proud between commutator segments
7 Brushes sticking, springs weak or broken
8 Field coil wires shorted, broken or burned

(f) Starter motor lacks power or will not operate

1 Battery discharged, loose cable connections
2 Starter pinion jammed in mesh with flywheel gear
3 Starter switch faulty
4 Brushes worn or sticking, leads detached or shorting
5 Commutator dirty or worn
6 Starter shaft bent
7 Engine obnormally stiff

(g) Starter motor runs but does not turn engine

1 Pinion sticking on screwed sleeve
2 Broken teeth on pinion or flywheel gears

(h) Noisy starter pinion when engine is running

1 Restraining spring weak or broken

(j) Starter motor inoperative

1 Check 1 and 4 in (f)
2 Armature or field coils faulty

(k) Starter motor rough or noisy

1 Mounting bolts loose
2 Damaged pinion or flywheel gear teeth
3 Main pinion spring broken

(l) Lamps inoperative or erratic

1 Battery low, bulbs burned out
2 Faulty earthing of lamps or battery
3 Lighting switch faulty, loose or broken wiring connections

(m) Wiper motor sluggish, taking high current

1 Faulty armature
2 Bearings out of alignment
3 Commutator dirty or shortcircuited
4 Wheelbox spindle binding, linkage joints stiff

(n) Wiper motor operates but does not drive arm

1 Wheelbox gear and spindle worn
2 Linkage faulty

(o) Fuel gauge does not register with ignition switched 'ON'

1 No battery supply to gauge
2 Gauge casing not earthed
3 Cable between gauge and tank unit broken or disconnected

(p) Fuel gauge registers 'Full' with ignition switched 'ON'

1 Cable between gauge and tank unit earthed

NOTES

CHAPTER 12

THE BODYWORK

12:1 Bodywork finish
12:2 Front door
12:3 Rear door
12:4 Front and rear screen glass
12:5 Engine compartment lid
12:6 Luggage compartment lid
12:7 Heated rear window
12:8 Sliding sun-roof

12:1 Bodywork finish

Large scale repairs to body panels are best left to expert panel beaters. Even small dents can be tricky, as too much hammering will stretch the metal and make things worse instead of better. Filling minor dents and scratches is probably the best method of restoring the surface. The touching up of paintwork is well within the powers of most car owners particularly as self-spraying cans of paint in the correct colours are now readily available. It must be recommended, however, that paint changes colour with age and it is better to spray a whole wing rather than try to touch-up a small area.

Before spraying it is essential to remove all traces of wax polish with white spirit. More drastic treatment is required if silicone polishes have been applied. Use a primer surface or paste stopper according to the amount of filling required, and when it is dry, rub it down with 400 grade 'Wet or dry' paper until the surface is smooth, and flush with the surrounding area. Spend time on getting the best finish as this will control the final effect. Apply retouching paint, keeping it wet in the centre and light and dry round the edges.

After a few hours of drying, use a cutting compound to remove the dry spray and finish with liquid polish.

12:2 Front door

Removal:

1 Mark the original position of the door hinges on the door pillar by marking the outline in pencil.

2 Using a chisel remove the lower flaired end of the rivet of the door check strap and drive upwards the rivet body using a parallel pin punch.

3 With the assistance of a second operator take the weight of the door from the hinges and remove the upper and lower hinge retaining screws to the door pillar. Gently ease outwards the lower hinge and lift away the door assembly.

Refitting:

Refitting the door is the reverse procedure to removal. Ensure that the hinges are correctly aligned with the pencil marks previously made before final tightening. Always fit a new rivet with its head uppermost and peen over the lower end so that it does not work loose.

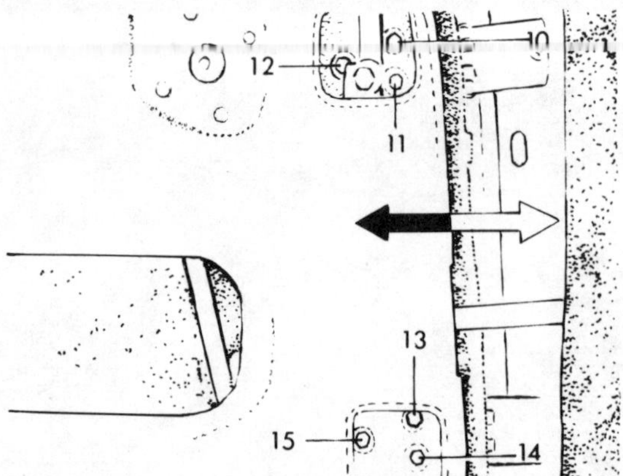

FIG 12:1 Front door hinge retaining bolts location

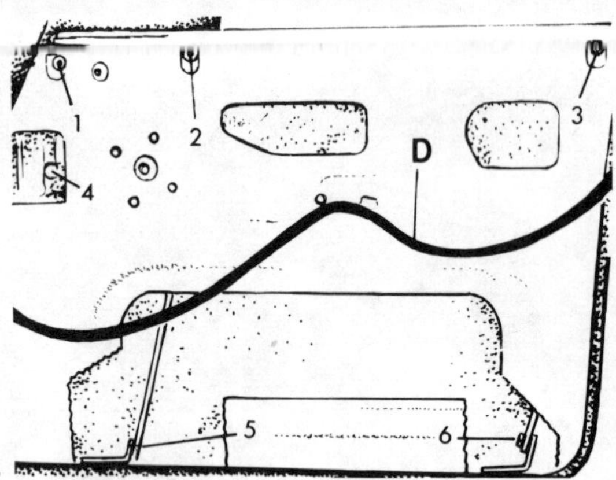

FIG 12:4 Window frame mounting locations

FIG 12:2 Pivoted quarter light hand wheel removal

FIG 12:3 Front door trim clip and retaining screw location

Adjustment:

Should difficulty be experienced in closing the door satisfactorily it should be correctly adjusted as follows:

1 Slacken the six retaining screws from the top and bottom hinges on the door pillar and adjust the position of the leading edge of the door inwards or outwards as required.
2 Slacken the three door catch screws and using a soft-faced hammer gently tap the door catch either inwards or outwards as required to give the required door closing action. It is important that the height of the door catch is not altered otherwise this will cause excessive strain on the catch mechanism.
3 Remove the inside door trim panel as detailed further in this section and carefully ease back the lining sheet from the apertures in the door panel.
4 Slacken the hinge clamp bolts 10 to 15 as shown in **FIG 12:1** and adjust the overall door clearance to ensure that it is correctly located in its position relative to the remainder of the body and also that the front and rear doors are in perfect alignment.

Door interior trim panel:

To remove the door trim panel proceed as follows:

1 Unscrew the door safety lock button. Using a piece of bent wire insert this behind the hole 'B' (see **FIG 12:2**) and push out the coverplate 2. Remove the hand wheel clamp screw and lift away the operating knob.
2 Push the coverplate of the window crank away from the handle using a screwdriver and lift away. Remove the window crank clamp screw and lift away the crank.
3 Remove the clamp screw on the inside door handle and carefully pull off the door handle.
4 Remove the two armrest clamp screws and swing the armrest forwards pulling clear from the door lining panel.
5 Remove the five door lining fastening screws and ease the door lining away from the door using a wide blade screwdriver as a lever. The locations for the clips are shown by the arrows in **FIG 12:3**.
6 Reassembly is the reverse procedure to dismantling.

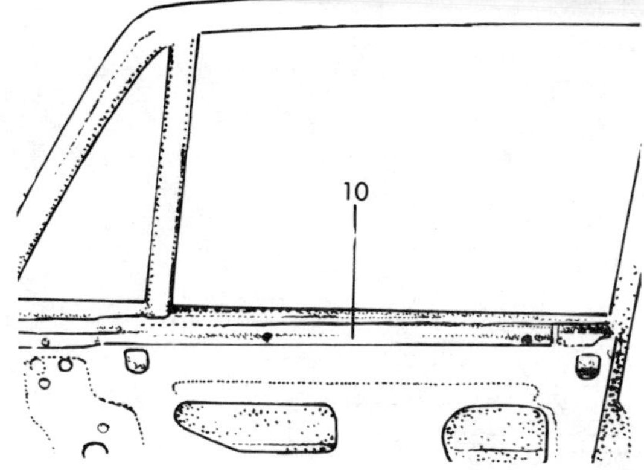

FIG 12:5 Window frame breast rail

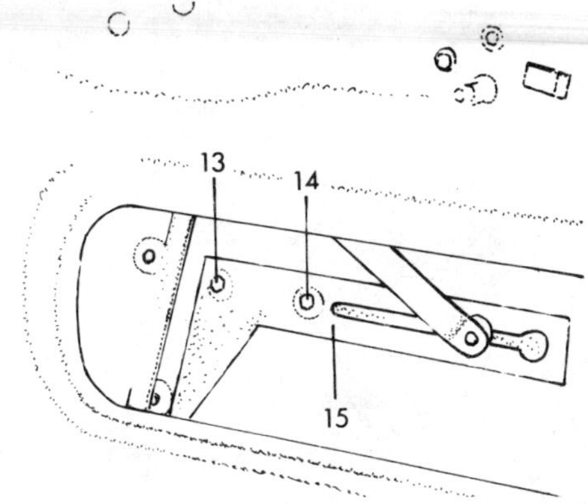

FIG 12:6 Window rail clamp

The small end of the conical spring on the inside door handle should face towards the door. When refitting the window crank ensure that the window is closed and the crank handle should point towards the armrest.

Door glass:

To remove the door glass from the door proceed as follows:

1 Remove the door lining trim as previously described and also the lining sheet.
2 Carefully ease away the door weather strip from around the window frame and using a pencil mark the position of the window frame.
3 Loosen the window frame clamp bolts 1 to 6 (see **FIG 12:4**), and carefully wind the window down and release the breast rail 10 (see **FIG 12:5**). Mark the location of the spacer tabs between the door and the window frame with a pencil.
4 Using a wide blade screwdriver, carefully ease out the rubber seal and also the cover rail. Detach the window rail clamp bolts 13 and 14 (see **FIG 12:6**), from the holder 15. Carefully lift the window frame from the door by tilting to one side and disconnecting the window raising arm from the window rail.
5 Should it be necessary to fit a new glass remove all traces of old glass and coat the inside and outside surfaces of the sealing strip with Terokal 503 adhesive. Press in the new window glass and sealing strip into the thoroughly cleaned window rail ensuring that the clearance between the window rail and the front edge of the door glass is approximately $\frac{7}{8}$ inch.
6 Reassembly is the reverse procedure to dismantling. It should be noted that the window rail should be correctly located between the two plastic guide washers as shown in **FIG 12:7**. Terokal 2444 is recommended for re-attaching the door lining sheet and also the door weather strip.

Adjust the window and window frame as detailed in the following section.

Window and window frame adjustment:

To adjust the window and window frame in the door panel proceed as follows:

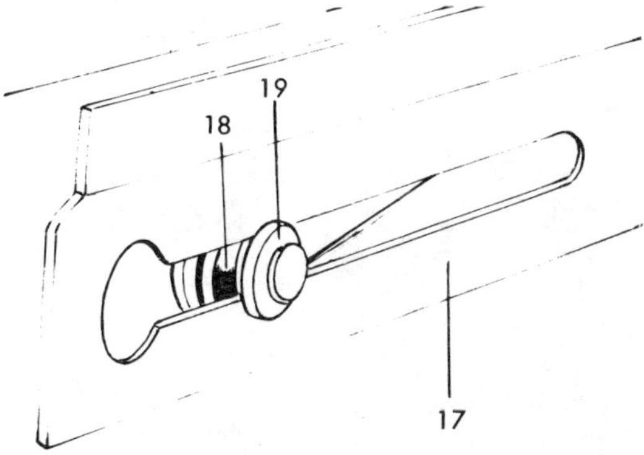

FIG 12:7 Window rail plastic guide washers

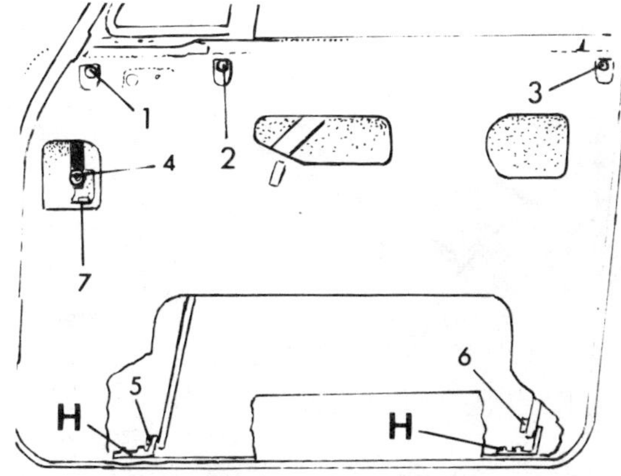

FIG 12:8 Window frame adjustment points

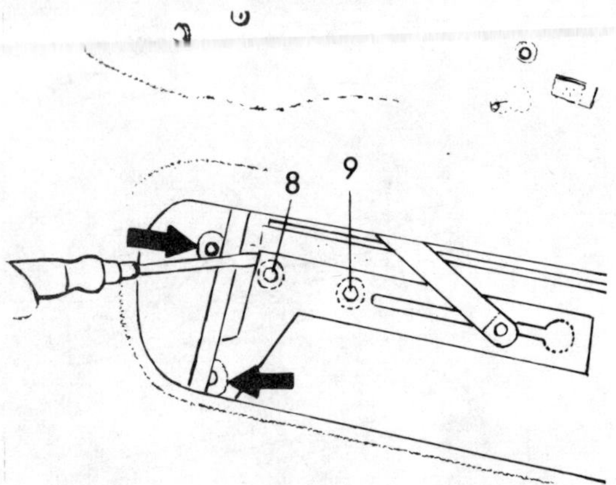

FIG 12:9 Door glass adjustment points

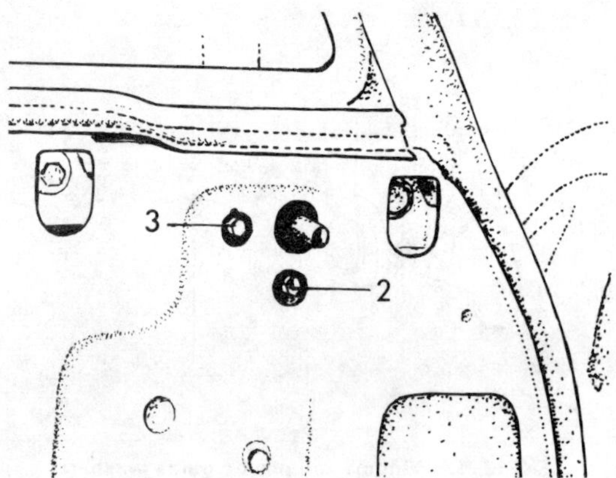

FIG 12:10 Worm gear retaining bolts

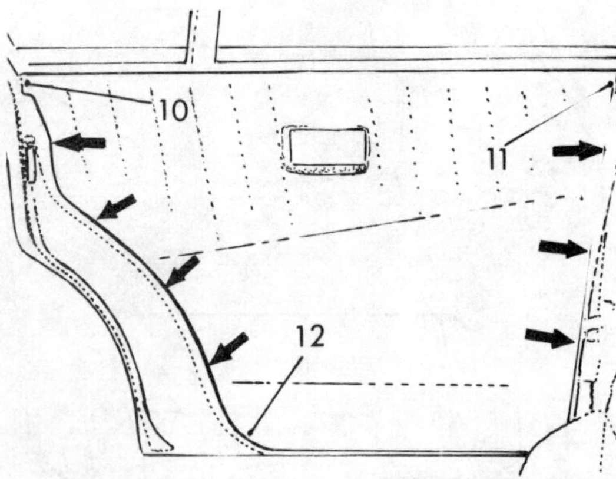

FIG 12:11 Rear door trim clip and retaining screw location

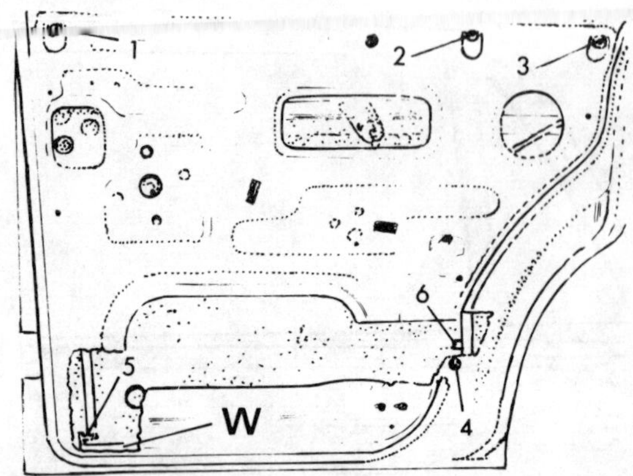

FIG 12:12 Window frame mounting locations, rear door

1 Remove the door interior trim panel as detailed previously in this section. Detach the weatherproof lining sheet.
2 Refer to **FIG 12:8** and slacken the clamp screws 1 to 7 and the retaining brackets 'H'.
3 Close the door and ensure that its adjustment is correct. If not complete this operation next.
4 Adjust the clearance between the window frame and the body ensuring that there is equal clearance all the way round. Tighten the frame retaining bolts 1 to 3 (see **FIG 12:8**), and also the retaining brackets 'H'. The rubber weather strip and the window frames must press evenly against the body with sufficient force to eliminate any wind noise whilst the vehicle is in motion. Finally tighten down the fastening bolts 4 to 7 (see **FIG 12:8**).
5 Wind down the window and slacken the retaining bolts 8 and 9 (see **FIG 12:9**), and carefully push the window forward in its rubber frame. Using a wide blade screwdriver push the holder and rollers up against the lifting rail and tighten the clamp bolts.
6 Refit all parts disturbed in the reverse order of dismantling.

Pivoted quarter light:

To remove the pivoted quarter light proceed as follows:
1 Open the pivoted quarter light so that the trailing edge is away from the glass frame by approximately two inches.
2 Remove the door interior trim panel as previously described in this section.
3 Refer to **FIG 12:10** and slacken the worm gear clamp bolts 2 and 3. Carefully but firmly push the quarter light assembly downwards and then pull upwards away from the door frame.
4 The worm gear may be removed by removing screws 2 and 3 (see **FIG 12:10**), and the worm gear withdrawn downwards.

12:3 Rear door

Removal:

1 Mark the original position of the hinges on the door

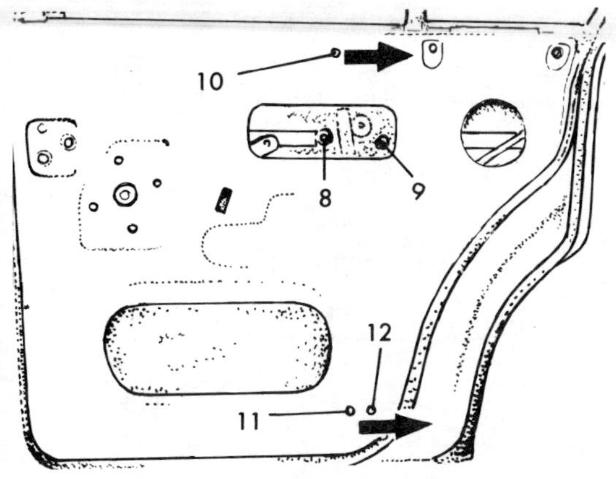

FIG 12:13 Window frame adjustment points

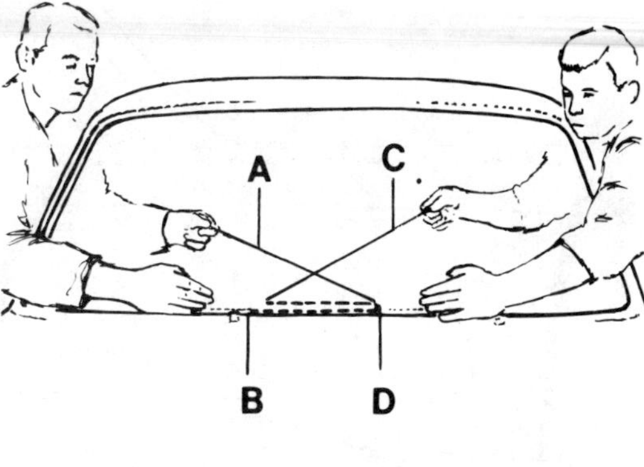

FIG 12:14 Windshield glass replacement

pillar by marking the outline in pencil.

2 Using a chisel remove the lower flaired end of the rivet of the door check strap and drive upwards the rivet body using a parallel pin punch.

3 With the assistance of a second operator take the weight of the door from the hinges and remove the upper and lower hinge retaining screws to the door pillar. Carefully lift away the door assembly.

Refitting:

Refitting the door is the reverse procedure to removal. Ensure that the hinges are correctly aligned with the pencil marks previously made before final tightening. Always fit a new rivet with its head uppermost and peen over the lower end so that it does not work loose.

Adjustment:

Should difficulty be experienced in closing the door satisfactorily it should be correctly adjusted as follows:

1 Remove the inside door panel as detailed further in this section and carefully ease back the lining sheet from the apertures in the door panel.

2 Slacken the upper and lower hinge clamp screws on the door pillar and adjust the position of the leading edge of the door inwards or outwards as required.

3 Slacken the three door catch screws and using a soft-faced hammer gently tap the door catch either inwards or outwards as required to give the required door closing action. It is important that the height of the door catch is not altered otherwise this will cause excessive strain on the catch mechanism.

4 Slacken the hinge clamp bolts to the outer door panel and adjust the overall door clearance to ensure that it is correctly located in its position relative to the remainder of the body and also that the front and rear doors are in perfect alignment.

Door interior trim panel:

To remove the door trim panel proceed as follows:

1 Unscrew the door safety lock button.

2 Push the coverplate of the window crank away from

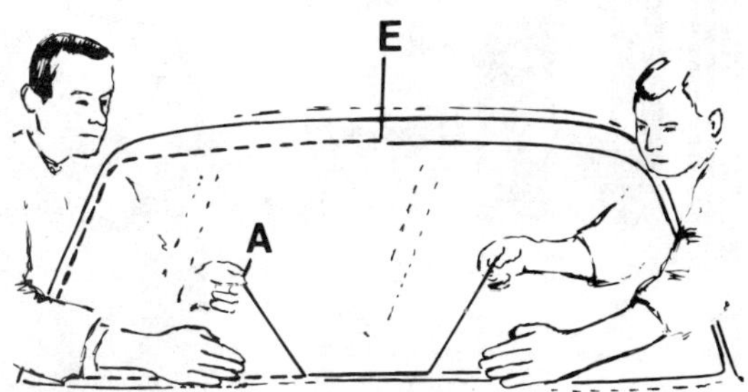

FIG 12:15 Draw cord movement stage one

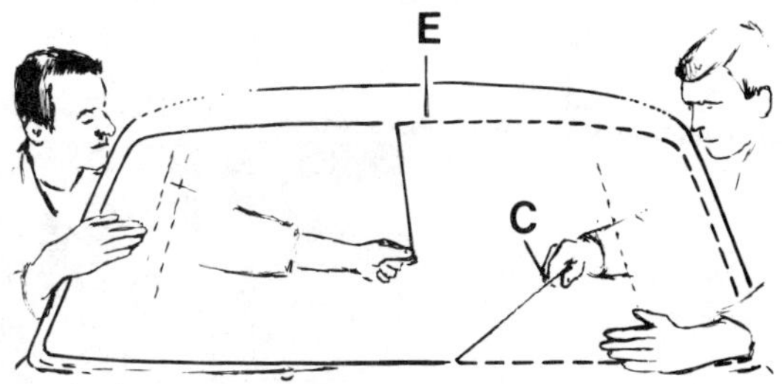

FIG 12:16 Draw cord movement stage two

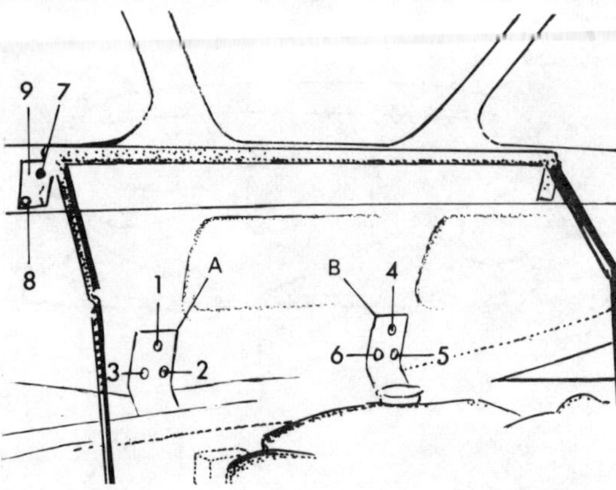

FIG 12:17 Bonnet hinge and main support retaining bolts location

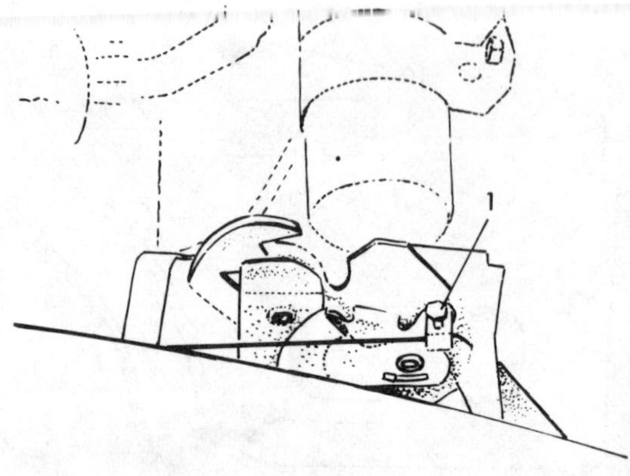

FIG 12:20 Lefthand bonnet release cable adjustment

FIG 12:18 Bonnet to front apron alignment

FIG 12:19 Bonnet lock adjustment

the handle using a screwdriver and lift away. Remove the window crank clamp screw and lift away the crank.

3 Remove the clamp screw on the inside door handle and carefully pull off the door handle.

4 Remove the two armrest clamp screws and swing the armrest forwards pulling clear of the door lining panel.

5 Lift out the ashtray and remove the ashtray retainer clamp screws. Lift away the ashtray container.

6 Remove the three door interior trim panel clamp screws and ease the door lining away from the door using a wide blade screwdriver as a lever. The locations of the clips are shown by the arrows in **FIG 12:11**.

Window and window frame:

Adjustment:

To correctly adjust the window and window frame to the door panel proceed as follows:

1 Remove the door interior trim panel as previously described, and also the lining sheet.

2 Slacken the clamp bolts 1 to 6 (see **FIG 12:12**), and also the bracket 'W'.

3 With the door closed adjust the window frame clearance relative to the bodywork so that there is an equal space all the way round. Tighten the clamp bolts 1 to 4 and bracket 'W' (see **FIG 12:12**). Ensure that the rubber seal on the window frame is firmly pressed against the body with sufficient force to eliminate any wind noise. Tighten the clamping bolts 5 and 6.

4 Open the window about two inches and loosen the holder clamping bolts 8 and 9 (see **FIG 12:13**). Loosen also the window rail clamping bolts 10 to 12 (see **FIG 12:13**). Carefully push the window rail upwards towards the door lock and tighten the clamping bolt 10. Push the window rail down in the direction of the door lock and tighten the fastening bolts 11 and 12. Finally with the aid of a wide blade screwdriver push the window rail up from the holder and simultaneously tighten down the clamping bolts 8 and 9.

Refitting the dismantled components is the reverse procedure to dismantling.

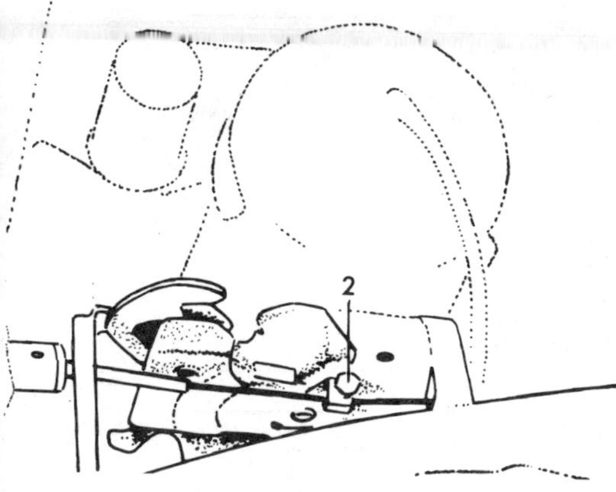

FIG 12:21 Righthand bonnet release cable adjustment

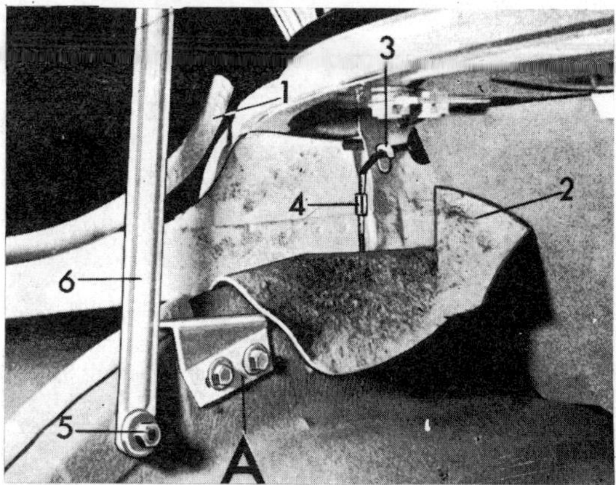

FIG 12:22 Boot lid hinge and support stay mounting points

12:4 Front and rear screen glass

The procedure for removing and refitting both the front and rear screen glass is identical.

Removal:

1 Ease the windscreen wiper arms from their spindles and lift away.
2 Using a windscreen rubber seal lip extractor or a suitably shaped tool detach the rubber window seal carefully from the body.
3 Commencing at one of the two top corners gently push the windscreen, together with the rubber seal and chrome trim away from the body. It is suggested that a second operator be located in front of the windscreen to ensure that when it is finally released from the windscreen aperture, the glass is not damaged.
4 Carefully remove all old sealing compound from the bodywork and the sealing rubber.

Refitting:

1 Place a thick woollen blanket on a flat surface so that the glass may be worked upon as necessary without damage.
2 Offer the glass to the body aperture to ensure that curvature is correct. Place the glass on the thick woollen blanket and starting at one corner gently ease the rubber seal onto the glass. Insert the chrome trim frame into place in the rubber seal and place a length of cord into the lip of the rubber frame with approximately one foot overlap at the bottom.
3 Carefully lay the assembled windscreen into position in the body aperture and hold firmly to prevent movement whilst it is being refitted.
4 Refer to **FIG 12:14** and start with end 'A' of the string and pull the rubber seal lip over the edge of the bodywork until point 'B' is reached. Carefully pull the end 'C' to point 'D'. During this procedure use the flat of the hand or a suitable pad to continuously strike the windscreen at about 6 to 10 inches in front of the point where the string protrudes.
5 Using end 'A' of the string pull the rubber seal lip over

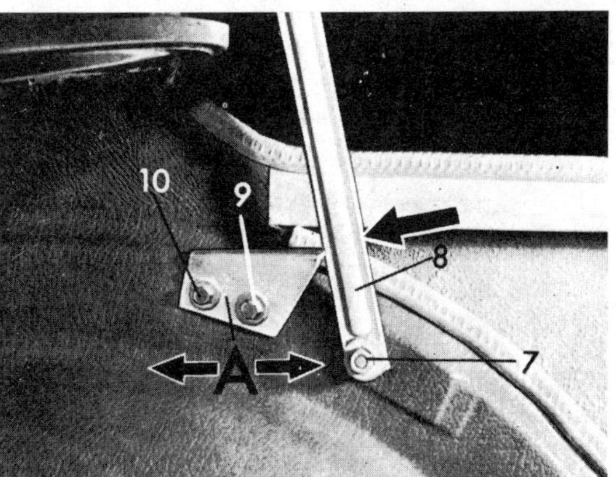

FIG 12:23 Boot lid hinge and support stay mounting points

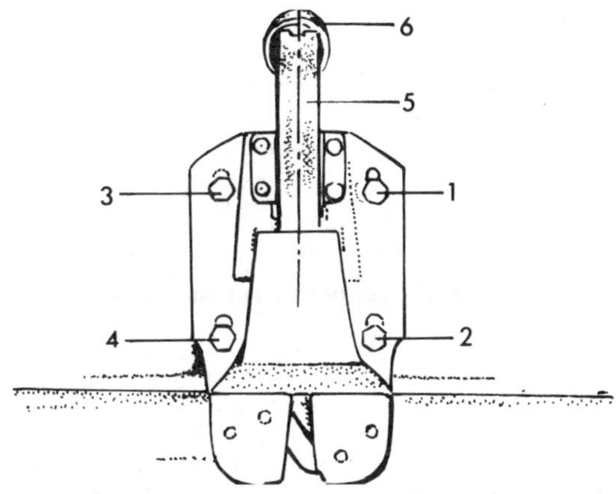

FIG 12:24 Boot lid lock

FIG 12:25 Heated rear window switch mounting point

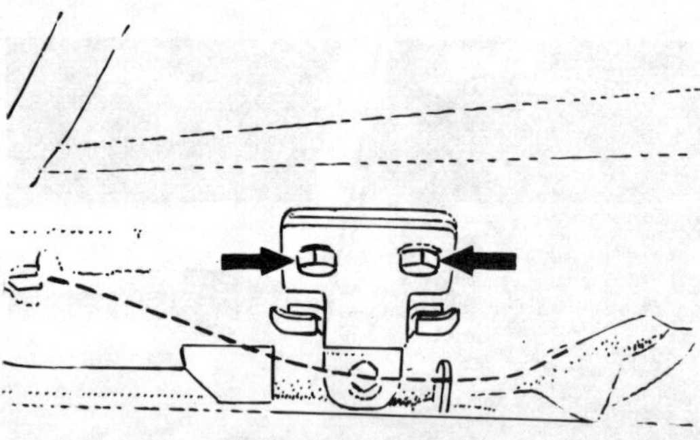

FIG 12:26 Guide retaining bolts

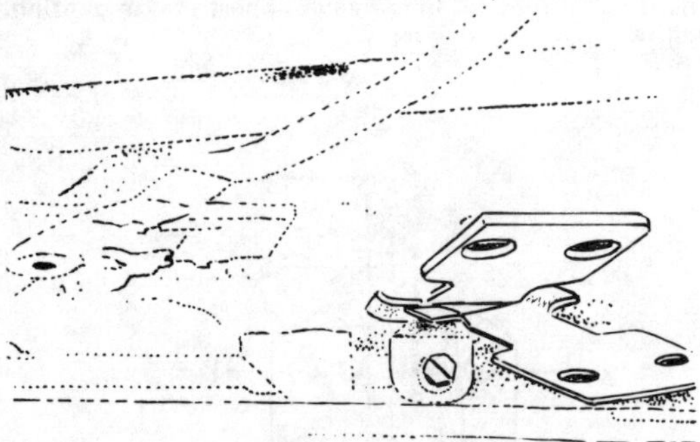

FIG 12:27 Locking plate removal

the edge of the bodywork until reaching point 'E' (see **FIG 12:15**).

6 Using the string end 'C' carefully pull the other half of the rubber seal over the edge of the windscreen aperture until reaching point 'E' (see **FIG 12:16**). Whilst this is being done continuously strike the windscreen. At any point where the rubber seal lip is not correctly seated in position this may be remedied by using a lip extractor or suitably shaped tool.

7 Using a weatherproof sealing compound in a sealer gun, seal the rubber frame into the windscreen ensuring that no gaps are lelt otherwise water ingress could occur.

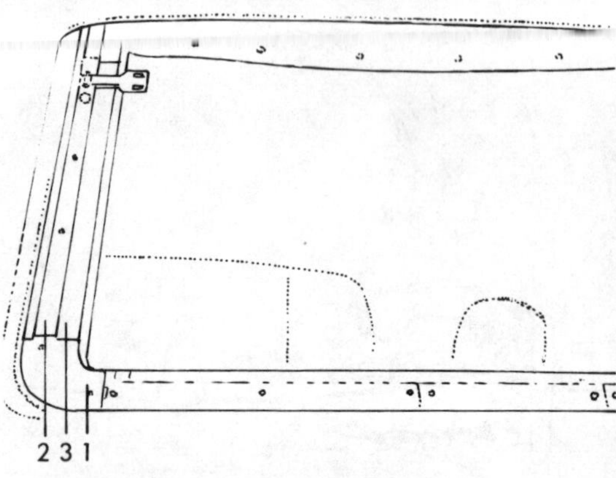

FIG 12:28 Roof bracking removal

12:5 Engine compartment lid

Removal:

1 Open the bonnet and using a pencil mark the position of the bonnet hinges on the bonnet lid.

2 Loosen the six bonnet hinge clamp bolts 1 to 6 (see **FIG 12:17**), and also the clamp bolts 7 and 8 on the mounting bracket 9. Lift away the mounting bracket.

3 Carefully remove the bonnet sliding the mounting bracket from the main support.

Adjustment:

To adjust the position of the bonnet relative to the engine compartment proceed as follows:

1 Slacken the clamp bolts on both hinges and adjust the position of the bonnet relative to the hinges until the correct location is found. This is made possible by elongated holes in the bonnet and hinges. Slacken the clamp bolts for both bonnet catches and move the catch forwards or backwards until the correct position is found. It should be noted that to prevent the bonnet from being pushed into the passenger compartment of the car in the event of a front collision, the bonnet catches must be adjusted to ensure that the bonnet catch plate recedes below the apron when the bonnet is closed. The clearance between the bonnet catch plate and the apron should not exceed $\frac{1}{8}$ inch.

2 Remove the front righthand and lefthand radiator grilles and slacken the righthand and lefthand hinge clamp bolts, 10 to 12 (see **FIG 12:18**). To centralize the bonnet in its correct basic setting, insert a centre punch into the bore 'C' and lock the bonnet mounting bracket into place. Gently ease the bonnet back until it rests on the apron. Close the bonnet. Ensure that

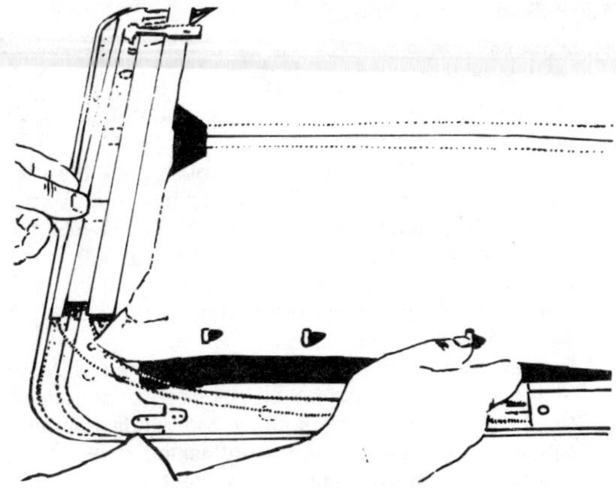

FIG 12:29 Head lining removal

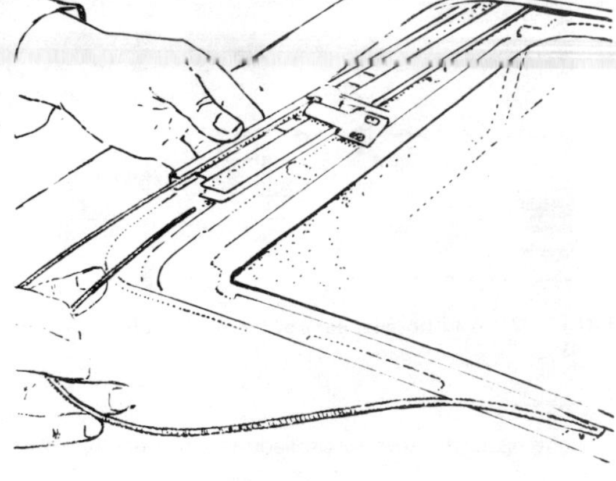

FIG 12:30 Guide rail assembly dismantling

when the bonnet clearance is being set the chrome beading on the bonnet is correctly aligned with that on the door.

3 Slacken the hinge clamp bolts and adjust the bonnet clearance 'D' (see **FIG 12:19**), at the front. The bonnet clearance 'D' at the rear is adjusted by moving the bonnet locks 'S' (see **FIG 12:19**). To eliminate excessive bonnet vibration or rattle by fitting rubber cushion pads of appropriate thickness between the wing panel and lower bonnet flange.

Refitting:

Refitting is the reverse procedure to dismantling. Adjust the location of the bonnet as previously described in this section and lubricate all pivot points using engine grade oil.

Bonnet catch release cable adjustment:

Refer to **FIG 12:20** and slacken the retaining bolt 1 for the control cable on the righthand bonnet catch. Also slacken the control cable fastening bolt 2 (see **FIG 12:21**), on the lefthand bonnet catch. Release the cover and pull the control lever back as far as it will go. In this position with the bonnet locks fully open tighten the cable control clamp bolts 1 and 2 as shown in **FIGS 12:20** and **12:21**.

12:6 Luggage compartment lid

Removal:

1 Open the boot lid and carefully lift away the top section of the weather strip 1 (see **FIG 12:22**), from the channel. Carefully ease away the plastic lining 2 and bend open the retaining strap 3.

2 Disconnect the licence plate light socket plug 4 and also the clamp nut 5 for the supporting strut 6. Remove the strut 8 clamp nut (see **FIG 12:23**) and prop open the boot lid using a suitably sized piece of wood.

3 Mark the position of the hinges using a pencil and remove the hinge clamp bolts having first ensured that the boot lid is firmly held by a second operator so that it does not slip, causing damage to the paintwork.

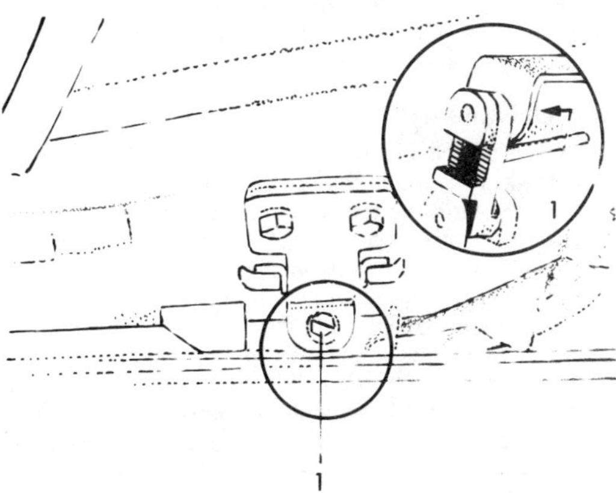

FIG 12:31 Sliding roof rear end height adjustment

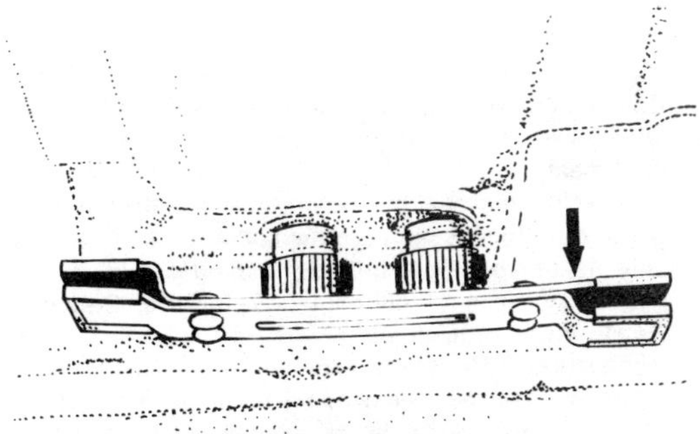

FIG 12:32 Sliding roof front end height adjustment

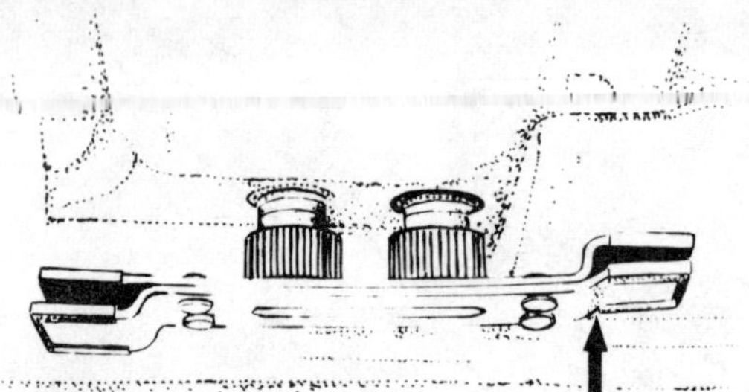

FIG 12:33 **Additional means of front end height adjustment**

Refitting:

Refitting is the reverse procedure to dismantling but the following points should be noted:

1 Slacken the clamp bolts 9 and 10 (see **FIG 12:23**) and move the limit stop 'A' until the torsion bar spring pressure pushes the stut 8 firmly against the limit stop 'A'.
2 When the boot lid is correctly located in place ensure that its front edge is correctly aligned with that of the rear wing panel.

Lock adjustment:

1 Slacken the clamping bolts 1 to 4 (see **FIG 12:24**), for the top section of the bonnet catch 5.
2 Correctly align the top section of the bonnet catch 5 with the bonnet lock 6. Push the top section of the bonnet catch 5 upwards in the elongated holes and fasten down firmly. It is important to ensure that the top section of the catch 5 is fitted flush with the lock 6.
3 Should the upper section of the boot catch 5 not lie in full contact with the lock 6 this may be corrected using a soft-faced hammer by gently tapping at the point 5 on the upper catch until it is correctly aligned.
4 Slacken the lower catch section and push upwards as far as it will go in the elongated holes. To correctly align the lower catch section relative to the upper section push it to the left or right as necessary until the guide bolt centre line is correctly aligned.

12:7 Heated rear window

To fit a rear window with a heater element as an accessory proceed as follows:

1 Remove the rear window as detailed in **Section 12:4**.
2 Disconnect the negative lead from the battery.
3 Refer to **FIG 12:25** and fit the push/pull switch as shown in the figure with dimension 'A' being 1.97 inch.
4 Connect the previous unused black/green leads in the wiring harness to the push/pull switch and fuse 6 underneath.
5 Remove the rear seat back cushion and fit the window glass with the heating element incorporated taking very great care that the little terminal on the side of the glass is not in any way damaged. Refer to **Section 12:4** for this procedure.
6 Connect up the loose black/green cable located on the wheel arch to the rear window terminal. Also attach the negative lead to the rear panel and to the rear window. Reconnect the battery terminal and refit the rear seat backrest cushion.

12:8 Sliding sun-roof

Removal:

1 Open the sliding roof approximately 6 to 8 inches and carefully lever off the head lining frame at the front of the sliding roof.
2 Referring to **FIG 12:26** carefully push back the roof bracing and twist off the retaining spring. Remove the two guide plate retaining bolts and slide away the locking plate from the guide (see **FIG 12:27**).
3 Close the sliding roof. Using a pencil mark the position of the locking plate and guide and then remove the two retaining screws.
4 Repeat the operations just performed on the other side of the sun-roof. Place an old blanket or protection sheet over the panel work above the windscreen and carefully lift out the sliding roof taking care not to damage any paintwork or lining material.
5 Refitting is the reverse procedure to dismantling.

Roof bracing removal and refitting:

1 Remove the sliding roof assembly as previously detailed in this section.
2 Refer to **FIG 12:28**, slacken the corner piece 1, the cover strip 2 and the guide rails 3. Lift the guide rail 3 slightly and lift out the head lining in a forward direction (see **FIG 12:29**).
3 Refitting is the reverse procedure to dismantling.

Guide removal and refitting:

1 Remove the sliding roof assembly as previously described in this section.
2 Remove the winder assembly by releasing the three Phillips head screws and remove the winder assembly.
3 Working from the top of the car remove corner piece, cover strip and guide rail by moving sideways and forwards. Carefully ease out the guide rail (see **FIG 12:30**).
4 Reassembly is the reverse procedure to dismantling. It is recommended that the guides be packed with Amblygon grease.

Sliding roof adjustment:

1 After removal of the winder it should be turned back in a clockwise direction up to the stop and then turned back two complete turns.
2 Push the sliding roof evenly onto the front edge of the roof ensuring that the guides line up correctly. Fit the winder and close the sliding roof several times.
3 Close the sliding roof fully and lift away the winder. Turn to the full righthand stop and refit the winder assembly with the knob in the central position in the winder knob recess.
4 The sliding roof should be set so that it is .039 inch lower at the front and .039 inch higher at the back than the roof outer skin. To adjust this refer to **FIG 12:31** and it will be seen that by slackening the screw 1 the guide may be adjusted using the serrations to lock the adjustment. To adjust the front refer to **FIG 12:32** and place the guide with the straight fork side on the guide rail. The milled nuts will rotate for fine adjustment. Should the cranked end of the fork be offered up to the guide rail as shown in **FIG 12:33**, the sliding roof will be lower at the front.

NOTES

NOTES

APPENDIX

TECHNICAL DATA

Engine Cooling system Fuel system Clutch
Transmission Steering Suspension Brakes
Electrical system Capacities Dimensions
Torque wrench settings

WIRING DIAGRAMS

FIG 13:1 BMW 1600
FIG 13:2 BMW 1600—2/6 volt
FIG 13:3 BMW 1600—2/12 volt
FIG 13:4 BMW 1600TI

HINTS ON MAINTENANCE AND OVERHAUL

GLOSSARY OF TERMS

INDEX

NOTES

TECHNICAL DATA

Dimensions are in inches unless otherwise stated

ENGINE

Bore and stroke	3.307 x 2.795
Capacity	107.5 cu in
Compression ratio	
1600/1600–2	8.6:1
1600TI	9.5:1
Engine lubrication	
System	Pressure oil circulation
Oil filter	Fullflow
Oil pump	Gear type
Warning light operation	2.84 to 7.11 lb/sq in
Oil capacity (pints)	7.1 + .44 in filter bowl
Oil grade	Branded HD oil for 4 stroke petrol engines
Viscosity:	
For operation above 10°C	SAE.30, SAE.20W40, SAE.20W50
For operation below 10°C	SAE.20, SAE.10W30
Valve operating clearances (cold)	
Inlet	.15 to .20 mm (.0059 to .0079)
Exhaust	.15 to .20 mm (.0059 to .0079)
Valve clearance adjustment	Eccentrics on rockers
Sequence of adjustment	*TDC on cylinder No.* / *Valve overlap on cylinder No.*
	1 / 4
	3 / 2
	4 / 1
	2 / 3
Valve timing	With .02 inch clearance between cam base circle and rocker pad
Inlet opens	4 deg. BTDC
Inlet closes	52 deg. ABDC
Exhaust opens	52 deg. BBDC
Exhaust closes	4 deg. ATDC
Inlet period	236 deg. at crankshaft
Exhaust period	236 deg. at crankshaft
Valves	
Overall length:	
Inlet	4.087 ± .0079
Exhaust	4.106 ± .0079
Valve head diameter:	
Inlet—1600 only	1.535
Inlet	1.654
Exhaust	1.378
Valve stem diameter:	
Inlet	.315—.00157—.00098
Exhaust	.315—.00157—.00217
Minimum head thickness at edge:	
Inlet	.039 ± .004
Exhaust	.059 ± .004
Maximum head runout:	
Inlet	.0008
Exhaust	.0008

Valve seats

External diameter:	
Inlet—1600 only	1.654—.00035—.00098
Inlet	1.791—.00035—.00098
Exhaust	1.502—.00035—.00098
Diameter of cylinder head bore for valve seat:	
Inlet—1600 only	1.654 + .00098
Inlet...	1.732 + .00098
Exhaust	1.496 + .00098
Interference fit in cylinder head:	.00394 to .00591
Valve seat angle:	45 deg.
Outer correction angle	15 deg.
Inner correction angle	75 deg.
Valve seat width:	
Inlet	.063 to .079
Exhaust	.079 to .095
Valve seat oversizes	.0079 in diameter larger

Valve guides

Overall length	2.047
External diameter	.5512 + .00173 + .0013
Internal diameter	.3150 + .00059
Projection in cylinder head	.591
Interference fit in cylinder head	.00173 —.00059
Temperature of cylinder head when fitting valve guides	220 to 240°C
Oversize diameters	.5551, .5590, .5630

Valve running clearances

Inlet	.00098 to .00216
Exhaust	.00157 to .00275
Maximum wear tolerance	.0059

Valve springs

Wire thickness	.167
External coil diameter	1.260
Free length	1.811
Spring force and test length	66 lbs at 1.496 inch 154 lbs at 1.102 inch

Rockers

Bore for rocker shaft	.6103 + .00071
Bore in cylinder head	.6103 + .00106
Rocker shaft diameter	.6103—.00063—.00134
Rocker shaft running clearance	.00063 to .00240
Rocker running clearance	.00063 to .00205

Camshaft

Diameters	1.3780—1.6536—1.6929
Tolerance	—.00098 —.00161
Bore in cylinder head	1.3780—1.6536—1.6929
Tolerance	+.00134 +.00035
Running clearance	.00134 to .00295
Axial play	.00079 to .00512
Maximum permitted vertical runout of press-fitted distributor pinion	.00079
Cam base circle diameter	1.054
Cam lift	.2756

Valve gear

Operation	Single overhead camshaft and rockers
Camshaft drive	$\frac{3}{8}$ x $\frac{7}{32}$ duplex roller chain
Number of links fitted:	

With tensioning rail ...	94
With tensioning pinion	96

Chain tensioner

Piston length:	
With tensioning rail ...	2.441
With tensioning pinion	2.520
Tensioning rail coil spring free length ...	6.122
Wire thickness ...	.0394 ± .00059
Tensioning pinion coil spring free length	6.575
Wire thickness ...	.0492 ± .00059
Bore in tensioning pinion	.669 + .0011
Tensioning pinion bush	.669—.00063—.00134
Running clearance	.00063—.00240
Tensioning lever bore ...	.394 + .00059
Tensioning lever shaft ...	.394—.00051—.00110
Running clearance	.00051 to .00169

Crankshaft

Main bearing bore in crankcase:	
Red ...	2.362 + .00039
Blue ...	2.362 + .00075 + .00039
Bearing shell thickness:	
Red:	
Original	.0984—.00039—.00079
Stage 1	.1033—.00039—.00079
Stage 2	.1082—.00039—.00079
Blue:	
Original	.0988—.00039—.00079
Stage 1	.1037—.00039—.00079
Stage 2	.1087—.00039—.00079
Bearing play—radial	.0019 to .0027
Main bearing journal diameter:	
Red:	
Original	2.165—.00079—.00114
Stage 1	2.155—.00039—.00079
Stage 2	2.1457—.00039—.00079
Blue:	
Original	2.165—.00079—.00114
Stage 1	2.155—.00079—.00114
Stage 2	2.1457—.00079—.00114
Big-end bearing journal diameter:	
Original	1.8898—.00114—.00098
Stage 1	1.8799—.0004—.0010
Stage 2	1.8701—.0004—.0010
Guide bearing thickness:	
Original	1.1811 + .0025 + .0010
Stage 1	1.1890 + .0025 + .0010
Stage 2	1.1969 + .0025 + .0010
Crankshaft axial play ...	.0024 to .0064
Maximum runout centre main: ...	.0008

Connecting rod

Overall length	5.315
Small-end bore in rod ...	.945 + .00083
External diameter of small-end bush ...	.94777 to .94860
Manufacturer ...	Messrs Vandevell
Big-end bearing bore diameter	2.047 + .00039
Bearing shell thickness	.0787—.00039—.00075
Manufacturer ...	Messrs Glyco
Bearing play—radial ...	.00114 to .00287

Cylinders

1600:	
Standard	3.228 + .00087
First rebore	3.2383
Second rebore	3.2481
All other models:	
Standard	3.3071 + .00087
First rebore	3.3170
Second rebore	3.3268
Maximum ovality	.00039
Maximum taper	.00039
Total wear tolerance on piston and cylinder	.0039 to .0059

Pistons

Design	Domed oval centre section to crown
Diameter:	
Standard	3.3055
First oversize	3.3154
Second oversize	3.3252
Piston installed clearance	.0016

Piston rings

First groove (rectangular):	1251760 84/76.4 x 175 S.G.
End gap	.0118 to .0177
Flank clearance	.0024 to .0034
Second groove (stepped):	84/76.8 x 2.0f (DIN 24930)
End gap	.0118 to .0177
Flank clearance	.0014 to .0024
Third groove (double chamfer ring):	84/76.8 x 5.0f (DIN 24948)
End gap	.0098 to .0157
Flank clearance	.00098 to .00205

Gudgeon pins

Offset from piston centre line	.0591
Gudgeon pin diameter:	
White	.8662 —.00012
Black	.8662 —.00024 —.00012
Gudgeon pin clearance in piston	.00012 to .00032
Gudgeon pin clearance in small-end bush:	
White—1600 only	.00039 to .00071
White—all other models	.00028 to .00059
Black—1600 only	.00052 to .00084
Black—all other models	.00039 to .00071

Oil pump

Type	Gear
Oil pressure at idle speed	7.1 to 21.3 lb/sq in
Oil pressure at maximum speed	71 to 85 lb/sq in
Relief valve opening pressure	54 to 71 lb/sq in
Output	341 galls/hr
Gear tooth backlash:	
Normal	.0012 to .0019
Maximum	.0028
Axial play:	
Normal—all models...	.0019
Maximum 1600	.0028
Maximum—all models	.0035
Maximum depth in cover	.0019
Pressure relief valve spring free length	2.68
Distance between housing bulkhead and gear wheel bearing surface at hub	1.358 + .0039

Type	Rotor
Housing to rotor face	.0013 to .0033
Inner to outer rotor	.0035 to .0106 ± .0012
Outer rotor to housing	.0020 to .0079

COOLING SYSTEM

Water capacity including heater	12.5 pints
Thermostat opening temperature	75 ± 1°C
Radiator pressure cap	14.2 ± 2.1 lb/sq in
Water pump clearance between housing and impeller ...	.039 ± .0008
Output at 5700 rev/min	1520 galls/hr

FUEL SYSTEM

Recommended fuel octane rating	
1600TI	99
All other models	95
Fuel tank capacity:	
1600	12.1 gallons
All other models	10.1 gallons
Fuel system filter	Fine mesh filter in fuel pump
Mechanical fuel pump	
Type	Solex PE
Pressure at 1000 rev/min	2.99 to 3.56 lb/sq in
Carburetters	
1600:	
Type	Solex 36.PDSI
Main jet	X140
Air correction jet	100
Venturi	26
Pilot jet	47.5
Idling air jet	100
Rich mixture valve	72.5 calibrated, .7 drilled
Port for air-to-mixing tube	.50
Float needle valve gasket	.04
Injection pump tube	.8 calibrated
Quantity per stroke	1.6 to 1.7 cc
Float needle valve	2.0
Butterfly valve angle	8 deg.
Bypass drillways	1.2 to 1.0
Depth of fuel below joint line	.67 to .75
1600–2:	
Type	Solex 38.PDSI
Main jet	X130
Air correction jet	110
Venturi	26
Pilot jet	47.5
Idling air jet	100
Rich mixture valve	90
Port for air-to-mixing tube	.50
Float needle valve gasket	.04
Injection pump tube	.8 calibrated
Quantity per stroke	1.4 to 1.7 cc
Float needle valve	2.0
Butterfly valve angle	8 deg.
Bypass drillways	1.0 to 1.2
Depth of fuel below joint line	.67 to .75

1600TI

Typo	Solex 40 PHH (Twin)
Main jet	0120
Air correction jet	155
Venturi	30
Pilot jet	50
Idling air jet	100
Float needle valve gasket	.04
Injection pump tube	.4 calibrated
Quantity injected per stroke	.6 to .8 cc
Float needle valve	2.0
Butterfly valve angle	13 deg.
Bypass drillways	1.3 to1.3
Depth of fuel below joint line	Mark on float chamber exterior

CLUTCH

Type	Dry single plate with torsional damper
Model	KFS.200K
Contact pressure:	
1600TI	1075 ± 33 lbs
All other models	880 ± 44 lbs
Spring colour coding:	
1600TI	blue/white/blue with yellow stripe on outer edge
All other models	green/yellow/green
Driving plate internal diameter	5.12
Driving plate external diameter	7.87
Lining:	
Engine side	T.450.W
Transmission side	T.50.S
Total thickness:	
1600TI and 1600	.41
1600-2	.37
Minimum thickness:	
1600	.32
1600–2	.29
1600TI	.32
Maximum runout at circumference	.016
Withdrawal arm clearance	.118 to .138
Free movement at pedal	.8 to 1.0
Clearance between thrust ring and arm ends	.059

Master cylinder

1600 model only up to chassis number 931262:	
Bore	.625
Stroke	.91
1600 model only from chassis number 931263:	
Bore	.75
Stroke	1.18

Slave cylinder

1600 model only up to chassis number 931262:	
Bore	.625
Stroke	.91
1600 model only from chassis number 931263:	
Bore	.75
Stroke	.945

GEARBOX

Type	Manual with Porsche synchro-mesh on all 4 forward speeds 1 reverse speed
Gear selection	Manual at floor mounted lever
Ratios:	
First	3.835:1
Second	2.053:1
Third	1.345:1
Fourth	1.0:1
Reverse	4.18:1
Oil grade	Branded SAE.80 gearbox oil
Oil capacity	1.8 pints (1600: 2.2 pts)
Mainshaft end float	.024 maximum
Layshaft end float	.0079 maximum
Pinion tooth backlash	.00236 to .00591
Shaft runout	.0008 maximum

REAR AXLE

Number of teeth crownwheel/pinion:	
1600	35:8
1600–2	37:9
1600TI...	39:10
Ratio:	
1600	4.375:1
1600–2	4.11:1
1600TI...	3.9:1
Backlash	.0028 to .0047
Friction coefficient of input pinion bearing	.87 to 1.23 lb ft
Total friction coefficient at 3-arm flange	1.23 to 1.74 lb ft
Crownwheel heating temperature for assembly	75°C
Axial play between driving flange and axle casing ...	.039 to .059
Final drive oil grade	Branded SAE.90 hypoid gear oil
Capacity	1.6 pints
Rear wheel bearing play	.0020 to .0039
Track:	
1600	53.75
All other models	52.36
Toe-in:	
1600	.039 ± .039 normally loaded
All other models	.059 ± .059 normally loaded
Camber	2 deg. negative
Coil spring free length:	
1600	11.38
All other models	12.93
Coil spring rating:	
1600:	
Red	1120 to 1158 lb
White	1160 to 1197 lb
Green	1200 to 1235 lb
All other models:	
Red	710 to 128 lb
White	730 to 769 lb
Green	772 to 789 lb
Wire diameter:	
1600	.559
All other models	.484

External coil diameter:	
1600	4.7
All other models	5.01
Length of rubber auxiliary spring	3.15
Anti-roll bar diameter:	
1600	.67
All other models	.63
Shock absorber	
Type:	
1600	Boge Atos 32
All other models	Boge 1–0201–27–908–0
Colour code:	
1600	1 green dot
All other models	Black finish
Maximum length	
1600	20.60 ± .098
All other models	20.63 ± .098
Minimum length:	
1600	13.3 ± .098
All other models	13.15 ± .098

STEERING

Type	ZF-Gemmer worm and roller
Steering box ratio	15.5:1
Number of turns lock to lock	3.5
Maximum free play at wheel rim	.79
Splines on steering roller shaft	$1\frac{1}{8}$ inch taper
Splines on worm	$\frac{11}{16}$ inch straight
Straight-ahead position	Mark on worm and steering box
Maximum lock:	
Inner wheel	42 deg.
Outer wheel	34 deg.
Oil grade (Steering box and idler arm bearing)	SAE.90 hypoid gear oil
Capacity of steering box	300 cc approximately
Capacity of idler arm bearing	25 cc approximately
Friction coefficient of steering box in straight-ahead position	.72 to 1.15 lb ft
Friction coefficient of worm bearing	.07 to .18 lb ft
Preload on steering column bearing	.079 to .098 lb ft

FRONT AXLE

Track:	
1600	51.97
All other models	52.36
Toe-in:	
1600	0 —.079 normally loaded
All other models	.059 ± .059 normally loaded
Camber angle	0 deg. 30′ ± 30′
Toe-out on 20 deg. turn	1 deg. ± 30′
Kingpin inclination:	
1600	8 deg. ± 30′
All other models	8 deg. 30′
Castor angle:	
1600	3 deg. ± 30′
All other models	4 deg. ± 30′
Wheel bearing play	.00079 to .00315

Coil spring free length:	
1600	12.11
All other models	12.78
Wire diameter:	
1600	.495
All other models	.465
External coil diameter:	
1600 up to chassis number 917583	4.98 ± .051
1600 from chassis number 917584	5.02 ± .039
All other models	4.99 ± .059
Coil spring rating:	
1600:	
Red	640 to 660 lb
White	662 to 682 lb
Green	684 to 706 lb
All other models:	
Red	564 to 584
White	584 to 606
Green	606 to 626
Length of auxiliary spring:	
1600	2.953
All other models	3.347
Diameter of anti-roll bar:	
1600	.67
All other models	.59
Shock absorber	
Oil grade	Shell 4001
Capacity:	
1600	395 ± 3 cc
All other models	285 ± 3 cc
Type:	
1600	Boge Ftos 32
All other models	Boge 1–0211–27–314–0
Colour code:	
1600	1 yellow dot
All other models	Black finish
Stroke	6.46
Fitted length:	
1600	18.58
All other models	18.27 ± .059

BRAKES

Front	ATE fixed caliper disc brakes with automatic wear adjustment
Rear	Leading and trailing shoe drums
Maximum free travel at brake pedal	$\frac{1}{4}$ to $\frac{1}{3}$ of total travel
Brake unit type (1600TI)	T50/29/10
Master cylinder piston diameter:	
1600	$\frac{11}{16}$
All other models	$\frac{3}{4}$
Front wheel piston diameter	1.89
Piston offset	20 deg.
Rear wheel cylinder piston diameter:	
1600	$\frac{5}{8}$
All other models	$\frac{11}{16}$
Brake disc diameter:	
1600	10.55

All other models	9.45	
Maximum brake disc runout	.0039	
Maximum disc thickness variation in rubbed area	.00079	
Minimum brake disc thickness:		
1600	.335	
All other models	.374	
Front brake pad lining	Necto244 (white/green/white)	
Minimum front brake pad total thickness	.276	
Brake drum diameter:		
1600:		
Diameter	9.84	
First oversize	9.84 ± .0197	
Second oversize	9.84 ± .0394	
All other models:		
Diameter	7.87	
First oversize	7.87 ± .0197	
Second oversize	7.87 + .0394	
Maximum ovality	.0039	
Brake shoe width	1.575	
Minimum brake lining thickness	.118	

WHEELS AND TYRES

Type	Steel disc	
Rim size		
1600	$4\frac{1}{2}$J x 14	
All other models	$4\frac{1}{2}$J x 13	
Maximum runout		
Radial	.039	
Lateral	.039	
Tyres		
Standard:		
1600	600S x 14	
1600–2	600S x 13	
Radial ply:		
1600	165SR x 14	
All other models	165SR x 13	
Tyre pressures		
Up to 4 persons:	*lb/sq in*	*lb/sq in*
Standard	Front 24	Rear 24
Radial ply	Front 26	Rear 26
Up to 5 persons:		
Standard	Front 24	Rear 27
Radial ply	Front 26	Rear 28

ELECTRICAL

Battery	
Voltage:	
1600TI	12 volt
All other models	6 volt
Capacity:	
1600TI	44 amp/hr
All other models	77 amp/hr
Earth lead	Negative
Lowest starting voltage:	
1600TI	7 volts
All other models	4.8 volts
Starter	
Type:	

1600TI	Bosch EF(R) 12V
All other models	Bosch GF (R) 6V
Shortcircuit current:	
1600TI	340 amps
All other models	552 amps
Output:	
1600TI	.8 hp
All other models	.6 hp
Generator 1600 and 1600–2 only	
Type	Bosch
Model	200/6/2400R
Cut-in speed	1600 rev/min
Zero watts speed	1550 rev/min
Maximum current	50 amps
Nominal speed	2400 rev/min
Maximum output speed	3100 rev/min
Alternator 1600TI only	
Type	Bosch
Model	K1 14V 35 A20
Maximum output	490 watts
Maximum current	35 amps
Charging begins	900 rev/min
Regulator 1600 and 1600–2 only	
Type	Bosch
Model	RS/VA 200/6A
Cut-in voltage	5.9 to 6.5 volts
Idling speed voltage	6.9 to 7.5 volts
On-load voltage	6.2 to 7.0 volts
On-load current	65 amps
Back current	2 to 7.2 amps
Regulator 1600TI only	
Type	Bosch
Model	AD1/14V (RS/VA 200/6A (1/1)—others)
Control voltage	13.5 to 14.2
Coil	
Type	Bosch
Model:	
1600TI	K12V
All other models	TE.6B4
Ignition voltage:	
1600TI	15,000 volts
All other models	13,000 volts
Spark plugs	
Thread	14 mm x 1.25
Type:	
Bosch	W.200T30
Champion	N9Y (except 1600TI)
Beru:	
1600TI	230/14/3/A
All other models	200/14/3/A
Electrode gap	.024 + .004
Distributor	
Type	Bosch
Model:	
1600TI	0231119033
All other models	0231115048

Ignition point on belt pulley with engine cold:	
1600TI ...	TDC
All other models ...	3 deg. BTDC
Firing order ...	1–3–4–2
Contact breaker points gap ...	.016
Points spring pressure ...	15.9 to 19.5 oz
Dwell angle ...	60 deg. ± 1 deg. or 67 per cent ± 2 per cent

Lighting	*1600* *Watt*	*1600–2 1600TI* *Watt*
Main and dipped beam headlight ...	45/40	45/40
Side and parking light ...	4	4
Front flashing indicator ...	18	21
Stoplight ...	18	21
Reversing light ...	15	15
Rear flashing indicator ...	18	21
Tail and parking light ...	5	5
Licence plate light ...	5	5
Interior light ...	5	10
Instrument lights ...	2	3
Battery charge telltale ...	2	4
Main beam telltale ...	2	3
Flashing indicator telltale ...	2	3
Oil pressure telltale ...	2	3
Choke and fuel level telltale ...	2	—

Fuse box

1600 ...	6 pole 4 x 8 amp, 2 x 25 amp
All other models ...	6 pole 5 x 8 amp, 1 x 16 amp

CAPACITIES

Engine ...	7.54 pints
Gearbox ...	1.8 pints
Final drive ...	1.6 pints
Fuel tank:	
1600 ...	12.1 gallons
All other models ...	10.1 gallons
Cooling system ...	12.5 pints (including heater)

DIMENSIONS

	1600	*1600–2 1600TI*
Overall length ...	177.2	166.5
Overall width ...	67.3	62.6
Overall height ...	57.1	55.5
Ground clearance ...	5.9	6.3
Front overhang ...	33.1	28.3
Rear overhang ...	41.3	39.8
Permitted trailer load:		
Unbraked ...	1100	1100
Braked ...	2645	2645

TORQUE WRENCH SETTINGS

Engine

	lb ft
Cylinder head studs (from centre, in cross-over pattern in 3 stages) ...	21.7 to 50.6 ± 1.4, 50.6 ± 1.4
Chain tensioner locking bolt ...	21.7 to 28.9
Main bearing caps ...	42.0 to 45.6
Connecting rod bolts (12K) ...	37.6 to 41.2

Suction pipe attachment-to-oil pump retainer	6.5 to 8.0
Flywheel shoulder stud M10 x 1 (12K)—induction hardened or non hardened	50.6 to 54.2
Expansion bolt M12 x 1.5 (12K) coated with Loctite on fitting ...	65.1 to 72.3
Expansion bolt not coated with Loctite	72.3 to 79.6
Crankshaft V-belt pulley	101.3
Closure plug on oil pump housing pressure relief valve	36.2
Water pump belt pulley	28.9
Gearbox attachment points-to-engine	18.1 (M8) 34.0 (M10)
Fitted bolts for clutch attachment	12.3 ± 1.4
Spark plugs	18.1 to 21.7
Fuel pump	8.7
Oil drain plug	43.4
Oil sump	57.8
Carburetter-to-manifold (single carb.)	7.2 to 10.1
Hollow bolt for oil suppy-to-camshaft	8.0 to 9.4
Timing case cover top-to-bottom (together with item 1)	6.5
Distributor flange M8	18.1
Distributor flange M6	8.0
Cylinder head cover	5.9 to 7.2
Gearbox	
Gearbox/engine attachment bolts M8	18.1
Gearbox/engine attachment bolts M10	34.0
Spacer plate	14.5
Bearing block retaining bolts	18.1
Output flange	108.4
Housing cover	18.1
Sealing flange	7.2
Front suspension	
Telescopic leg shock absorber, centre top	57.8
Telescopic leg shock absorber, support	18.0
Shock absorber, screw ring	86.8 + 14.5
Shock absorber piston-to-piston rod	18.0
Tie rod lever-to-stub axle	18.0
Guide joint-to-tie rod lever	50.6 minimum
Wishbone-to-front axle carrier	108.5 minimum
Front axle carrier-to-body frame	34.0
Traction strut-to-wishbone and front axle carrier	43.4 minimum
Caliper-to-stub axle	68.7
Steering lever bearing	18.0
Steering gear-to-front axle carrier	34.0
Rear axle	
Bolts fastening final drive casing to body floor	65.0
Rear axle carrier mounting on body floor	87.0
Thrust rod on body floor	18.0
Trailing arm on axle beam	54.0
Lower shock absorber mounting	54.0
Final drive attachment points	65.0
Large cover on casing	36.0
3-point coupling on pinion (with Loctite AVV)	108 minimum
Giubo joint	33.0
Crownwheel-to-differential body	60.0 (12K)
Crownwheel-to-differential body	61.5 + 7.2
Driving flange-to-halfshaft pinion	65.1 + 7.2
Three-arm flange-to-input bevel pinion	108.5
Output shaft-to-driving flange	17.4 + 4.3
Final drive-to-rear axle carrier	47.0 + 7.2

Rubber mounting-to-body floor	30.4 + 3.6
Final drive-to-rubber mounting	58.6 + 6.5
Propeller shaft-to-final drive	32.5
Crossmember-to-final drive	32.5
Side casing cover	18.0
Hexagon bolt on drive flange	65.0 + 7.2
Halfshaft castellated nuts	217.0 + 36.0
Output shaft at driving flange	22.0 (12K)
Output shaft at halfshaft	22.0 (12K)
Propeller shaft at gearbox driven shaft flange	22.0 (12K)
Rubber bearing at rear axle carrier	22.0 (M8 32.5 (M10
Housing cover	14.5 + 3.6

Steering

Steering damper-to-clamp	30.4 + 3.6
Steering damper-to-retaining strap	30.4 + 3.6
Steering wheel retaining nut	39.8 + 3.6
Joint disc attachment	10.8 + 3.6
Joint flange attachment	18.0
Steering arm-to-steering box	101.3
Castellated nut on steering guide arm	57.8 minimum
Retaining strap-to-engine mounting	13.7 + 3.6
Clamp-to-track rod	13.7 + 3.6
Track rod castellated nuts	25.3
Steering box-to-front axle beam	34.0
Guige lever-to-front axle beam	18.0
Track rod clamp bolts	18.0

Brakes

Caliper-to-kingpin pivot	68.7
Brake disc-to-wheel hub	43.4 + 5.0
Brake hose-to-caliper	8.7 to 11.6
Pre-pressure valve	13.7
Wheel nuts	65.1
Collar nut on brake line	8.7 to 11.6
Retainer on rear of brake unit 1600-2 only	13.7+3.6
Retainer on front of brake unit 1600-2 only	11.6+2.9
Brake unit holder-to wheel arch 1600-2 only	11.6+2.9
Caliper halves	24.6

WIRING DIAGRAMS

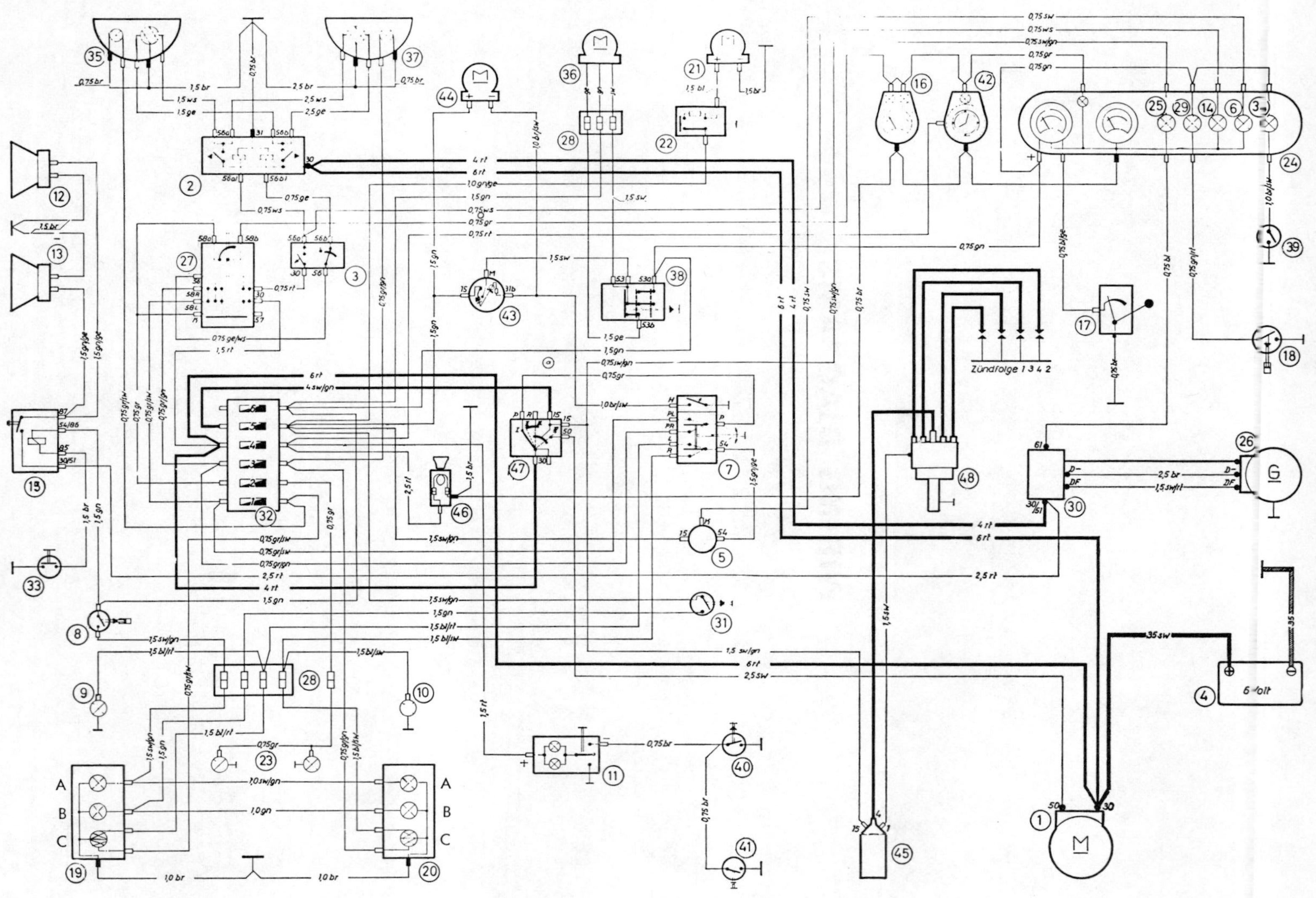
Zündfolge 1 3 4 2
6 Volt

FIG 13:1 BMW 1600

Key to Fig 13:1 1 Starter 2 Dip relay 3 Dipswitch 4 Battery 5 Flasher unit 6 Flasher telltale 7 Flasher/parking light switch with washer contact 8 Stoplight switch 9 Turn indicator front LH 10 Turn indicator front RH 11 Roof light 12 Two-tone horn 1 13 Two-tone horn 2 14 Main beam telltale 15 Horn relay 16 Speedometer 17 Fuel gauge mechanism 18 Oil pressure contact 19 Rear light LH A Stoplight B Reversing light C Turn indicator/parking light rear 21 Heater blower motor 22 Heater switch 23 Number plate light 24 Combined instrument 25 Battery charge telltale 26 Generator 27 Light switch 28 Cable connector 29 Oil pressure telltale 30 Regulator 31 Reversing light switch 32 Fuse box 33 Horn button 34 Choke telltale 35 Headlight LH 36 Screenwiper motor 37 Headlight RH 38 Screenwiper switch 39 Choke cable contact 40 Door switch LH 41 Door switch RH 42 Clock 43 Delay relay 44 Screenwasher pump 45 Coil 46 Cigar lighter 47 Ignition/starter switch 48 Distributor

Cable colour coding .75 sq mm cross-section **BL** Blue **BR** Brown **GE** Yellow **GN** Green **GR** Grey **RT** Red **SW** Black **WS** White

Fuses 1, 2, 3 and 5=8 amp 4 and 6=25 amp

Ignition/starter switch positions 1 Halt 2 Garage 3 Fahrt (Drive) 4 Start

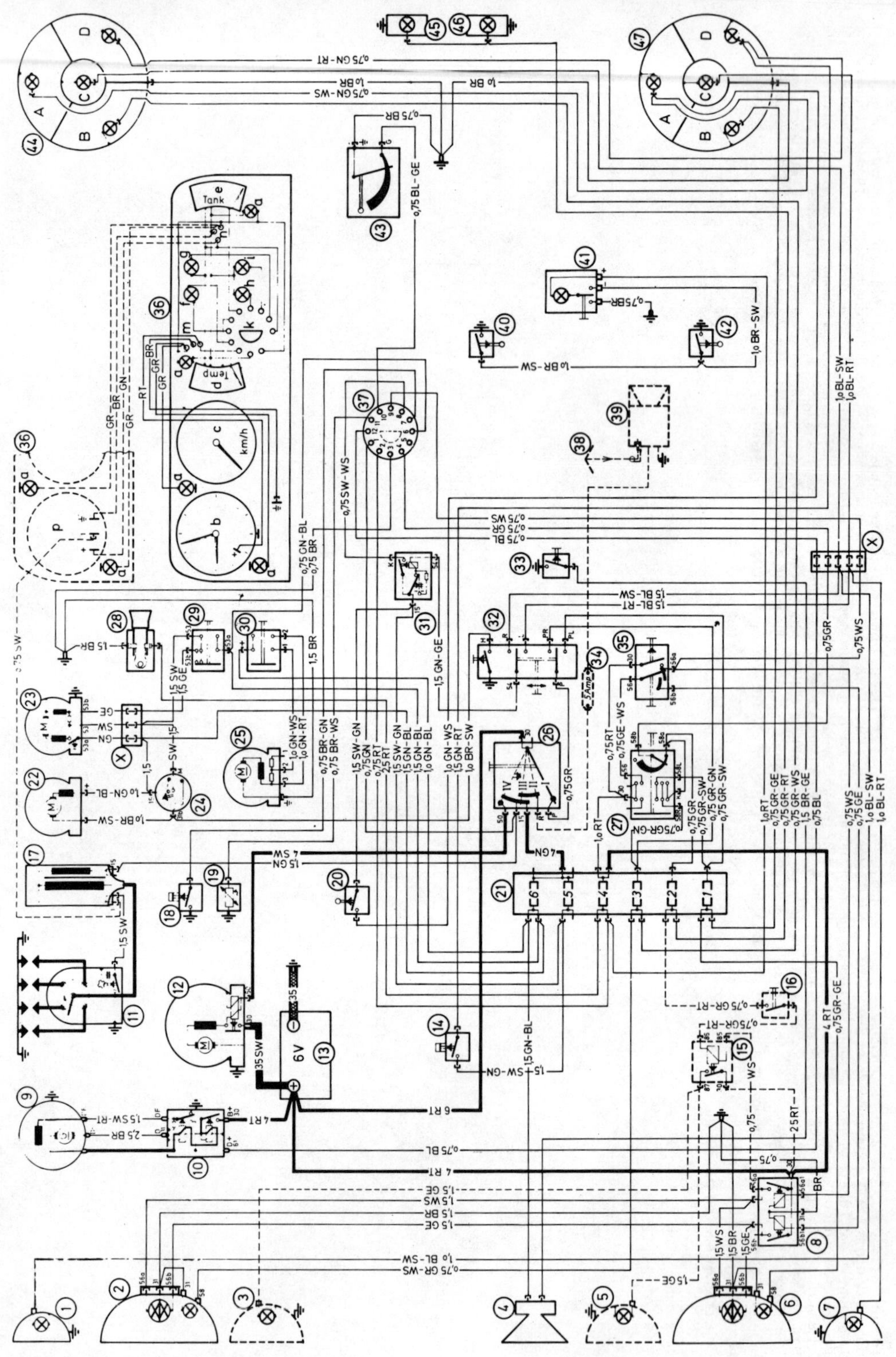

Tank
Temp
km/h
6V
0,75 GN-RT
1,0 BR
0,75 GN-WS
0,75 BR
0,75 BL-GE
0,75 SBR
1,0 BR-SW
1,0 BL-SW
1,0 BL-RT
0,75 SW-WS
0,75 WS
0,75 GR
0,75 BL
0,75 GN-BL
1,5 BL-SW
1,5 BL-RT
1,5 BR
1,5 SW
1,5 GE
1,5 GN-GE
1,0 GN-BL
1,0 BR-SW
1,0 GN-WS
1,0 GN-RT
0,75 BR-GN
0,75 BR-WS
1,5 SW-GN
0,75 GN
0,75 RT
2,5 RT
1,5 GN-BL
1,0 GN-WS
1,5 GN-RT
1,0 BR-SW
0,75 GR
0,75 RT
0,75 GE-WS
1,0 RT
0,75 GR-GN
0,75 GR-SW
0,75 GR-GN
0,75 GR-SW
1,0 RT-GE
0,75 GR-RT
0,75 GR-WS
1,5 BR-GE
0,75 BL
0,75 WS
0,75 GE
4 SW
1,5 GN
4 GN
35 SW
6 RT
4 RT
1,5 SW-RT
2,5 BR
0,75 BL
1,5 SW-GN
4 RT
0,75 GR-GE
0,75 GR-RT
25 RT
1,5 GE
1,5 WS
1,5 BR
1,5 GE
1,0 BL-SW
0,75 GR-WS
1,5 GE
15 WS
1,5 BR
15 GE
0,75 SW
5 Amp

FIG 13:2 BMW 1600 2/6 volt

Key to Fig 13:2 1 Turn indicator RH 2 Headlight RH with parking light 3 Foglamp RH 4 Horn 5 Foglamp LH 6 Headlight LH with parking light 7 Turn indicator LH 8 Dip relay 9 Generator 10 Regulator/switch unit 11 Distributor 12 Starter 13 Battery (6 volt) 14 Stoplight switch 15 Foglamp relay 16 Foglamp switch 17 Coil 18 Oil pressure contact 19 Water temperature sensor 20 Reversing light switch 21 Fuse box 22 Screenwasher pump 23 Screenwasher motor 24 Delay relay 25 Heater blower motor 26 Ignition/starter switch 27 Light switch 28 Cigar lighter 29 Screenwiper switch 30 Heater switch 31 Flasher unit 32 Turn indicator/parking light/screenwasher switch 33 Horn ring 34 Flying fuse for radio 35 Dipswitch 36 Instrument panel 37 12-pole plug for 'k' on instrument panel (view from cable side) 38 Radio aerial 39 Radio 40 Door switch RH 41 Interior light 42 Door switch LH 43 Fuel gauge mechanism 44 Rear light RH 45 Number plate light RH 46 Number plate light LH 47 Rear light LH X Flat pin connector

Cable colour coding 1.5 sq mm cross-section **BL** Blue **BR** Brown **GE** Yellow **GN** Green **GR** Grey **RT** Red **SW** Black **WS** White

Instrument panel **a** Instrument lighting **b** Clock **c** Speedometer **d** Thermometer **e** Fuel gauge **f** Charge telltale (red) **g** Oil pressure telltale (orange) **h** Main beam telltale (blue) **i** Turn indicator telltale (green) **k** 12-pole plug for position 37 (seen from connection side) **m** 3-pole plug for clock cable **n** 3-pole plug for revolution counter cable **p** Revolution counter (special equipment, replaces clock)

Special equipment (position numbers) 3, 5, 15 and 16=Foglamps , 38 and 39=Radio and aerial 36p=Revolution counter

Fuses 1, 2, 3, 4 and 5=8 amp 6=25 amp Radio=5 amp

Firing order 1–3–4–2

Ignition/starter switch positions 1 Halt 2 Garage 3 Fahrt (Drive) 4 Start

Rear lights **A** Reversing light **B** Rear light **C** Turn indicator **D** Stoplight

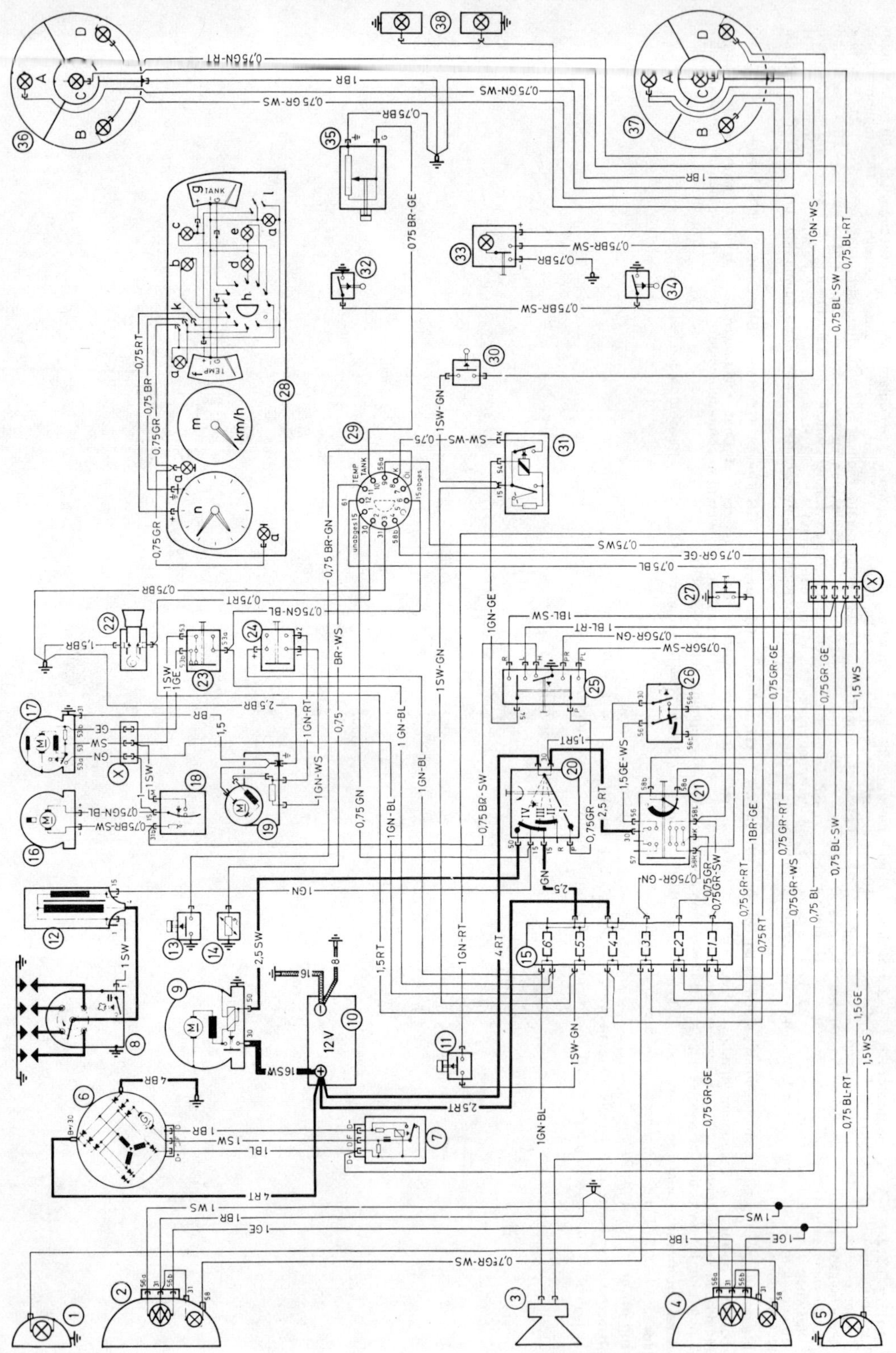

FIG 13:3 BMW 1600 2/12 volt

Key to Fig 13:3 1 Turn indicator front RH 2 Headlight RH with parking light 3 Horn 4 Headlamp LH with parking light 5 Turn indicator front LH 6 Alternator 7 Voltage regulator 8 Distributor 9 Starter 10 Battery 11 Stoplight switch 12 Coil 13 Oil pressure contact 14 Remote thermometer contact 15 Fuse box 16 Screenwasher pump 17 Screenwiper motor 18 Delay relay 19 Heater blower 20 Ignition/starter switch 21 Light switch 22 Cigar lighter 23 Screenwiper switch 24 Blower switch 25 Turn indicator/parking light/screenwasher switch 26 Dipswitch/headlight flasher 27 Horn ring 28 Instrument panel 29 12-pole plug for instrument panel (seen from cable side) 30 Reversing light switch 31 Flasher unit 32 Door switch RH 33 Interior light 34 Door switch LH 35 Fuel gauge tank mechanism 36 Rear light RH 37 Rear light LH 38 Number plate light X Flat pin connector

Instrument panel **a** Instrument lighting **b** Charge telltale (red) **c** Oil pressure telltale (orange) **d** Main beam telltale (blue) **e** Turn indicator telltale (green) **f** Water temperature gauge **g** Fuel gauge **h** 12-pole plug **k** 3-pole plug for clock **l** 3-pole plug for revolution counter **m** Speedometer **n** Clock

Ignition/starter switch positions 1 Halt 2 Garage 3 Fahrt (Drive) 4 Start

Rear lights **A** Reversing light **B** Rear light **C** Turn indicator **D** Stoplight

Firing order 1–3–4–2

Cable colour coding 1.5 sq mm cross-section **BL** Blue **BR** Brown **GE** Yellow **GN** Green **GR** Grey **RT** Red **SW** Black **VI** Violet **WS** White

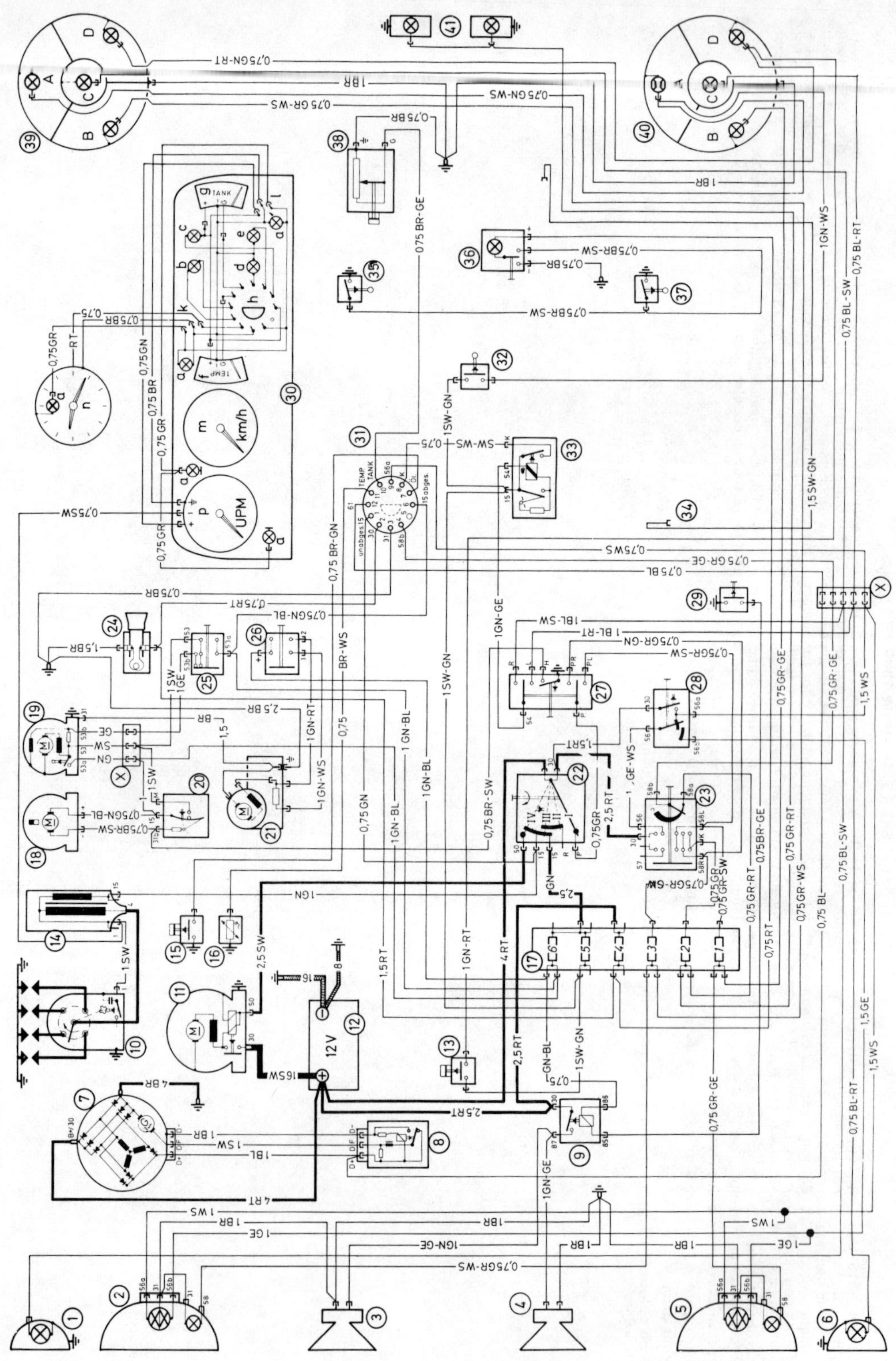

FIG 13:4 BMW 1600TI

Key to Fig 13:4 1 Turn indicator front RH 2 Headlight RH with parking light 3 Horn RH 4 Horn LH 5 Headlight RH with parking light 6 Turn indicator front LH 7 Alternator 8 Voltage regulator 9 Horn relay 10 Distributor 11 Starter 12 Battery 13 Stoplight switch 14 Coil 15 Oil pressure contact 16 Remote thermometer contact 17 Fuse box 18 Screenwasher pump 19 Screenwiper motor 20 Delay relay 21 Heater blower 22 Ignition/starter switch 23 Light switch 24 Cigar lighter 25 Screenwiper switch 26 Blower switch 27 Turn indicator/parking light/screenwasher switch 28 Dipswitch/headlight flasher 29 Horn ring 30 Instrument panel 31 12-pole plug for instrument panel (seen from cable side) 32 Reversing light switch 33 Flasher unit 34 Cable for heated rear window (Special equipment) 35 Door switch RH 36 Interior light 37 Door switch LH 38 Fuel gauge tank mechanism 39 Rear light RH 40 Rear light LH 41 Number plate light X Flat pin connector

Instrument panel **a** Instrument lighting **b** Charge telltale (red) **c** Oil pressure telltale (orange) **d** Main beam telltale (blue) **e** Turn indicator telltale (green) **f** Water temperature gauge **g** Fuel gauge **h** 12-pole plug **k** 3-pole plug for clock **l** 3-pole plug for revolution counter **m** Speedometer **n** Clock **p** Revolution counter

Ignition/starter switch positions 1 Halt 2 Garage 3 Fahrt (Drive) 4 Start

Rear lights **A** Reversing light **B** Rear light **C** Turn indicator **D** Stoplight

Firing order 1–3–4–2

Cable colour coding 1.5 sq mm cross-section **BL** Blue **BR** Brown **GE** Yellow **GN** Green **GR** Grey **RT** Red **SW** Black **VI** Violet **WS** White

Inches	Decimals	Millimetres	Inches to Millimetres		Millimetres to Inches	
			Inches	mm	mm	Inches
1/64	.015625	.3969	.001	.0254	.01	.00039
1/32	.03125	.7937	.002	.0508	.02	.00079
3/64	.046875	1.1906	.003	.0762	.03	.00118
1/16	.0625	1.5875	.004	.1016	.04	.00157
5/64	.078125	1.9844	.005	.1270	.05	.00197
3/32	.09375	2.3812	.006	.1524	.06	.00236
7/64	.109375	2.7781	.007	.1778	.07	.00276
1/8	.125	3.1750	.008	.2032	.08	.00315
9/64	.140625	3.5719	.009	.2286	.09	.00354
5/32	.15625	3.9687	.01	.254	.1	.00394
11/64	.171875	4.3656	.02	.508	.2	.00787
3/16	.1875	4.7625	.03	.762	.3	.01181
13/64	.203125	5·1594	.04	1.016	.4	.01575
7/32	.21875	5.5562	.05	1.270	.5	.01969
15/64	.234375	5.9531	.06	1.524	.6	.02362
1/4	.25	6.3500	.07	1.778	.7	.02756
17/64	.265625	6.7469	.08	2.032	.8	.03150
9/32	.28125	7.1437	09	2.286	.9	.03543
19/64	.296875	7.5406	1	2.54	1	.03937
5/16	.3125	7.9375	2	5.08	2	.07874
21/64	.328125	8.3344	3	7.62	3	.11811
11/32	.34375	8.7312	4	10.16	4	.15748
23/64	.359375	9.1281	5	12.70	5	.19685
3/8	.375	9.5250	6	15.24	6	.23622
25/64	.390625	9.9219	.7	17.78	7	.27559
13/32	.40625	10.3187	.8	20.32	8	.31496
27/64	.421875	10.7156	.9	22.86	9	.35433
7/16	.4375	11.1125	1	25.4	10	.39370
29/64	.453125	11.5094	2	50.8	11	.43307
15/32	.46875	11.9062	3	76.2	12	.47244
31/64	.484375	12.3031	4	101.6	13	.51181
1/2	.5	12.7000	5	127.0	14	.55118
33/64	.515625	13.0969	6	152.4	15	.59055
17/32	.53125	13.4937	7	177.8	16	.62992
35/64	.546875	13.8906	8	203.2	17	.66929
9/16	.5625	14.2875	9	228.6	18	.70866
37/64	.578125	14.6844	10	254.0	19	.74803
19/32	.59375	15.0812	11	279.4	20	.78740
39/64	.609375	15.4781	12	304.8	21	.82677
5/8	.625	15.8750	13	330.2	22	.86614
41/64	.640625	16.2719	14	355.6	23	.90551
21/32	.65625	16.6687	15	381.0	24	.94488
43/64	.671875	17.0656	16	406.4	25	.98425
11/16	.6875	17.4625	17	431.8	26	1.02362
45/64	.703125	17.8594	18	457.2	27	1.06299
23/32	.71875	18.2562	19	482.6	28	1.10236
47/64	.734375	18.6531	20	508.0	29	1.14173
3/4	75	19.0500	21	533.4	30	1.18110
49/64	.765625	19.4469	22	558.8	31	1.22047
25/32	.78125	19.8437	23	584.2	32	1.25984
51/64	.796875	20.2406	24	609.6	33	1.29921
13/16	.8125	20.6375	25	635.0	34	1.33858
53/64	.828125	21.0344	26	660.4	35	1.37795
27/32	.84375	21.4312	27	685.8	36	1.41732
55/64	.859375	21.8281	28	711.2	37	1.4567
7/8	.875	22.2250	29	736.6	38	1.4961
57/64	.890625	22.6219	30	762.0	39	1.5354
29/32	.90625	23.0187	31	787.4	40	1.5748
59/64	.921875	23.4156	32	812.8	41	1.6142
15/16	.9375	23.8125	33	838.2	42	1.6535
61/64	.953125	24.2094	34	863.6	43	1.6929
31/32	.96875	24.6062	35	889.0	44	1.7323
63/64	.984375	25.0031	36	914.4	45	1.7717

UNITS	Pints to Litres	Gallons to Litres	Litres to Pints	Litres to Gallons	Miles to Kilometres	Kilometres to Miles	Lbs. per sq. In. to Kg. per sq. Cm.	Kg. per sq. Cm. to Lbs. per sq. In.
1	.57	4.55	1.76	.22	1.61	.62	.07	14.22
2	1.14	9.09	3.52	.44	3.22	1.24	.14	28.50
3	1.70	13.64	5.28	.66	4.83	1.86	.21	42.67
4	2.27	18.18	7.04	.88	6.44	2.49	.28	56.89
5	2.84	22.73	8.80	1.10	8.05	3.11	.35	71.12
6	3.41	27.28	10.56	1.32	9.66	3.73	.42	85.34
7	3.98	31.82	12.32	1.54	11.27	4.35	.49	99.56
8	4.55	36.37	14.08	1.76	12.88	4.97	.56	113.79
9		40.91	15.84	1.98	14.48	5.59	.63	128.00
10		45.46	17.60	2.20	16.09	6.21	.70	142.23
20				4.40	32.19	12.43	1.41	284.47
30				6.60	48.28	18.64	2.11	426.70
40				8.80	64.37	24.85		
50					80.47	31.07		
60					96.56	37.28		
70					112.65	43.50		
80					128.75	49.71		
90					144.84	55.92		
100					160.93	62.14		

UNITS	Lb ft to kgm	Kgm to lb ft	UNITS	Lb ft to kgm	Kgm to lb ft
1	.138	7.233	7	.967	50.631
2	.276	14.466	8	1.106	57.864
3	.414	21.699	9	1.244	65.097
4	.553	28.932	10	1.382	72.330
5	.691	36.165	20	2.765	144.660
6	.829	43.398	30	4.147	216.990

HINTS ON MAINTENANCE AND OVERHAUL

There are few things more rewarding than the restoration of a vehicle's original peak of efficiency and smooth performance.

The following notes are intended to help the owner to reach that state of perfection. Providing that he possesses the basic manual skills he should have no difficulty in performing most of the operations detailed in this manual. It must be stressed, however, that where recommended in the manual, highly-skilled operations ought to be entrusted to experts, who have the necessary equipment, to carry out the work satisfactorily.

Quality of workmanship:

The hazardous driving conditions on the roads to-day demand that vehicles should be as nearly perfect, mechanically, as possible. It is therefore most important that amateur work be carried out with care, bearing in mind the often inadequate working conditions, and also the inferior tools which may have to be used. It is easy to counsel perfection in all things, and we recognize that it may be setting an impossibly high standard. We do, however, suggest that every care should be taken to ensure that a vehicle is as safe to take on the road as it is humanly possible to make it.

Safe working conditions:

Even though a vehicle may be stationary, it is still potentially dangerous if certain sensible precautions are not taken when working on it while it is supported on jacks or blocks. It is indeed preferable not to use jacks alone, but to supplement them with carefully placed blocks, so that there will be plenty of support if the car rolls off the jacks during a strenuous manoeuvre. Axle stands are an excellent way of providing a rigid base which is not readily disturbed. Piles of bricks are a dangerous substitute. Be careful not to get under heavy loads on lifting tackle, the load could fall. It is preferable not to work alone when lifting an engine, or when working underneath a vehicle which is supported well off the ground. To be trapped, particularly under the vehicle, may have unpleasant results if help is not quickly forthcoming. Make some provision, however humble, to deal with fires. Always disconnect a battery if there is a likelihood of electrical shorts. These may start a fire if there is leaking fuel about. This applies particularly to leads which can carry a heavy current, like those in the starter circuit. While on the subject of electricity, we must also stress the danger of using equipment which is run off the mains and which has no earth or has faulty wiring or connections. So many workshops have damp floors, and electrical shocks are of such a nature that it is sometimes impossible to let go of a live lead or piece of equipment due to the muscular spasms which take place.

Work demanding special care:

This involves the servicing of braking, steering and suspension systems. On the road, failure of the braking system may be disastrous. Make quite sure that there can be no possibility of failure through the bursting of rusty brake pipes or rotten hoses, nor to a sudden loss of pressure due to defective seals or valves.

Problems:

The chief problems which may face an operator are:

1 External dirt.
2 Difficulty in undoing tight fixings.
3 Dismantling unfamiliar mechanisms.
4 Deciding in what respect parts are defective.
5 Confusion about the correct order for reassembly.
6 Adjusting running clearance.
7 Road testing.
8 Final tuning.

Practical suggestions to solve the problems:

1 Preliminary cleaning of large parts—engines, transmissions, steering, suspensions, etc.,—should be carried out before removal from the car. Where road dirt and mud alone are present, wash clean with a high-pressure water jet, brushing to remove stubborn adhesions, and allow to drain and dry. Where oil or grease is also present, wash down with a proprietary compound (Gunk, Teepol etc.,) applying with a stiff brush—an old paint brush is suitable—into all crevices. Cover the distributor and ignition coils with a polythene bag and then apply a strong water jet to clear the loosened deposits. Allow to drain and dry. The assemblies will then be sufficiently clean to remove and transfer to the bench for the next stage.

On the bench, further cleaning can be carried out, first wiping the parts as free as possible from grease with old newspaper. Avoid using rag or cotton waste which can leave clogging fibres behind. Any remaining grease can be removed with a brush dipped in paraffin. If necessary, traces of paraffin can be removed by carbon tetrachloride. Avoid using paraffin or petrol in large quantities for cleaning in enclosed areas, such as garages, on account of the high fire risk.

When all exteriors have been cleaned, and not before, dismantling can be commenced. This ensures that dirt will not enter into interiors and orifices revealed by dismantling. In the next phases, where components have to be cleaned, use carbon tetrachloride in preference to petrol and keep the containers covered except when in use. After the components have been cleaned, plug small holes with tapered hard wood plugs cut to size and blank off larger orifices with grease-proof paper and masking tape. Do not use soft wood plugs or matchsticks as they may break.

2 It is not advisable to hammer on the end of a screw thread, but if it must be done, first screw on a nut to protect the thread, and use a lead hammer. This applies particularly to the removal of tapered cotters. Nuts and bolts seem to 'grow' together, especially in exhaust systems. If penetrating oil does not work, try the judicious application of heat, but be careful of starting a fire. Asbestos sheet or cloth is useful to isolate heat.

Tight bushes or pieces of tail-pipe rusted into a silencer can be removed by splitting them with an open-ended hacksaw. Tight screws can sometimes be started by a tap from a hammer on the end of a suitable screwdriver. Many tight fittings will yield to the judicious use of a hammer, but it must be a soft-faced hammer if damage is to be avoided, use a heavy block on the opposite side to absorb shock. Any parts of the steering system which have been damaged should be renewed, as attempts to repair them may lead to cracking and subsequent failure, and steering ball joints should be disconnected using a recommended tool to prevent damage.

3 It often happens that an owner is baffled when trying to dismantle an unfamiliar piece of equipment. So many modern devices are pressed together or assembled by spinning-over flanges, that they must be sawn apart. The intention is that the whole assembly must be renewed. However, parts which appear to be in one piece to the naked eye, may reveal close-fitting joint lines when inspected with a magnifying glass, and, this may provide the necessary clue to dismantling. Left-handed screw threads are used where rotational forces would tend to unscrew a right-handed screw thread.

Be very careful when dismantling mechanisms which may come apart suddenly. Work in an enclosed space where the parts will be contained, and drape a piece of cloth over the device if springs are likely to fly in all directions. Mark everything which might be reassembled in the wrong position, scratched symbols may be used on unstressed parts, or a sequence of tiny dots from a centre punch can be useful. Stressed parts should never be scratched or centre-popped as this may lead to cracking under working conditions. Store parts which look alike in the correct order for reassembly. Never rely upon memory to assist in the assembly of complicated mechanisms, especially when they will be dismantled for a long time, but make notes, and drawings to supplement the diagrams in the manual, and put labels on detached wires. Rust stains may indicate unlubricated wear. This can sometimes be seen round the outside edge of a bearing cup in a universal joint. Look for bright rubbing marks on parts which normally should not make heavy contact. These might prove that something is bent or running out of truth. For example, there might be bright marks on one side of a piston, at the top near the ring grooves, and others at the bottom of the skirt on the other side. This could well be the clue to a bent connecting rod. Suspected cracks can be proved by heating the component in a light oil to approximately 100°C, removing, drying off, and dusting with french chalk, if a crack is present the oil retained in the crack will stain the french chalk.

4 In determining wear, and the degree, against the permissible limits set in the manual, accurate measurement can only be achieved by the use of a micrometer. In many cases, the wear is given to the fourth place of decimals; that is in ten-thousandths of an inch. This can be read by the vernier scale on the barrel of a good micrometer. Bore diameters are more difficult to determine. If, however, the matching shaft is accurately measured, the degree of play in the bore can be felt as a guide to its suitability. In other cases, the shank of a twist drill of known diameter is a handy check.

Many methods have been devised for determining the clearance between bearing surfaces. To-day the best and simplest is by the use of Plastigage, obtainable from most garages. A thin plastic thread is laid between the two surfaces and the bearing is tightened, flattening the thread. On removal, the width of the thread is compared with a scale supplied with the thread and the clearance is read off directly. Sometimes joint faces leak persistently, even after gasket renewal. The fault will then be traceable to distortion, dirt or burrs. Studs which are screwed into soft metal frequently raise burrs at the point of entry. A quick cure for this is to chamfer the edge of the hole in the part which fits over the stud.

5 **Always check a replacement part with the original one before it is fitted.**

If parts are not marked, and the order for reassembly is not known, a little detective work will help. Look for marks which are due to wear to see if they can be mated. Joint faces may not be identical due to manufacturing errors, and parts which overlap may be stained, giving a clue to the correct position. Most fixings leave identifying marks especially if they were painted over on assembly. It is then easier to decide whether a nut, for instance, has a plain, a spring, or a shakeproof washer under it. All running surfaces become 'bedded' together after long spells of work and tiny imperfections on one part will be found to have left corresponding marks on the other. This is particularly true of shafts and bearings and even a score on a cylinder wall will show on the piston.

6 Checking end float or rocker clearances by feeler gauge may not always give accurate results because of wear. For instance, the rocker tip which bears on a valve stem may be deeply pitted, in which case the feeler will simply be bridging a depression. Thrust washers may also wear depressions in opposing faces to make accurate measurement difficult. End float is then easier to check by using a dial gauge. It is common practice to adjust end play in bearing assemblies, like front hubs with taper rollers, by doing up the axle nut until the hub becomes stiff to turn and then backing it off a little. Do not use this method with ballbearing hubs as the assembly is often preloaded by tightening the axle nut to its fullest extent. If the splitpin hole will not line up, file the base of the nut a little.

Steering assemblies often wear in the straight-ahead position. If any part is adjusted, make sure that it remains free when moved from lock to lock. Do not be surprised if an assembly like a steering gearbox, which is known to be carefully adjusted outside the car, becomes stiff when it is bolted in place. This will be due to distortion of the case by the pull of the mounting bolts, particularly if the mounting points are not all touching together. This problem may be met in other equipment and is cured by careful attention to the alignment of mounting points.

When a spanner is stamped with a size and A/F it means that the dimension is the width between the jaws and has no connection with ANF, which is the designation for the American National Fine thread. Coarse threads like Whitworth are rarely used on cars to-day except for studs which screw into soft aluminium or cast iron. For this reason it might be found that the top end of a cylinder head stud has a fine thread and the lower end a coarse thread to screw into the cylinder block. If the car has mainly UNF threads then it is likely that any coarse threads will be UNC, which are not the same as Whitworth. Small sizes have the same number of threads in Whitworth and UNC, but in the $\frac{1}{2}$ inch size for example, there are twelve threads to the inch in the former and thirteen in the latter.

7 After a major overhaul, particularly if a great deal of work has been done on the braking, steering and suspension systems, it is advisable to approach the problem of testing with care. If the braking system has been overhauled, apply heavy pressure to the brake pedal and get a second operator to check every possible source of leakage. The brakes may work extremely well, but a leak could cause complete failure after a few miles.

Do not fit the hub caps until every wheel nut has been checked for tightness, and make sure the tyre pressures are correct. Check the levels of coolant, lubricants and hydraulic fluids. Being satisfied that all is well, take the car on the road and test the brakes at once. Check the steering and the action of the handbrake. Do all this at moderate speeds on quiet roads, and make sure there is no other vehicle behind you when you try a rapid stop.

Finally, remember that many parts settle down after a time, so check for tightness of all fixings after the car has been on the road for a hundred miles or so.

8 It is useless to tune an engine which has not reached its normal running temperature. In the same way, the tune of an engine which is stiff after a rebore will be different when the engine is again running free. Remember too, that rocker clearances on pushrod operated valve gear will change when the cylinder head nuts are tightened after an initial period of running with a new head gasket.

Trouble may not always be due to what seems the obvious cause. Ignition, carburation and mechanical condition are interdependent and spitting back through the carburetter, which might be attributed to a weak mixture, can be caused by a sticking inlet valve.

For one final hint on tuning, never adjust more than one thing at a time or it will be impossible to tell which adjustment produced the desired result.

NOTES

GLOSSARY OF TERMS

Allen key Cranked wrench of hexagonal section for use with socket head screws.

Alternator Electrical generator producing alternating current. Rectified to direct current for battery charging.

Ambient temperature Surrounding atmospheric temperature.

Annulus Used in engineering to indicate the outer ring gear of an epicyclic gear train.

Armature The shaft carrying the windings, which rotates in the magnetic field of a generator or starter motor. That part of a solenoid or relay which is activated by the magnetic field.

Axial In line with, or pertaining to, an axis.

Backlash Play in meshing gears.

Balance lever A bar where force applied at the centre is equally divided between connections at the ends.

Banjo axle Axle casing with large diameter housing for the crownwheel and differential.

Bendix pinion A self-engaging and self-disengaging drive on a starter motor shaft.

Bevel pinion A conical shaped gearwheel, designed to mesh with a similar gear with an axis usually at 90 deg. to its own.

bhp Brake horse power, measured on a dynamometer.

bmep Brake mean effective pressure. Average pressure on a piston during the working stroke.

Brake cylinder Cylinder with hydraulically operated piston(s) acting on brake shoes or pad(s).

Brake regulator Control valve fitted in hydraulic braking system which limits brake pressure to rear brakes during heavy braking to prevent rear wheel locking.

Camber Angle at which a wheel is tilted from the vertical.

Capacitor Modern term for an electrical condenser. Part of distributor assembly, connected across contact breaker points, acts as an interference suppressor.

Castellated Top face of a nut, slotted across the flats, to take a locking splitpin.

Castor Angle at which the kingpin or swivel pin is tilted when viewed from the side.

cc Cubic centimetres. Engine capacity is arrived at by multiplying the area of the bore in sq cm by the stroke in cm by the number of cylinders.

Clevis U-shaped forked connector used with a clevis pin, usually at handbrake connections.

Collet A type of collar, usually split and located in a groove in a shaft, and held in place by a retainer. The arrangement used to retain the spring(s) on a valve stem in most cases.

Commutator Rotating segmented current distributor between armature windings and brushes in generator or motor.

Compression The ratio, or quantitative relation, of the total volume (piston at bottom of stroke) to the unswept volume (piston at top of stroke) in an engine cylinder.

Condenser See capacitor.

Core plug Plug for blanking off a manufacturing hole in a casting.

Crownwheel Large bevel gear in rear axle, driven by a bevel pinion attached to the propeller shaft. Sometimes called a 'ring gear'.

'C'-spanner Like a 'C' with a handle. For use on screwed collars without flats, but with slots or holes.

Damper Modern term for shock-absorber, used in vehicle suspension systems to damp out spring oscillations.

Depression The lowering of atmospheric pressure as in the inlet manifold and carburetter.

Dowel Close tolerance pin, peg, tube, or bolt, which accurately locates mating parts.

Drag link Rod connecting steering box drop arm (pitman arm) to nearest front wheel steering arm in certain types of steering systems.

Dry liner Thinwall tube pressed into cylinder bore

Dry sump Lubrication system where all oil is scavenged from the sump, and returned to a separate tank.

Dynamo See Generator.

Electrode Terminal, part of an electrical component, such as the points or 'Electrodes' of a sparking plug.

Electrolyte In lead-acid car batteries a solution of sulphuric acid and distilled water.

End float The axial movement between associated parts, end play.

EP Extreme pressure. In lubricants, special grades for heavily loaded bearing surfaces, such as gear teeth in a gearbox, or crownwheel and pinion in a rear axle.

Fade Of brakes. Reduced efficiency due to overheating.

Field coils Windings on the polepieces of motors and generators.

Fillets Narrow finishing strips usually applied to interior bodywork.

First motion shaft Input shaft from clutch to gearbox.

Fullflow filter Filters in which all the oil is pumped to the engine. If the element becomes clogged, a bypass valve operates to pass unfiltered oil to the engine.

FWD Front wheel drive.

Gear pump Two meshing gears in a close fitting casing. Oil is carried from the inlet round the outside of both gears in the spaces between the gear teeth and casing to the outlet, the meshing gear teeth prevent oil passing back to the inlet, and the oil is forced through the outlet port.

Generator Modern term for 'Dynamo'. When rotated produces electrical current.

Grommet A ring of protective or sealing material. Can be used to protect pipes or leads passing through bulkheads.

Grubscrew Fully threaded headless screw with screwdriver slot. Used for locking, or alignment purposes.

Gudgeon pin Shaft which connects a piston to its connecting rod. Sometimes called 'wrist pin', or 'piston pin'.

Halfshaft One of a pair transmitting drive from the differential.

Helical In spiral form. The teeth of helical gears are cut at a spiral angle to the side faces of the gearwheel.

Hot spot Hot area that assists vapourisation of fuel on its way to cylinders. Often provided by close contact between inlet and exhaust manifolds.

HT High Tension. Applied to electrical current produced by the ignition coil for the sparking plugs.

Hydrometer A device for checking specific gravity of liquids. Used to check specific gravity of electrolyte.

Hypoid bevel gears A form of bevel gear used in the rear axle drive gears. The bevel pinion meshes below the centre line of the crownwheel, giving a lower propeller shaft line.

Idler A device for passing on movement. A free running gear between driving and driven gears. A lever transmitting track rod movement to a side rod in steering gear.

Impeller A centrifugal pumping element. Used in water pumps to stimulate flow.

Journals Those parts of a shaft that are in contact with the bearings.

Kingpin The main vertical pin which carries the front wheel spindle, and permits steering movement. May be called 'steering pin' or 'swivel pin'.

Layshaft The shaft which carries the laygear in the gearbox. The laygear is driven by the first motion shaft and drives the third motion shaft according to the gear selected. Sometimes called the 'countershaft' or 'second motion shaft.'

lb ft A measure of twist or torque. A pull of 10 lb at a radius of 1 ft is a torque of 10 lb ft.

lb/sq in Pounds per square inch.

Little-end The small, or piston end of a connecting rod. Sometimes called the 'small-end'.

LT Low Tension. The current output from the battery.

Mandrel Accurately manufactured bar or rod used for test or centring purposes.

Manifold A pipe, duct, or chamber, with several branches.

Needle rollers Bearing rollers with a length many times their diameter.

Oil bath Reservoir which lubricates parts by immersion. In air filters, a separate oil supply for wetting a wire mesh element to hold the dust.

Oil wetted In air filters, a wire mesh element lightly oiled to trap and hold airborne dust.

Overlap Period during which inlet and exhaust valves are open together.

Panhard rod Bar connected between fixed point on chassis and another on axle to control sideways movement.

Pawl Pivoted catch which engages in the teeth of a ratchet to permit movement in one direction only.

Peg spanner Tool with pegs, or pins, to engage in holes or slots in the part to be turned.

Pendant pedals Pedals with levers that are pivoted at the top end.

Phillips screwdriver A cross-point screwdriver for use with the cross-slotted heads of Phillips screws.

Pinion A small gear, usually in relation to another gear.

Piston-type damper Shock absorber in which damping is controlled by a piston working in a closed oil-filled cylinder.

Preloading Preset static pressure on ball or roller bearings not due to working loads.

Radial Radiating from a centre, like the spokes of a wheel.

Radius rod Pivoted arm confining movement of a part to an arc of fixed radius.

Ratchet Toothed wheel or rack which can move in one direction only, movement in the other being prevented by a pawl.

Ring gear A gear tooth ring attached to outer periphery of flywheel. Starter pinion engages with it during starting.

Runout Amount by which rotating part is out of true.

Semi-floating axle Outer end of rear axle halfshaft is carried on bearing inside axle casing. Wheel hub is secured to end of shaft.

Servo A hydraulic or pneumatic system for assisting, or, augmenting a physical effort. See 'Vacuum Servo'.

Setscrew One which is threaded for the full length of the shank.

Shackle A coupling link, used in the form of two parallel pins connected by side plates to secure the end of the master suspension spring and absorb the effects of deflection.

Shell bearing Thinwalled steel shell lined with antifriction metal. Usually semi-circular and used in pairs for main and big-end bearings.

Shock absorber See 'Damper'.

Silentbloc Rubber bush bonded to inner and outer metal sleeves.

Socket-head screw Screw with hexagonal socket for an Allen key.

Solenoid A coil of wire creating a magnetic field when electric current passes through it. Used with a soft iron core to operate contacts or a mechanical device.

Spur gear A gear with teeth cut axially across the periphery.

Stub axle Short axle fixed at one end only.

Tachometer An instrument for accurate measurement of rotating speed. Usually indicates in revolutions per minute.

TDC Top Dead Centre. The highest point reached by a piston in a cylinder, with the crank and connecting rod in line.

Thermostat Automatic device for regulating temperature. Used in vehicle coolant systems to open a valve which restricts circulation at low temperature.

Third motion shaft Output shaft of gearbox.

Threequarter floating axle Outer end of rear axle halfshaft flanged and bolted to wheel hub, which runs on bearing mounted on outside of axle casing. Vehicle weight is not carried by the axle shaft.

Thrust bearing or washer Used to reduce friction in rotating parts subject to axial loads.

Torque Turning or twisting effort. See 'lb ft'.

Track rod The bar(s) across the vehicle which connect the steering arms and maintain the front wheels in their correct alignment.

UJ Universal joint. A coupling between shafts which permits angular movement.

UNF Unified National Fine screw thread.

Vacuum servo Device used in brake system, using difference between atmospheric pressure and inlet manifold depression to operate a piston which acts to augment brake pressure as required. See 'Servo'.

Venturi A restriction or 'choke' in a tube, as in a carburetter, used to increase velocity to obtain a reduction in pressure.

Vernier A sliding scale for obtaining fractional readings of the graduations of an adjacent scale.

Welch plug A domed thin metal disc which is partially flattened to lock in a recess. Used to plug core holes in castings.

Wet liner Removable cylinder barrel, sealed against coolant leakage, where the coolant is in direct contact with the outer surface.

Wet sump A reservoir attached to the crankcase to hold the lubricating oil.

NOTES

INDEX

A

Air cleaner maintenance 38
Air pump 27
Alternator description 126
Alternator removal 126
Anti-roller 89
Armature/generator 120
Armature/starter 122
Antifreeze 52
Axle shaft assembly 77
Axle shaft removal 77
Axle shaft inspection 77

B

Ball joints steering 88
Battery maintenance 118
Battery testing 118
Beam setting—headlamp 124
Belt tension 49
Big-end bearings, fitting 20
Big-end bearings, removal 20
Bleeding, brake system 106
Bodywork renovation 129
Brake adjustment rear 106
Brake bleeding 106
Brake caliper servicing 101
Brake disc removal 102, 104
Brake flexible hose removal 110
Brake layout description 99
Brake linings 105
Brake maintenance 100
Brake master cylinder removal 107
Brake master cylinder servicing 108
Brake shoes 106
Brake wheel cylinders 109
Brushes, generator 119
Brushes, starter 122

C

Caliper front brakes 101
Camshaft bearings 14
Camshaft drive removal 14
Camshaft drive replacement 14
Camshaft removal 14
Camshaft replacement 14
Capacitor distributor 43
Carburetter operation and adjustment Solex PDSI 33
Carburetter operation and adjustment Solex 40.PHH 35
Carburetter removal and refitting Solex PDSI .. 32
Carburetter removal and refitting Solex 40.PHH 34
Clutch construction 53
Clutch description 53
Clutch hydraulic system 56
Clutch inspection 56
Clutch master cylinder 57
Clutch pedal removal and adjustment .. 58
Clutch pedal removal and adjustment, 1600–2 59
Clutch removal 53
Clutch replacement 54
Clutch shaft pilot bearing 23
Clutch slave cylinder 57
Coil spring front suspension 90
Condenser (capacitor) distributor 43
Connecting rod removal 19
Connecting rod reassembly 20
Contact breaker points 41
Contact renovation, distributor 42
Contact breaker points adjustment 43
Control box (electrical) 123
Cooling system, description 47
Cooling system, maintenance 47
Cooling system, testing 48
Crankpin and journal alignment 23
Crankshaft balance 23
Crankshaft bearings 22
Crankshaft pulley removal 18
Crankshaft sprocket removal and refitting .. 17
Crankshaft removal 21
Crankshaft thrust bearing end float 21
Crownwheel and pinion renewal 81
Current regulator adjustment 124
Cylinder block and crankcase 23
Cylinder bores 24
Cylinder head dismantling and reassembly .. 15
Cylinder head nut sequence 13
Cylinder head removal 11
Cylinder head replacement 12
Cylinder head servicing 16

D

Decarbonizing 16
Differential dismantling 80
Differential housing removal and replacement 79
Differential reassembly 80
Disc brake pads 101
Disc removal 105
Distributor cap leads 44
Distributor dismantling 43
Distributor drive spindle 44
Distributor reassembly 43
Distributor removal 43
Distributor replacement 43
Door dismantling, front 130
Door dismantling, rear 133
Door hinge adjustment, front 130
Door hinge adjustment, rear 133
Draining cooling system 47

E

Electrically heated rear screen 125
Electrical system, description 117
Electrolyte, battery 118
Engine compartment lid 136
Engine description 9
Engine removal 9
Engine replacement 11
Exhaust emission control unit 26
Exhaust gas control valve 27

F

Factory exchange engine installation 25
Fan belt 49
Field coil testing, generator 120
Field coil testing, starter 123
Final drive unit removal and replacement .. 79
Float adjustment, Solex 38.PDSI 34
Float adjustment, Solex 40.PHH 36
Flywheel removal 21
Flywheel replacement 21
Flywheel starter ring 21
Friction pad renewal, disc brakes 101
Front axle carrier 85
Front door servicing 129
Front hub bearings 87
Front suspension description 85
Front screen glass 135
Front suspension guide joints 89
Frost precautions 52
Fuel pump description 31
Fuel pump dismantling 31
Fuel pump examination 32
Fuel pump installation 32
Fuel pump maintenance 31
Fuel pump reassembly 32
Fuel system description 31
Fuel tank sender unit 125

G

Gearbox description 63
Gearbox dismantling 64
Gearbox refitting 64
Gearbox removal 63
Gearbox shifter forks 70
Generator armature 120
Generator bushes 119
Generator dismantling 119
Generator refitting 119
Generator removal 118
Generator testing 120
Glossary of terms 171
Grinding in valves 16
Guide joint servicing 89

H

Halfshaft removal 77
Halfshaft servicing 77
Handbrake cable 110
Headlamp lens and reflector renewal 124
Head nut tightening sequence 13
Head removal 11
Head replacement 12
Hints on maintenance and overhaul 167
Hub bearings, front 87
Hub bearings, rear 77
Hydraulic brake operation 99
Hydraulic flexible hose removal 110
Hydraulic brake servo unit, description .. 113
Hydraulic shock absorbers 77
Hydrometer test of electrolyte 118

I

Idler arm and support steering 98
Ignition faults 42
Ignition system description 41
Ignition timing 43
Injection pipes 28
Input shaft 71

L

Layshaft 68
Lighting circuit faults 125
Low-tension circuit test 42
Luggage compartment lid 137

M

Main bearing oversizes 22
Main bearing shell 22
Master cylinder overhaul 108
Master cylinder refitting 107
Master cylinder removal 107

O

Oil filter 25
Oil pump dismantling and reassembly .. 24
Oil pump removal and refitting 24
Oilways crankshaft cleaning 22
Output shaft 67

P

Pedal travel adjustment, brake 111
Pedal travel adjustment, clutch 60
Petrol tank removal and cleaning 38
Piston classes and oversizes 19
Piston and connecting rod replacement .. 22
Piston removal 19
Piston rings 19
Piston ring gap 20
Piston ring replacement 19
Propeller shaft removal 73
Propeller shaft servicing 73

R

Radiator removal 48
Rear axle assembly 74
Rear axle carrier renewal 75
Rear brake servicing 105
Rear brake shoes 105
Rear hub bearings 77
Rear hub lubrication 77
Rear hub oil seal 77
Rear hub removal 77
Rear light renewal 124
Rear screen glass 135
Regulator unit 123
Removing engine 9
Rocker clearance adjustment 15
Rocker shaft and support assembly 16

S

Selector shaft and forks 70
Sliding sunroof 138
Spark plug condition 44
Spark plug gap 44
Spark plug leads 44
Specific gravity 118
Starter motor armature 122

Starter motor brushes 122
Starter motor pinion drive 123
Starter motor switch 122
Starter motor testing 123
Starter ring gear 21
Steering box overhaul 94
Steering box removal and replacement .. 93
Steering box universal joint 94
Steering description 93
Steering guide lever 97
Steering lubrication 98
Steering rack 98
Steering wheel removal and replacement .. 97
Stroboscopic timing 44
Suspension arm silentbloc 76
Synchromesh assembly 66

T
Technical data 143
Telescopic leg shock absorber 90
Tie rod lever 88
Timing chain and timing gear 17
Timing marks, ignition 43
Torque wrench settings 154
Trailing arm servicing 75
Trailing arm silentbloc bushes 76

Transmission dismantling 64
Transmission removal 63
Trim, front door panel 130
Trim, rear door panel 133

U
Universal joint servicing 78

V
Valve clearance adjustment 15
Valve dismantling 16
Valves, fuel pump 32
Valve guide replacement 16
Valve seat renovation 16
Valve timing gear overhaul 17

W
Water pump overhaul 50
Water pump removal and replacement .. 49
Wheel hub and bearing servicing 87
Window, back, removal and replacement .. 135
Window, front, removal and replacement .. 135
Window front door, removal and replacement 132
Window rear door, removal and replacement .. 134
Windshield wiper motor 124
Wiring diagrams 158, 160, 162, 164

Alfa Romeo Giulia 1962 on
Aston Martin 1921-58
Audi 100 1969 on
(Austin, Morris etc.) 1100 Mk. 1 1962-67
(Austin, Morris etc.) 1100 Mk. 2, 1300 Mk. 1, 2, America 1968 on
Austin A30, A35, A40 Farina
Austin A55 Mk. 2, A60 1958-69
Austin A99, A110 1959-68
Austin J4 1960 on
Austin Maxi 1969 on
Austin, Morris 1800 1964 on
BMC 3 (Austin A50, A55 Mk. 1, Morris Oxford 2. 3 1954-59)
Austin Healey 100/6, 3000 1956-68
(Austin Healey, MG) Sprite, Midget 1958 on
BMW 1600 1964 on
BMW 1800 1964-68
BMW 2000, 2002 1966 on
Chevrolet Corvair 1960-69
Chevrolet Corvette V8 1957-65
Chevrolet Vega 2300 1970-71
Chevrolet Corvette V8 1965-71
Chrysler Valiant V8 1965 on
Chrysler Valiant Straight Six 1966-70
Citroen DS 19, ID 19 1955-66
Citroen ID 19, DS 19, 20, 21 1966-70
Datsun 1200 1970 on
Datsun 1300, 1600 1968 on
Datsun 240Z Sport 1970 on
De Dion Bouton 1899-1907
Fiat 124 1966 on
Fiat 124 Sport 1966 on
Fiat 125 1967 on
Fiat 500 1957 on
Fiat 600, 600D 1955-69
Fiat 850 1964 on
Fiat 1100 1957-69
Fiat 1300, 1500 1961-67
Ford Anglia Prefect 100E 1953-62
Ford Anglia 105E, Prefect 107E 1959-67
Ford Capri 1300, 1600 1968 on
Ford Capri 2000 GT, 3000 GT 1969 on
Ford Classic, Capri 1961-64
Ford Consul, Zephyr, Zodiac, 1, 2 1950-62
Ford Corsair Straight Four 1963-65
Ford Corsair V4 1965-68
Ford Corsair V4 1969 on
Ford Cortina 1962-66
Ford Cortina 1967-68
Ford Cortina 1969-70
Ford Cortina Mk. 3 1970 on
Ford Escort 1967 on
Ford Falcon V8 1964-69
Ford Thames 10, 12, 15 cwt 1957-65
Ford Transit 1965 on
Ford Zephyr Zodiac Mk. 3 1962-66
Ford Zephyr V4, V6, Zodiac 1966 on
Hillman Avenger 1970 on
Hillman Hunter 1966 on
Hillman Imp 1963-68
Hillman Imp 1969 on
Hillman Minx 1 to 5 1956-65
Hillman Minx 1965-67
Hillman Minx 1966-70
Hillman Super Minx 1961-65
Holden Straight Six 1948-66
Holden Straight Six 1966 on
Jaguar XK120, 140, 150, Mk. 7, 8, 9 1948-61
Jaguar 2.4, 3.4, 3.8 Mk. 1, 2 1955-69
Jaguar 'E' Type 1961 on
Jaguar 'S' Type 420 1963-68
Jaguar XJ6 1968 on
Jowett Javelin Jupiter 1947-53
Landrover 1, 2 1948-61
Landrover 2, 2a, 3 1959 on
Mercedes-Benz 190b, 190c 200 1959-68
Mercedes-Benz 220 1959-65
Mercedes-Benz 220/8 1968 on
Mercedes-Benz 230 1963-68
Mercedes-Benz 250 1965-67
Mercedes-Benz 250 1968 on
Mercedes-Benz 280 1968 on
MG TA to TF 1936-55
MGA MGB 1955-68
MG MGB 1969 on
Mini 1959 on
Mini Cooper 1961 on
Morgan 1936-69
Morris Marina 1971 on
Morris Minor 2, 1000 1952-71
Morris Oxford 5, 6 1959-71
NSU 1000 1963 on
NSU Prinz 1 to 4 1957 on
Opel Ascona, Manta 1970 on
Opel G.T. 1900 1968 on
Opel Kadett, Olympia 993 cc, 1078 cc 1962 on
Opel Kadett, Olympia 1492, 1698, 1897 cc 1967 on
Opel Rekord C 1966 on
Peugeot 204 1965 on
Peugeot 404 1960 on
Peugeot 504 1968-70
Porsche 356a, 356b, 356c 1957-65
Porsche 911 1964-69
Porsche 912 1965-69
Reliant Regal 1962 on
Renault R4, R4L, 4 1961 on
Renault 6 1968 on
Renault 8, 10, 1100 1962 on
Renault 12 1969 on
Renault R16 1965 on
Renault Dauphine Floride 1957-67
Renault Caravelle 1962-68
Rover 60 to 110 1953-64
Rover 2000 1963 on
Rover 3 Litre 1958-67
Rover 3500, 3500S 1968 on
Saab 95, 96, Sport 1960-68
Saab 99 1969 on
Saab V4 1966 on
Simca 1000 1961 on
Simca 1100 1967 on
Simca 1300, 1301, 1500, 1501 1963 on
Skoda One (440, 445, 450) 1957-69
Sunbeam Rapier Alpine 1955-65
Toyota Corolla 1100 1967 on
Toyota Corona 1500 Mk. 1 1965-70
Toyota Corona 1900 Mk. 2 1969 on
Triumph TR2, TR3, TR3A 1952-62
Triumph TR4, TR4A 1961-67
Triumph TR5, TR250, TR6 1967 on
Triumph 1300, 1500 1965 on
Triumph 2000 Mk. 1, 2.5 PI Mk. 1 1963-69
Triumph 2000 Mk. 2, 2.5 PI Mk. 2 1969 on
Triumph Herald 1959-68
Triumph Herald 1969-71
Triumph Spitfire Vitesse 1962-68
Triumph Spitfire Mk. 3 1969 on
Triumph GT6, Vitesse 2 Litre 1969 on
Triumph Toledo 1970 on
Vauxhall Velox, Cresta 1957 on
Vauxhall Victor 1, 2, FB 1957-64
Vauxhall Victor 101 1964-67
Vauxhall Victor FD 1600, 2000 1967 on
Vauxhall Viva HA 1963-66
Vauxhall Viva HB 1966-70
Vauxhall Viva, HC Firenza 1971 on
Vauxhall Victor 3300, Ventura 1968 on
Volkswagen Beetle 1954-67
Volkswagen Beetle 1968 on
Volkswagen 1500 1961-66
Volkswagen 1600 Fastback 1965 on
Volkswagen Transporter 1954-67
Volkswagen Transporter 1968 on
Volvo P120 1961-70
Volvo P140 1966 on
Volvo 160 series 1968 on
Volvo 1800 1961 on